Tradition and Revolution
in
Russian Art

SPONSORED BY SIEMENS

2003

003

JAN 2006

Cornerhouse Publications in association with the Olympic Festival 1990 2008

This is the catalogue of the *Leningrad in Manchester* exhibitions:

Russian Faces, Soviet Lives: figure painting 1910-45, paintings from the State Russian Museum, Leningrad, at the City Art Gallery, Princess Street, Manchester, 16 June-22 July, 1990.

The Russian Lubok: Two Hundred Years of Popular Prints, from the Saltykov-Shchedrin State Public Library, Leningrad, at the Whitworth Art Gallery, University of Manchester, 15 June-21 July, 1990.

Bolshevik Posters, 1917-25, from the Saltykov-Shchedrin State Public Library, Leningrad, at the Whitworth Art Gallery, University of Manchester, 15 June-21 July, 1990.

Street Art of the Revolution: Petrograd 1918, artists' designs from the State Russian Museum, the State Museum of the Great October Socialist Revolution, and the Museum of the History of Leningrad, and banners also from the State Museum of the Great October Socialist Revolution, all in Leningrad, at Cornerhouse, Manchester, 16 June-22 July, 1990.

Posters of Perestroika, competitive exhibition of poster designs *Sovest'* 89, organised by Interplakat, Leningrad, at Cornerhouse, Manchester, 16 June-22 July, 1990.

St Petersburg, exhibition of paintings and prints from the State Museum of the History of Leningrad, Leningrad, at the City Art Gallery, Mosley Street, Manchester, 16 June-22 July, 1990.

Seventh exhibition: *The View from Leningrad: photographs by Anatolii Medvednikov*, Sir William Siemens House, Princess Road, Manchester 20, 16 June-14 July, has a separate illustrated catalogue.

Committee of Honour
Lord Birkett, Director, Olympic Festival 1990
Natalia Dementeva, Director, State Museum of the History of Leningrad
Councillor John Gilmore, Lord Mayor of Manchester
Richard Gray, Director, Manchester City Art Galleries
Margarita Gromyko, Head of the Foreign Cities Department, Leningrad City Council
Vladimir Gusev, Director, State Russian Museum
Dewi Lewis, Director, Cornerhouse
Councillor Peter Morrison, Chair, Art Galleries Committee, Manchester City Council
Marta Potiforova, Director, State Museum of the Great October Socialist Revolution
Robert Scott, Chairman, Manchester Olympic Bid Committee
Alastair Smith, Director, Whitworth Art Gallery
Councillor Graham Stringer, Leader, Manchester City Council
Vladimir Zaitsev, Director, Saltykov-Shchedrin State Public Library

Gita Conn, Coordinator Olympic Festival 1990
Elaine Goddard, Administrator Olympic Festival 1990

Exhibitions Committee
Elena Barkhatova, Saltykov-Shchedrin State Public Library
Andrew Causey, University of Manchester (chairman)
Olga Chekhanova, State Museum of the History of Leningrad
Vernon Cressey, Manchester City Council
Gerald Deslandes, Cornerhouse
Vladimir Filippov, Interplakat
Richard Gray, Manchester City Art Galleries
Sarah Hyde, Whitworth Art Gallery
Evgeniia Petrova, State Russian Museum
Greg Smith, Whitworth Art Gallery

Catalogue edited and *Leningrad in Manchester* organised by Susan Causey
Catalogue designed by Christopher Lord
Typeset by Manchester Free Press
Made and Printed in Great Britain by
Jackson · Wilson, Leeds

Photography by Vladimir Dorokhov, Aleksandr Kashnitskii, Anatolii Shishkov, Peter Burton, Michael Pollard, Counter Image
Text translations by Brian Pearce, Martin Taylor, Gillian Hogg, Alan Pinch; further help with translations from Valentina Shakhlai, Vladimir Vishniak, Lilia Payne
Numbered illustrations in section 4 courtesy Thames and Hudson;
illustration p98 courtesy David King

The organisers are grateful to Her Majesty's Government for agreeing to indemnify the exhibition under the National Heritage Act 1980 and the Museums and Galleries Commission for their help in arranging this indemnity.

ISBN 0 948797 26 6

Cover illustration
Boris Kustodiev: **Festivities in Uritskii Square on the Opening Day of the Second Congress of the Comintern in July 1920**, 1921 (1.22)

Contents

Introduction

The tension between traditional Russia and desire for urgent change is a topical theme with a long history. The paintings, graphic works and essays collected for this series of exhibitions focus on the period immediately before and after 1917, until now the most fundamental upheaval the country has known. Those years are put into perspective by a look backward to the attempt to leap into the modern world under Peter the Great, and forward to contemporary transformations through the graphic satire of Glasnost. All are concerned with ways in which, as political change cuts across established traditions, the arts respond, stepping in with radical innovation or reforging existing ideas for a new age.

Traditionalism is a particular characteristic of Russia. Product of the country's geography, its Eastern Christian religion, and the need to unify remote locations, this character crystallised during Russia's isolation from the rest of Europe under the two-hundred-year Mongol and Tatar domination; it was strengthened by the long serfdom of its population, many of whom remained tied by various obligations to the same locality right down to 1917. But Leningrad, from which these exhibitions come, is the setting for profound shifts of direction for Russia. As St Petersburg, founded by Peter in 1703, it represents a vision of the classically ordered, educated and cultured society planned by Peter and his successor Catherine the Great; as Petrograd — the Slavonic name given it for patriotic reasons in 1914 — the city was the capital of the Russian revolution and pacesetter for the most radical change of all.

Russian art had begun to observe West European currents in Peter's time. By the first decade of the 20th century Russian artists faced the same turmoil of radical renewal as artists in the West, but Russia's particular situation imposed its own conditions. Rapid, late industrialisation and the liberation of the serfs had destabilised the worn-out social and political structure, which were put under further pressure by the First World War. Political revolution coincided with a ferment of artistic innovation, and with the first Soviet government's readiness to make use of artists who had already rejected the old aesthetic order. The scene was set for a moment of explosive creativity.

The artistic achievements of the first Soviet years are remarkable. A brilliant generation of artists under 40 at the time of the revolution broke new ground in *avant-garde* painting, re-thought the responsibilities of art by their involvement in poster campaigns, advertising, theatre and industrial design. They were united in the idea that art was central to life and needed to emerge from aristocratic drawing-rooms and fashionable exhibitions into all aspects of the everyday world.

The exhibitions engage with this theme. *Russian Faces, Soviet Lives* presents figure paintings that span the revolutionary era and continue into the period of Socialist Realism. The fierce debates in the traumatic late 1920s and 30s about the nature of art in a socialist society have resulted in a simplistic Western view that, because artistic experiment was soon under severe official pressure, only the abstract work of the period should be considered of value. This exhibition looks specifically at non-abstract work, emphasising the distinguished artists who found a way of making the lessons of modernism relevant to their commitment to the new society.

Russia's unique creation of art for the streets is described in *Bolshevik Posters* and *Street Art of the Revolution*. The first is the better known: its juxtaposition with the designs for the Petrograd revolutionary festival of 1918 reveals a much fuller picture of artists' involvement in mass communication, especially as some artists have work represented in two or even all three of these exhibitions.

The theme of Russian traditionalism is parallel to that of revolution. The subjects of *The Russian Lubok*, popular prints sold at village fairs for over two hundred years, are of considerable aesthetic appeal and sociological interest on their own account. Of particular relevance here is the value of this tradition to the revolutionary generation. *Lubki* were important formally and culturally for Russian modernists' break with what they considered the oversolemn and salon-oriented art of the 19th century. The bright, unnatural colours and shallow space in these works made the kind of direct contact with the senses that modernists valued; these features and the terse and metaphoric story-telling helped the artists as they looked for ways to make complex ideas accessible to broad masses of people.

Issues raised by *St Petersburg* include the 19th-century perception of this planned environment as autocratic, and the way the city's orderly concept — radical at the outset — had by the modern era become a symbol of discredited authority. *Posters of Perestroika* shows how courageous artists have cut across moribund practices and injected new life into the distinguished tradition initiated by the first Soviet graphic artists.

*   *   *   *   *

Leningrad in Manchester has been made possible by the collaboration of Leningrad City Council; we are particularly grateful for the support of Mrs Margarita Gromyko, Head of the Foreign Cities Department, and for the coordinating role of her assistant, Irina Iliushenko. We also owe special thanks to Vladimir Gusev and Evgeniia Petrova, director and deputy director of the State Russian Museum, who have not only lent us an outstanding selection of oil paintings from the museum's collections at a time when the surge of interest in Russian and Soviet art has led to requests for loans from all over the world, but have substantially contributed to a second exhibition as well. The Saltykov-Shchedrin State Public Library has also been particularly generous in the loan of two exhibitions. Our thanks go to all the lending institutions.

In the administration of *Leningrad in Manchester* we have received unstinting help from the Union of Soviet Friendship Societies: its chairman, Mrs Natalia Eliseeva, deputy chairman Andrei Ibragimov, general secretary Margarita Mudrak, and their colleagues. In making the initial contacts and at several moments of crisis we have greatly benefited from the support and advice of Neil Gilroy, secretary of the Manchester branch of the British Soviet Friendship Society. Thanks also for help in Leningrad to Professor Nina Kalitina, Dr Vsevolod Morozov, Professor Tatiana Kuzmicheva, Evgenii Artëmov, Beltina Dianova and Inga Lander. Preparation of the catalogue was only possible thanks to personal help with couriering by Colin Barnett, Elena Crosbie, Annie Feltham, Sue Hall, Laura Hawkins, Sue Jones, Colin Laycock, Les Pattison, Catherine Phillips and Julia South.

Manchester's special relationship with the great city of Leningrad began in 1949 with links between trade unionists; this progressed to an exchange of civic delegations in 1956 and the signing of a Friendship Agreement in 1963. *Leningrad in Manchester* is very grateful for the support of Manchester City Council and the assistance given by the Leader of the council, Councillor Graham Stringer.

Leningrad in Manchester is particularly grateful to Siemens, whose generous sponsorship has made it possible for this rich series of exhibitions to be mounted in Manchester. We thank Richard Caithness of Siemens for his support and advice during the planning. The sponsorship of Siemens has been recognised by an award under the Government's Business Sponsorship Incentive Scheme, which is administered by the Association for Business Sponsorship of the Arts (ABSA). We are grateful to the Patrons and Associates of Manchester City Art Galleries for a generous grant and for the support of the Visiting Arts Unit of the British Council. The Philips Price Memorial Trust, founded in memory of the *Manchester Guardian* correspondent in Russia during the revolution, has very kindly given a donation.

Many thanks for help with the notes to Dr Catherine Cooke, Dr Colin Imber, Nina and Vladimir Vishniak, and Valentina Shakhlai. We are grateful for help in the Soviet Embassy from Mr Sergei Paramonov and Mrs Tatiana Formicheva. Many thanks to Dr Jennifer Harris for approving the Leningrad projects for the Whitworth Art Gallery when she was acting keeper in 1989. A special debt is owed to Katharine Ridler of Thames and Hudson, for help with the visual material for *Street Art of the Revolution: Petrograd* 1918. Dr Robert Russell very kindly let us read his forthcoming paper 'The Arts in Russia during the Civil War'. Many thanks to Caroline Warhurst and to the North West Museums Service (Blackburn), also to Jane Ades, Alison Buchan, Sue Clive, Kathryn Cope, Ruth Floate, Sara Holdsworth, Kate Horton, Imogen Lock, Sarah Prendergast of Fiat, Peter Ramsay, Howard Smith and Julian Tomlin.

SUSAN CAUSEY, organiser and catalogue editor
ANDREW CAUSEY, chairman of the exhibition committee

NOTE ON THE TEXT

In transliterating names from the Cyrillic alphabet the Library of Congress system is used, with modifications for such familiar names as Trotsky and Mayakovsky; people who are not royal have their names directly transliterated, but monarchs appear as they are known in the West: Catherine the Great, rather than Ekaterina. Russia moved from the Julian calendar to the Gregorian system on 14 February 1918, after which the next day became 1 March: dates here follow this pattern. Catalogue numbers appear in the text in bold type to show that an illustration is close by or that a cross reference is illustrated in another section: in reading the catalogue sections a single star indicates a black and white illustration in the text, a double star colour. All dimensions of works are given in centimetres, height before width.

I.32

Russian Faces, Soviet Lives

By 1917 a brilliant generation of young artists in St Petersburg and Moscow were at the forefront of European experiment in form and colour. The revolution stimulated an unprecedented outburst of artistic activity, as this talent found expression in all spheres of life, before the official imposition of Socialist Realism in the early 30s set strict rules for artists and put an end to *avant-gardism*. Movements in art mirror the political change and the often bitter debates — about the role of art and the nature of a socialist culture. The range of Soviet art in the 1920s and 30s is still unfamiliar. But the pictures here, with their different concepts and styles, their shifting relationship to modernism, deny the simple view that after the revolution artists faced a straightforward choice between *avant-garde* art and a banal, lifeless realism.

Revolutionary Morning: Visions of a New Life

by Evgeniia Petrova, deputy director, State Russian Museum

Russian art in the first half of this century was altogether richer and more dramatic in expression than might appear to one familiar only with the work of our *avant-garde*. In the years of Glasnost, it has become possible for the State Russian Museum to show works from the particularly fertile 1920s and 30s at home and in countries all over the world. The paintings exhibited in Manchester were largely made during this same rich period, but in focusing on works showing the human figure portrayed in a mainly representational way, the exhibition reveals a less familiar face of the art of this time. The works are occasionally abstract and a few are fully realistic. But for the most part they represent a tendency in which artists pursue an image that is understandable, while at the same time benefiting from the lessons of modernism. The image is clearly readable, but the elaborate realism characteristic of the late 19th century is replaced by a pared-down

1.19 P. Konchalovskii, *Portrait of Konchalovskaia and Tatiana*, 1916

presentation, concentrated and immediate.

This painting had its roots in the turn of the century. Already then, when the World of Art* group associated with Sergei Diaghilev was founded, the sway in art of wholly 'life-like' presentation and solemn, formal content was broken. Headed by Alexandre Benois, World of Art painters evolved an art of historical and symbolic reference, combined with a richly decorative manner to counter the academic and heavily naturalistic work of the period. The new art was permeated by poetic feeling and intimacy, and for its subject-matter it turned nostalgically to the period of Peter the Great and Louis XIV, to Kievan Russia, to historical costumes and manners, portraying them with a wit, irony and even frivolity that cut through the reverential attitude to the past customarily shown by Russian artists. As well as Benois, the group's members included such brilliant figures as Mstislav Dobuzhinskii, Leon Bakst, Boris Kustodiev, Konstantin Somov and Nikolai Roerich, who together revived theatre and costume design, book production and art criticism, as well as painting. The *World of Art*

1.18 P. Konchalovskii, *Portrait of Denike and Pokrovskii*, 1913

1.33 Kuzma Petrov-Vodkin, *Dream*, 1910

1.29 Mikhail Nesterov, *Self-portrait*, 1915

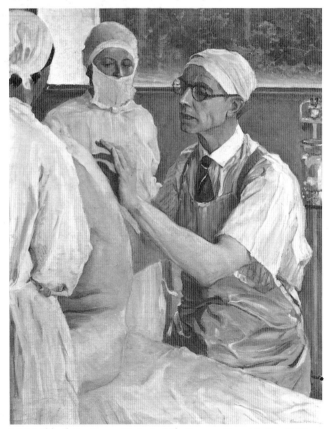

1.30 Mikhail Nesterov, *Portrait of the Surgeon Sergei Iudin*, 1933

journal published regular articles about recent and past developments in Russian and also West European art, stimulating a new wave of interest in European works, especially in France and Germany.

In this context rich men again became art patrons. The businessmen Sergei Shchukin and Savva Morozov brought to Russia paintings by Cézanne, Matisse and Gauguin at a time when the work of these artists was not highly valued. Both at home and in the studios of Paris and Munich, Russian artists saw at first hand the work of their West European contemporaries; nearly all the best artists of the first decade of the 20th century travelled abroad to study and observe. Remarkably, on their return home, they were able to find their own personal themes and artistic language; in the years before the First World War Russian art is marked by an amazing range of individual constructions of reality and of fantasies born of the imagination.

Typical of this period is the art of such different artists as Mikhail Vrubel and Valentin Serov, emerging in quite unsimilar ways from the school of the Modern Style. In 1907 and 1910 the Knave of Diamonds and Blue Rose exhibiting groups were formed, representing diametrically opposed artistic principles. The tough, but rich and life-affirming art of the first, in which the work of Pëtr Konchalovskii (**1.18-19**) and Ilia Mashkov (**1.26**) was outstanding, contrasted with the refined aestheticism and colourful symbolism of the latter, in the paintings of such artists as Pavel Kuznetsov and Viktor Borisov-Musatov.

Contemporary exhibitions also showed works by artists who had developed a creative idiom independent of the groups they belonged to. Mikhail Nesterov rediscovered the purity and spirituality of devout Kievan Rus. His pictures of holy men are not portraits in naturalistic settings. Rather, Nesterov finds images to express the essence of Russian religious feeling, its roots in the specific way of life and the Russian countryside of limitless distances, broad steppes and dense forest. Without making use of prescribed iconic forms, his work represents an understanding of early icon-painting, its starting point being the poetic concept of renunciation of a former way of life.

In his *Self-portrait* (**1.29**), Nesterov portrays himself in formal city dress but against a broad Russian landscape. Painted when the artist was 53, it marks a transitional period in his art between the early poetics and his post-revolutionary concentration on portrait-painting. In the new genre Nesterov nevertheless remains true to the spirit of the earlier work: asceticism and spiritual power always distinguish the images he created. The artistry of the surgeon Iudin (**1.30**), of whom Nesterov made several portraits, is conveyed in a remarkably acute and expressive way.

Nesterov, who was at one time closely connected with the imperial family, also flourished under Stalin's regime: he was highly valued in official circles as an artist who incarnated the continuity between past and present. Here was one of the paradoxes of those days: especially as the realism of Nesterov was remote from the academic, grandiose naturalism of the Stalin era.

While Nesterov's historical compositions made him heir to the spirit of the Russian icon, but not to its form, Kuzma Petrov-Vodkin proved to be the most brilliant interpreter of the flat, coloured surfaces and basic formal concerns of the Russian church art. This makes Petrov-Vodkin markedly unlike Nesterov. It was Petrov-Vodkin who returned Russian painting to its iconic tradition, choosing as the basis of his colour range in 1910 and after the native purity and transparency of the red, blue and yellow used by icon-painters **(see 1.34)**. But the content of Petrov-Vodkin's images, of his allegories and metaphors, is far from religious; it is oriented rather to the profound philosophical questions of existence that were a major preoccupation at the beginning of the 20th century (1.33). The themes of existence — its beginning, flowering and extinction — of love and suffering, suffuse all his work. They lose nothing of their penetration through being embodied in deeply subjective representations.

If Russia, its history, landscape and enigmatic future was a particular theme of artists at the end of the 19th century and beginning of the 20th, the work of Boris Kustodiev presents a quite different vision from that of Nesterov or Petrov-Vodkin. The festively cheerful, fairground world of Kustodiev's richly coloured canvases evokes the breadth and boldness, the luxury and eccentricity of the old Russian merchant class. Inspiration for Kustodiev's imagery came from the traditional popular culture still surviving, especially in provincial life: tales of old-time heroes and a golden age of sunshine and abundance, the *lubok* pictures made for sale at country fairs (see pp 61-96) and the shop signs produced by local craftsmen, which held great attraction for artists at the beginning of the 20th century. Kustodiev carried the cheery amplitude of life in this idealised view, the picture of old Russia that so appealed to him, over into the 1920s, managing to translate its spirit into celebration of the festivities and 'happenings' of the finally achieved revolution **(1.22)**.

Zinaida Serebriakova, member of a distinguished family of artists, designers and architects, was an outstanding contemporary of Kustodiev, Petrov-Vodkin and Nesterov. In a style that chang-

1.36 Kuzma Petrov-Vodkin, *Morning*, 1917

ed little throughout a long creative career, Serebriakova shared with her generation of artists a preoccupation with 20th-century classicism, based on the Renaissance art of France and Italy. The monumentality and stillness of the Italian Quattrocento **(1.47)** is combined in some of her works, such as *The Bath-house, study* of 1912 **(1.48)**, with a complex figure composition: studies of similar models are repeated, with variations and on differing, almost unrelated, scales. This fragmented complexity is typical of mid 16th-century Mannerism.

Another influence in Serebriakova's work is French Romanticism, especially, it is considered, the work of Ingres; her paintings are also close to those of such Russian classicists as Aleksei Egorov. To the Russian spectator, clear also is the closeness of Serebriakova to Aleksei Venetsianov, the first artist to portray sympathetically the population of the Russian countryside. Serebriakova makes the life and work of the peasants one of her main subjects, in paintings like *Peasants* **(1.49)**, of 1914, *Harvest* (1915), and *Bleaching Canvas* (1917).

In the first decades of this century Russian art manifested itself

1.34 Kuzma Petrov-Vodkin, *Thirsty Warrior*, 1915

1.24 Aristarkh Lentulov, *Self-portrait*, 1913

1.49 Zinaida Serebriakova, *Peasants*, 1914

in a rich variety of styles and made widely differing use of the inherited traditions. To the names of the artists discussed and exhibiting one may add those of Kazimir Malevich and Vasilii Kandinsky, Aristarkh Lentulov (**1.24**) and Natan Altman (**1.1**), Marc Chagall (**1.7**) and Boris Grigorev (**1.15-16**). Still continuing their work were artists of the older generation, especially the Itinerants. This group, against whom the younger artists had reacted, had themselves represented fundamental change when in 1863 they rejected the Academy of Arts in favour of travelling exhibitions and a fresher, more genuine subject-matter. In 1900-17 Ilia Repin (see **1.42**) and Vasilii Surikov (**1.54**), the leading exponents of traditional realism, were still exhibiting, although most of their typically very large narrative work was now behind them.

Russian art had embarked on the mastery of West European creative forms in Peter's time. Two hundred years later, after intensive and swift progress in the later period, Russian modernism was evolving innovatory concepts in many ways unknown in the West. The revolutions of 1917 swiftly opened up the possibilities for the new artistic ideas that had appeared so strikingly from 1910 onwards. Many artists greeted the revolution with joy in the expectation of creative renewal. Leading painters, sculptors and graphic artists of all the different movements responded positively by plunging into the transformation of streets and squares for the first revolutionary festivals. The sketches and designs that have survived (see pages 135-52) bear witness to commitment, adventurousness and a high level of achievement. This was a unique phase in the history of art, when for a short period social radicalism and the art *avant-garde* were united in harmony on the basis of the new freedom.

The process of revolutionary transformation stimulated the creative intelligentsia, often to the use of their art in new areas. Painters worked on porcelain (Malevich, Suetin, Chashnik) and textiles (Popova, Ekster), while also building on the experimental work of precursors: in theatre design (Ekster, Chagall, Malevich) and books (Kustodiev, Miturich, Annenkov, Altman). Some artists believed that the social revolution must inevitably and immediately bring a revolution in people's understanding of the world, their thinking and perception; they associated the remaking of social forms with a permanent shift, a sort of 'explosion' of the forms of art. Others tried to record the face of their own era in an expressive way that would nevertheless be familiar and comprehensible to their contemporaries, many of whom had no conception of the artistic language of modernism.

Much debate was conducted in manifestoes issued by the numerous groupings that swiftly sprang up and often, equally quickly, disappeared. After the revolution and in the early 1920s there was little to presage the ideological terror of Stalinism. Suprematists and Realists, Constructivists and Symbolists, Futurists and Impressionists were all equal participants in the discussion. Blood was spilt for social, political and ideological reasons, but with all the many problems of the time no aesthetic control was possible: diversity prevailed in exhibition policy, with works by painters with fundamentally opposed artistic convictions often appearing side by side. Attempts to make art part of an ideological debate met with no backing from the government or the ruling party before the mid 1920s. Lenin was an admirer of traditional realism, but considered that he had no right to impose his personal taste on artists. Anatolii Lunacharskii, People's Commissar for Enlightenment, emphasised in speeches and articles that the party ought not to give its backing to any one of the different groupings. For the time being art remained outside the realm of ideology, although by the mid 1920s it became clear that political forces favouring bans, supervision and the distortion of artistic life were gathering strength and influence.

The problem nevertheless remained that the changed way of life, the new rhythms and heroes, needed to be expressed in a visual language comprehensible to the new Soviet public. It was no accident that the goal of many art associations of the 1920s was to find content and form to correspond to the fundamental changes in people's lives. In a desire to understand the contemporary situation, some artists went into industrial plants and factories and spent time on building sites. The art they produced often bore no indication of direct ideological briefing, although of course its subject-matter — the industrialised nation that was being born, the socialist achievements — told a specific story. Romanticisation of the ordinary and everyday, compression into a single image of the whole dynamic of that time, the forging of forms that were direct and expressive — all these qualities are characteristic of the art in the 1920s of Aleksandr Deineka, Iurii Pimenov, Pëtr Osolodkov, Sergei Gerasimov, and Fëdor Bogorodskii. The paintings make an original form of visual diary of a whole era, while at the same time remaining the inspired works of considerable artists.

But the sincere patriotic impulses of the majority of the artists were not valued for what they were. On 23 April 1932 an ominous document was published, the decision of the Communist Party 'On the Restructuring of Literary and Artistic Organisations', which in essence gave only a single artistic tendency the right to legal existence. This tendency was to be given the name 'Socialist Realism'. To this day it is not fully clear what this is. What is well known is the emasculation suffered by the art of the Soviet Union of that time.

Even such artists as Petrov-Vodkin, Aleksandr Samokhvalov, and Deineka were not considered to fulfil Socialist Realist criteria. The art of Samokhvalov, for example, had by 1931 (**1.46**) lost the strange perspective and modernist forms of an early work like *Hairwashing* (**1.45**), of 1922, when the artist was much influenced by his teacher, Petrov-Vodkin. But the dogmatic narrowness of this compulsory aesthetic made it always possible to find one more batch of 'heretics' not to the liking of the administrative or professional bureaucracy. Artists went on working but their pictures were not shown or purchased. Right down to the 1960s periodicals and newspapers made no mention of their names.

The circle of artists whose work was shown then was very narrow. This impoverishment and limitation was reflected in the depictions of allegedly 'real' life in the works of these few official artists, with their inflated glorifications and pompous images.

1.45 Aleksandr Samokhvalov, *Hairwashing*, 1922-3

However, the terrible situation by no means meant that true art had been destroyed. Until his death in 1939 Kuzma Petrov-Vodkin went on working in his usual style: to the exasperation of official circles. Pavel Filonov, persecuted but unbroken, continued painting without changing either his subject-matter or his style, until his death in frightening poverty during the blockade of Leningrad; right up to the mid 1980s his works continued to strike fear into the hearts of the censors, who removed them from almost all exhibitions. Until the end of the 1950s the brilliant colourist Robert Falk continued to live quietly and modestly in Moscow, stubbornly insisting on his right to paint according to the promptings of his creative intuition.

Fate dealt harshly with many of the artists whose artistic flowering occurred in the first decades of the 20th century. Some of them, like Petrov-Vodkin, Falk and Filonov, chose a difficult freedom. As a rule they lived in poverty and protracted uncer-

1.47 Zinaida Serebriakova, *Bather*, 1911

1.48 Zinaida Serebriakova, *The Bath-house, study* 1912

1.42 Ilia Repin, *Portrait of Vladimir Bekhterev*, 1913

1.53 Konstantin Somov, *Portrait of Rakhmaninov*, 1925

tainty as to what the next day would bring. Others, unable to endure the burdensome changes, went permanently abroad and for a long time lost their public (Filipp Maliavin, Aleksandr Iakovlev, Dobuzhinskii, Konstantin Korovin). Very few followed the path laid down by the official aesthetics.

The lives of the painters who embarked on their creative journey together, in the period of the epoch-making upheavals in Russia, were often very different. Today the disputes and quarrels centring on 'leftists' and 'rightists', emigrés and patriots, have fallen silent. All the artists — regardless of their biographies or their ideological or aesthetic affiliations — are once more part of our culture. In the sum of their work is reflected the varying perceptions of contemporaries and of the ancestors we share with them.

And so this collection of paintings opens the door a little on Russia, showing her distinctive view of the world and of herself, through the prism of the art of a few decades of the 20th century.

* * * * *

The Russian Museum in Leningrad holds the largest collection of Russian art in the USSR and in the whole world. This comprises more than 360,000 items. Besides paintings, sculpture and graphics, this museum — unlike, for example, the State Tretiakov Gallery in Moscow — collects decorative and popular (peasant) art, and also coins. The Museum was opened to the public in 1898, as Russia's first state gallery. To it came the splendid collections of St Petersburg's rich art patrons, the Russian sections of the Hermitage and the museum of the Academy of Arts. After 1917, it received many works from palaces and private houses, monasteries and cathedrals.

A number of distinguished figures in the art world have had direct links with the Russian Museum. Ilia Repin made certain his oeuvre was properly represented, making gifts of later works, including the *Portrait of Vladimir Bekhterev*, of 1913 (**1.42**). A collection took shape — superb in its completeness and the variety of artists represented — of the work of Russia's *avant-garde*. When Inkhuk, the *avant-garde*'s 'laboratory', was closed in 1926, as one of the first signs of the triumph of dogma in art, Nikolai Punin and Malevich helped ensure that works held by the museum department of Inkhuk were transferred to the Russian Museum. Having been expelled from Inkhuk, Malevich himself found work in the Russian Museum in the early 1930s.

It was not easy to preserve innovatory work during the 1930s and 40s. But the direction and staff of the museum always appreciated the unique historical importance of the collection: not one picture belonging to it was sold even in the darkest period, nor were any destroyed on government orders, as happened, unfortunately, in other museums. In the late 1950s and early 60s, during the Khrushchev 'Thaw', the museum's director, Vasilii Pushkarëv, resumed enthusiastically the inclusion of works by formerly banned artists when making additions to the collections. The museum's reputation thus acquired resulted in many artists seeing the Russian Museum as a safe refuge for their work. In the 1950s, 60s and later, the museum received almost the entire legacy of Petrov-Vodkin, Anna Ostroumova-Lebedeva, Filonov, Aleksandr Shevchenko, and others. The collection today provides a complete record of Russian art history from the 15th to the 20th century.

Exhibitions are an important part of the museum's programme: although, alas, the history of exhibitions here — as in all Russian museums — was governed for a long time by ideology. The move away from Socialist Realism was slow, but the Russian Museum was the leader in gradually during the 1960s exhibiting works of other tendencies, even the most adventurous. At this time, the first great one-man retrospectives of such artists as Petrov-Vodkin, Serebriakova, and Konstantin Somov took place, and recognition was accorded to the Russian icon, long persecuted because of the official atheistic ideology.

For the several generations of the Soviet public who had from childhood been accustomed to the idea that all the best work had been done by the artists of 'critical' realism in the 19th century — by Vasilii Perov, Repin, and Ivan Kramskoi — and by their 20th-century 'socialist' realist successors, these exhibitions were striking revelations. After three decades of bans, persecutions and the Iron Curtain, Russian people once again had access to the work of Cézanne and Matisse, Van Gogh and Gauguin, which could now be seen without restrictions in the Hermitage in Leningrad and the Pushkin Museum in Moscow. As if fearful of losing the new opportunities, everyone queued for the exhibitions, read about them in trams and at home, poured in in a mighty flood. An exhibition of British art held in the late 1950s made a great impression on the people of Leningrad. For the first time they saw works of Turner, Constable, the Pre-Raphaelites, Graham Sutherland and the abstractionists. People came to understand that art is not confined to realism, or to the problems of life and nothing else: on the contrary, realism itself is a many-sided concept, rich in nuances. Artists too were encouraged by this lesson.

In the 20 years that followed there were fresh bans and persecutions, contemporary exhibitions not sanctioned by the authorities were broken up, works of the innovatory artists of the 20s and 30s were arbitrarily removed from the gallery displays and the museums' programmes subjected to severe censorship. But although these measures caused considerable harm they did not frighten people much. The Russian artistic underground came increasingly to the fore. Unseen by the authorities, our museum continued, sometimes using subtle means, to acquire the most interesting works and to prepare for the next leap forward by studying the banned artists. Russia's museum staff knew that sooner or later they would be able to show the country and the world our nation's art in all its richness. When the period of Glasnost and Perestroika came in the mid 1980s, it did not find the creative intelligentsia unprepared.

The Russian Museum, once freed from the censor and ideological diktat, hurried to show its visitors the art which had been hitherto under ban. In 1987-9 there were one-man exhibitions of Filonov, Malevich and Kandinsky. Art of the 1920s and 30s, a show with almost one thousand exhibits, covered the artists of all the varied creative movements that flourished in the post-revolutionary period before the Stalinist decrees. The museum first began arranging exhibitions abroad in the 1960s, but this programme has lately gathered huge impetus. Following the great 1988 Malevich exhibition prepared by Soviet and Dutch specialists, three cities in the United States will see this artist's work in 1990: New York, Los Angeles and Washington. In February 1990 the Pompidou Centre in Paris mounted the first comprehensive exhibition of Filonov, little known till then in the West; in the autumn work of Filonov and his pupils will be seen in Düsseldorf.

The Russian Museum's many foreign exhibitions of the past decade have mainly had one common feature: their concentration on the Russian avant-garde of the first wave. While the canvases of those artists adorn any exhibition in which they appear, their work has for some time been well enough known in the West, whereas that of even their contemporaries, not to speak of their predecessors, has been little shown to the rest of the world. At this unusual point in our history, as we move to recover the whole of our past, it is valuable to shift attention in the direction of figure painting, which speaks in an immediate way about aspects of Russian life and art in the 20s and 30s. To look at names, works and movements that are important for a fuller picture of art in the Soviet period.

1.26 Ilia Mashkov, *Portrait of a Woman with Pheasants*, 1911

1.22 Boris Kustodiev, *Festivities in Uritskii Square on the Opening Day of the Second Congress of the Comintern in July 1920*, 1921

Art and Revolutionary Society: Factions and Debates

by Andrew Causey, department of art history, University of Manchester

Changes in Russia from the last years of the tsarist empire to the harshly repressive Stalinist 1930s and the trauma of the Second World War are reflected in art. A simple view has been to see the rich and progressive work of the immediate pre-war years developing briefly after 1917 into an unparalleled outburst of innovation, which was soon squeezed out in favour of politically-dictated arid realism. By taking figure painting as the subject of study, a more complex picture emerges. Often the move away from experiment was the initiative of artists themselves, while it was measures taken by the Communist Party and the art authorities that ensured a degree of artistic pluralism in the 20s. When restrictions on art were finally made official in 1932, there still remained in the succeeding years artists of distinction and integrity who managed to retain some personal independence within the narrow, illiberal system.

In the early 1900s the St Petersburg World of Art Group finally rejected Russia's 19th-century realism as practised by the group of Itinerants. Gathering together the threads of Symbolism and Post-Impressionism, World of Art brought art to the brink of more radical change in a vivid, elegant, sometimes fantastic art. The plunge into modernism was taken in 1910 by Moscow artists, when four friends, expelled from art school for extremism, established the Jack of Diamonds group, Mashkov, Lentulov, Falk and Konchalovskii were soon joined by Altman, Chagall and Puni, who were all away in Paris in 1910, as well as Tatlin and others.

The *avant-garde* valued Russia's own folk traditions for their primitive conceptual forms and colours and their oblique and flexible expression, which was in contrast to the portentous Slavonic historicism of the Itinerants. Turning their backs on Russia's 19th century, the artists made it clear that Russian art was breaking out of a period of isolation, and would now take part in the experiments going on all over Europe. Internationalist and open to Cubism and other progressive trends, members of Jack of Diamonds and like-minded artists such as Grigorev and Shevchenko were only outstripped in their radicalism by the more anarchic practices of the Russian Futurists, who were engaged in looking for new social contexts for art, taking theatre, poetry and painting out onto the streets.

Bolshevik theorists were in the main taken by surprise when the revolution occurred in their own relatively underdeveloped country. In cultural matters, as in much else, the new leaders had no previously agreed plan. The next decade was marked by wide-ranging discussion in many areas; but as people tired of argument and unsolved problems, the debate gradually narrowed and central authority came to be accepted, even welcomed. Artistic policy needs to be seen in terms of a combative ten-year discussion about the purposes of art that eventually ended with the imposition from outside of a fixed role within a static system.

In 1917-18 there was broad consensus in the new government in a desire for continuity to make best use of the talent of all groups who wanted to be involved in the cause of the revolution. There was less agreement on a related issue: did Russia need a shared art of the masses as an essential force within the contemporary drive for a new socialist society? — or, conversely, would the establishment of a proletarian art follow the actual achievement of the new society? Among the leaders, Trotsky adhered firmly to the second belief, that the practice and enjoyment of art needed leisure and that present attention should be concentrated elsewhere. Lenin and his former colleague in exile, Anatolii Lunacharskii, now head of Narkompros, took a middle position, believing that, given political direction, art had an important role; the policy was a pluralist one of maintaining good relations with the existing intelligentsia as a whole. Aleksandr Bogdanov, another comrade from the years in exile, took a different stance. As the intellectual leader of Proletkult, a radical body just pre-dating the October Revolution, Bogdanov wanted to bring all the people into education and artistic activity, as makers of cultural change who would help form the character of the new society. The more pragmatic Lenin, with his advocacy of gradual evolution of socialist culture and steady assimilation of existing ideas, mistrusted the zeal of Proletkult and in 1920 brought it under the control of Narkompros.

Neither Lenin nor Trotsky liked advanced art, and even Lunacharskii was cautious about it. Insofar as Lenin had artistic preferences, they were for the tradition of Repin, the late 19th-century painter of romantic realist subject pictures, and the other

Ilia Repin, *Religious Procession in Kursk Province*, 1880-83 (175 x 280), State Tretiakov Gallery

Itinerants. Trotsky was interested in Futurism, because he saw that it was trying to bring art to working people. But he described it as a closet revolution within a middle-class framework: most workers had no appropriate experience to help them evaluate it. Culture depended on knowledge, the people needed a period in which to learn, and it was impossible, Trotsky declared — with the Constructivists' ideas in mind — to create a class culture behind the back of the class'.[1]

The leadership's interest was in practical programmes, of which the first was for monuments to revolutionary heroes, and the second the street decorations of 1918. In these, the Bolsheviks were at first most actively supported by the radical artists, but although these groups could claim to be both collective and oriented towards the proletariat, advanced art was not what ultimately interested the leaders. Lenin made occasional private outbursts against the 'left' movements, describing a poem by Mayakovsky as 'rubbish, stupid, absolutely silly and pretentious'.[2] Lunacharskii declared himself in 1923 a champion of realism, 'the sort of realism that would proceed approximately from the Itinerants'[3]

— where Lenin's taste also lay.

Repin, an artist sympathetic to the revolution, died as late as 1930 at the age of 86, and was the exemplary practitioner looked up to by many Bolsheviks. Repin had said of late tsarist society that the role of art was to 'criticise mercilessly all the monstrosities of our vile reality';[4] his ideological mentor, Nikolai Chernyshevskii, held that 'the content of art is life in its social aspect',[5] and was also admired by Lenin. Repin's large subject paintings are brave in their social criticism, particularly successful being his *Volga Boatmen* of 1870-3 and *Religious Procession in Kursk Province* **(ill)**, of 1880-3, with its maimed, credulous peasants, arrogant mounted police, and hillside denuded of trees by industry. But although Repin rejected the socially irrelevant subjects of academic artists, he made little advance formally; his painting style remains most appropriate for the grand bourgeois salon, the middle-class audience for whom pictures were an essential part of interior furnishing. It was against the solid, serious paintings of Repin and the Itinerants that the pre-war World of Art group had reacted, offering instead an art that was elegant and modern, avoiding

1.35 Kuzma Petrov-Vodkin, *Midday*, 1917

1.37 Kuzma Petrov-Vodkin, *Death of the Commissar*, 1928

political issues. The Bolshevik leadership was tolerant in art matters, but its inner conviction was backward-looking, admiring artists who were of no interest to the *avant-garde*.

The contemporary painter who satisfied the values of the new establishment as well as any was Boris Kustodiev, in whose work popular realism was combined with a guardedly modern technique. Widely successful before 1917, Kustodiev had been singled out in reviews of a World of Art show in 1911 by two different commentators: Alexandre Benois complimented him on his brilliant colour and the native Russian character of his images; Repin himself also valued Kustodiev as the guardian of national traditions. This double accolade is interesting, coming on one hand from Benois, master of the cosmopolitan St Petersburg aestheticism that would recognise the Renoir-like glamour of Kustodiev's colour, and on the other from Repin, the formally conservative social critic.

Kustodiev committed himself at once to the October Revolution, as he had to the dress rehearsal of 1905. In 1920, by then crippled although only 42, he was given a car by the authorities in Petrograd to tour the events connected with the second congress of the Third International, and later received the prestigious commission to make his painting *Festivities on Uritskii Square* **(1.22)**. Showing men and women of different races and age groups, civilians and members of the armed forces, the canvas embodies both the complex make-up of the new Soviet republic and its internationalist aspirations. It is executed with studied elation and a considerable element of conscious naïveté: particular situations and gestures appear emblematic, as Kustodiev captures the excitement of the moment by concentrating on a series of separate incidents, the comparatively shallow space and primitive colours denying literal representation. Kustodiev achieved a synthesis of high-keyed modernism with a historical Russian feeling proceeding from Repin and the Itinerants: the treatment is only semi-realist. This dynamic and entertaining painting uses devices evolved through study of traditional popular art that had also been important for modernists like Mashkov and Lentulov, but not to the point of mystifying a wide audience. No wonder Lunacharskii was happy. He wrote to Lenin at this time describing Kustodiev as a 'democratically minded and great painter in his own way, perhaps the greatest we have in Russia today'.[6] (see also p 140).

The pre-war Russian *avant-garde* had embraced a network of shifting, disputatious groups, reacting upon one another with statements and manifestoes as well as through their painting. The events of 1917 stimulated an outburst of creative activity which took such varied forms as agitational art, street art, productivism, and Constructivist theatre. Group debate and conflict continued to be a feature of the Soviet art of the 20s, but with the difference that the government itself was by then a participant. Factional activity was a sign of independence and ensured that innovation would continue, but the years that separate the revolutionary euphoria and Stalin's decree of 1932 abolishing artistic groups saw increasingly heated arguments.

The year 1922 was a watershed, with attacks on Narkompros from both radicals and champions of a popularly accessible art. Constructivists in groups like Obmokhu and LEF argued with increasing vigour against 'individualist' easel painting, preferring a more 'collective' activity; they asserted that artists' real concern should be not painting, but experiment — to bring innovative concepts into everyday life. In *Constructivism* (1922), Aleksei Gan sentenced easel painting to death, accusing Narkompros of archaism and concern for old-fashioned subjectivity. But even within the *avant-garde* there were those who recognised that although Constructivism was theoretically collective and consonant with a socialist society, in reality it was likely to remain for many years an élite activity. Understanding this led Constructivists gradually away from abstract 'laboratory' art to more practical areas like photography, graphics and exhibition design. Although there was no sudden change or programme of exclusion, life became perceptibly more difficult. Some artists emigrated, some found their work and teaching opportunities confined and former students turning against them.

NOZh, a group of recently graduated artists, declared in their manifesto in 1922: 'We, former Leftists in art, were the first to feel the utter rootlessness of further analytical and scholastic aberrations. . . . We want to create realistic works of art'.[7] Among the signatories was Georgii Riazhskii, a former pupil of Malevich and author of abstract paintings who was later to be a Socialist Realist. At the same time as youth was turning to tradition, the Itinerants held their last exhibition before dissolving the group, some members joining the new Association of Artists of Revolutionary Russia (AKhRR).

AKhRR was to become the largest artists' organisation in the 20s, embracing NOZh artists, former Itinerants, and young painters like Bogorodskii and Dormidontov who had not passed through a modernist phase. Even the four founders of the pre-war Jack of Diamonds group all joined AKhRR in the mid-20s, despite its declared opposition to the 'decadence' of French influence on Russian art. The change in Mashkov's painting between 1911 and

26

1.27 Ilia Mashkov, *Portrait of Z.D.P.* (*Woman in Blue*), 1927

1927 **(1.26-7)** shows how, in the new context, a brilliantly expressionist use of colour and primitivist design developed into elegant but reserved realism.

AKhRR's central platform was 'documentary' realism. It promised 'a true picture of events and not abstract concoctions discrediting our revolution in the face of the international proletariat';[8] with this aim, some members visited factories and other industrial plants, looking for subjects. A circular issued in 1924 called for an end to 'vacuous philosophising', advocating an 'invigorating', heroic realist style, that would be concerned with such subjects as 'the production worker, electrification and the heroes of labour'.[9] The theme of the heroic worker had its immediate source in recent street and agitational art, although the suffering of the toiling people was an established Itinerant subject in the work of Kasatkin, Arkhipov and Iaroshenko as well as Repin. In 1922, under AKhRR influence, emphasis returned to the traditional salon medium of oil and canvas, a change that coincided in the field of commercial and industrial life with the introduction of the New Economic Policy, itself reflecting a limited surrender of the collective principle.

Here in 1922 are premonitions of Socialist Realism, and in the attacks on both Narkompros and Constructivism are evidence that, however much heroic realism reflected the taste of leading Bolsheviks, its immediate source was often artists themselves. Radicals had been a major force in the reform of art education, but they did not always carry their students with them. After the strong polemics of 1922, friction was constant up to 1927, when tenth anniversary exhibitions offered important art commissions. The debate was not just between representation and abstraction, but increasingly within the field of figuration itself.

The war of words was often acrimonious.[10] The successors of Bogdanov and Proletkult within AKhRR pursued the conviction that only working people could create cultural change. Advocates of gradualism, while declaring common ground with workers, maintained the need to see cultural issues in pluralist terms. In 1924 a conference convened by the Communist Party supported the second standpoint, and early in 1925 a panel of leading government figures produced a paper, soon extended to art, 'On the Party's Policy in the Field of Literature', which concluded: 'All attempts to bind the Party to a single direction at the present stage of cultural development of the country must be firmly rejected'.[11] AKhRR's persistent claims to hegemony lead early in 1926 to a joint protest by five other artists' groups: OST, of which — among the artists represented here — Deineka and Pimenov were members; *Makovets* (Shevchenko); Four Arts (Petrov-Vodkin, Miturich, Bruni); *Bytie* (Konchalovskii, Bogorodskii); and Union of Youth, a reconvened pre-1917 radical group. The artists protested that AKhRR was disproportionately well resourced, arguing that all groups contributing to the making of a socialist art should be funded equally. A commission set up by the Central Committee of the Party upheld the complaint and 10 or more leading AKhRR figures were replaced.

The outcome of this debate, a victory for Lunacharskii's pluralism, had considerable impact in the second half of the decade. To celebrate the first ten years of the revolution, two prestigious art exhibitions were planned in Moscow, *Ten Years of the Workers' and Peasants' Red Army* and the *Exhibition Dedicated to the Tenth Anniversary of the October Revolution*. Early in 1926, before the decision against AKhRR, the Red Army had reserved commissions exclusively for that group's artists, but Lunacharskii now intervened

1.38 Kuzma Petrov-Vodkin, 1919, *The Alert*, 1934

1.9 Aleksandr Deineka, *White HQ: Interrogation*, 1933

Aleksandr Deineka, *The Defence of Petrograd*, 1927 (218 x 354), Museum of the USSR Armed Forces

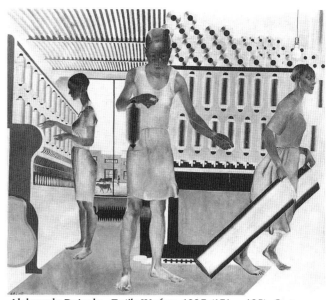

Aleksandr Deineka, *Textile Workers*, 1927 (171 x 195), State Russian Museum

and on the order of the Council of Ministers commissions were given to Petrov-Vodkin as well as rising painters like Pimenov and Deineka. In effect, the government was protecting artists who tackled popular subjects but — unlike AKhRR painters — were modernist although not *avant-garde* in their approach.

As a result of Lunacharskii's intervention, Deineka painted *The Defence of Petrograd* (ill), probably his most famous work, and commissions were extended to distinguished pre-1917 painters like Lentulov and Konchalovskii. At the anniversary of the revolution exhibition, Deineka showed *Textile Workers* (ill) and Pimenov *Forward Heavy Industry* (ill), both highly successful expressions of a vision of the new technological society and emblematic works of this period. OST painters emphasised contemporaneity and clarity of subject, a high degree of finish, and opposed the fragmentation of form that had been common in art since Cézanne and Cubism; equally they rejected what they saw as the overblown and old fashioned realism of the Itinerants. In their modernity of style and subject, OST artists shared something with the aesthetic of *l'esprit nouveau* in France.

Petrov-Vodkin's *Death of the Commissar* (1.37), was a key work in the Red Army exhibition. The central figures follow the form of a traditional *pietà* in a design focusing on the anguish of the irreversible moment of death, a lament for the single individual even in the mass conflict of civil war. As with *Midday*, 1917 (1.35), painted on the death of Petrov-Vodkin's father and made up of vignettes of the different stages of peasant life in his native Volga

region, the similar setting of village and river in *Death of the Commissar* gives personal intensity to a painting on a public theme. As a major public commission, it could not have the private meaning or folk character of *Midday*; but although the subject is heroism there is nothing of the detached rhetoric soon to be associated with Socialist Realism. The traditional subject is given a fresh compositional dynamic through Petrov-Vodkin's strange, widely varying perspectives; despite acceptance of a heroic realist idea, the artist's commitment to innovatory forms of expression makes the picture surprising.

Much remains to be discovered about Soviet figure painting in the 20s, but its rich invention clearly relates to the efforts of a multiplicity of groups resisting AKhRR pressure to conform. Pluralism survived while Lunarcharskii directed Narkompros. His departure was a consequence of Stalin's achievement of power and a new political ethos of moving from debate to action and the resolving of problems through central direction. Stalin, less educated than most early Bolshevik leaders, had not, like them, had his cultural horizons broadened by long periods of foreign exile; he was not interested in the arts for their own sake, but only insofar as they had a part in his programme of national regeneration. His arts policy was contained in the Communist Party's decree 'On the Restructuring of Literary and Artistic Organisations', which paved the way for the official introduction of Socialist Realism two years later. Imposed from above, artistic limitation was a logical extension of other policies pursued now.

Iurii Pimenov, *Forward Heavy Industry*, 1927 (260 x 212), State Tretiakov Gallery

Socialist Realism set up models for art to conform to and established compliant groups within the art world to assess projects and pictures. Art was to be optimistic and create a favourable attitude to work, family life, and to recreation as the reward of labour. Qualities associated with modernism were rejected — stylistic innovation in particular, but also surprise, wit, irony and ambiguity, all of which permit flexibility of interpretation, encourage the use of critical faculties, and leave the ultimate meaning of a painting open. Although the theorisation of Socialist Realism made it appear a positive movement, offering service to the nation or to party loyalty, its effects were mainly negative, leading to static, reductive art that asserts its authority as of right rather than persuading through argument.

There is nothing specifically Russian about Socialist Realism. Contact with national traditions, like that of *lubki* — which Russian modernism had cultivated and which is full of underground currents of satire and subversion — was cast aside in what is in effect a kind of late academicism. Socialist Realism does hark back,

in a limited way, to the precedent of the Itinerants. Although this was an independent and democratically oriented group, which did not have access to the complex critical language of modernist art and should thus not be associated too closely with what followed, its aesthetic language is nevertheless relatively narrow and its art as a result is exhortatory rather than wholly persuasive.

Soviet art did not change overnight, but it is not difficult to see how the new policy took effect during the 30s. Of the artists discussed here, Kustodiev died in 1927, had large, well received retrospective exhibitions in Leningrad in 1928 and Moscow in 1929, but subsequently virtually disappeared from public view till the 1960s. Petrov-Vodkin was at the height of his fame when he showed *Death of the Commissar* in Moscow and at the Venice Biennale in 1928, and his work was exhibited in international exhibitions up to the mid-30s. His became first president of the Leningrad branch of the new Union of Artists in 1932 and was extensively praised at the time of his large one-man show in Leningrad and Moscow in 1936-7, but at his death in 1939 his star was waning and, as with Kustodiev, it was not till the 1960s that serious attention was paid to him again.

The greater naturalism and narrative character of Petrov-Vodkin's 1919. *The Alert* **(1.38)**, of 1934, is in keeping with the new official policy. An anxious urban family peer out into the dark night in anticipation of the advancing White army's attack on Petrograd, while a copy of *Red Gazette* on the chair calls citizens to the defence of their city. Petrov-Vodkin had sketched the design in 1925, and the motive for his return to it now could have been the existence of a different threat, that of the arrests and persecutions of the 1930s. It was at almost the same moment, in 1933, that the artist looked back at his 1910 painting *Dream* **(1.33)** and analysed it in terms of the political immobility of the time and the premonition of sudden change implied by the distant eruption.[12] Tensions, ambiguities of interpretation, and the theatrical simplification of the images: the knowing devices proclaiming 'this is art' — distinguish clearly even a late design like this 1934 painting from Socialist Realism.

Aleksandr Deineka, younger than Petrov-Vodkin or Kustodiev, was trained within the Soviet system, graduating from the Vkhutemas, innovatory institutions of higher education that combined fine and applied art in a unitary system parallel to the Bauhaus in Germany. Deineka was a graphic artist who worked on posters, including Rosta windows, under Moor (see p 101). With his OST collaborator, Iurii Pimenov, he admired the satirical bite of Weimar art, as Pimenov's *Disabled War Veterans* **(1.39)** testifies.

1.10 Aleksandr Deineka, *Air Ace Shot Down*, 1943

1.11 Aleksandr Deineka, *Freedom of the Open Spaces*, 1944

In his 1933 painting *White HQ: Interrogation* (**1.9**) Deineka depicts the White officers as sleazy rogues, tunics unbuttoned, drinks and cigars on the table, with the isolated figure of a half-dressed woman at the side. It is as much a German painting as a Russian one, evoking the nastiness of the naturally corrupt in the manner of Grosz and others. In general, Deineka's skill at satire and caricature makes him antithetic to Socialist Realism, which was an affirmative rather than a critical art, mainly concerned with promoting the nobility of the favoured side and projecting optimism (however groundless) rather than criticising the decadence of opponents.

Deineka did not suffer the same eclipse as Kustodiev and Petrov-Vodkin. Although in the 40s he appears to have angered Zhdanov, the successor of Lunacharskii, his career was not seriously handicapped and he continued to exhibit and travel abroad. While his paintings are popular and heroic, the designs are sharply realised with simple monumental forms and clear lighting adding an apparitional effect. Deineka's capacity to arrest and stimulate with huge canvases such as *Air Ace Shot Down* (**1.10**) and *Freedom of the Open Spaces* (**1.11**) has no parallel. The monumental stillness he projects in designs depicting movement is mysterious: it is as if from a sequence of passing images he had extracted one, stopping the world for a split second to pinpoint a unique drama. The strangeness of the girls running and the horror of the falling pilot lies in their frozen immobility in a realistic, but otherwise unpeopled and dreamlike world.

The flourishing state of Soviet painting around 1930 is clear: some of the most vivid images here are Bogorodskii's portraits of sailors (**1.4-5**) and Osolodkov's miner (**1.32**), all sharply observed, fully realised, credible images that belong to life. There is a difference between these and, for example, the later Pimenov, *Station in Autumn* (**1.40**), of 1945, where a moody picturesqueness and loose paintwork sap the emotion by comparison with Pimenov's intense 1920s picture *Disabled War Veterans*. While the later work is certainly representative of the mood of exhaustion and dislocation at the end of the war, the artistic distancing and slightly sentimental presentation deprive it of the impetus to change that was originally the emblem of revolutionary art.

Understanding the early years of Soviet art means looking at the context in which artists were working and the way political values are reflected in art. Uncertainty over how art would represent the new world the Bolsheviks wanted to create left them caught between highly theorised Constructivism, which was collective and modern but not widely accessible, and a fully available

1.4 Fëdor Bogorodskii, *Red Navy Sailor-Poet*, 1931

realism that often perpetuated moribund art concepts and forms. Interest lies in the quality of the debate, and the bridges it was possible to build — with the help of subtle political leadership in cultural affairs — between these two extremes.

NOTES

1. Leon Trotsky, *Literature and Revolution* (1924), Allen & Unwin, 1925, p194.
2. V.I. *Lenin on Literature and Art*, Moscow, 1970, p 214.
3. Letter to A.K. Voronsky, qu C. Vaughan James, *Soviet Socialist Realism: Origins and Theory*, Macmillan, 1973, p 52.
4. Qu Vaughan James, *op cit*, p 28.
5. *ibid*, p 22.
6. *Lenin and Lunacharskii: Letters, Reports and Documents*, Moscow, 1971, p 260, qu Mark Etkind (intr), *Boris Kustodiev*, Leningrad, 1983.
7. Qu by John Bowlt, *Russian Art of the Avant-Garde: Theory and Criticism*, Thames & Hudson, 1988, p xxxix.
8. From 'Declaration of the Association of Artists of Revolutionary Russia', qu Bowlt, *op cit*, p 265.
9. Qu Bowlt, *op cit*, p 269.
10. Details of these arguments are in A. Pavliuchenkov, 'Politika kommunisticheskoi partii v oblasti kul'tury (1917-1927)', *Iskusstvo*, Moscow, 11, 1988.
11. Document published in full in Vaughan James, *op cit*, pp 116-19.
12. Petrov-Vodkin qu from stenographic record of a meeting devoted to his career, Moscow, 25.5.1933., qu Iurii Rusakov, *Petrov-Vodkin*, Leningrad, 1986, p 44.

CATALOGUE

Notes by Anna Antonova (12, 30); Elena Basner, (2, 13, 15-16, 28, 52); Anatolii Dmitrenko (4-5, 8-11, 14, 21-3, 27, 31-2, 37-40, 43-6); Valentina Kniazeva (42, 47, 49-51, 53, 55); Galina Krechina (18-19, 24, 26, 48, 54); Vladimir Kruglov (1, 3, 6-7, 20, 25, 29, 33-6, 41); Olga Shikhireva (17); with biographical data by Irina Kokurina (4-5, 31-2, 39-40, 43-4). All works belong to the State Russian Museum, Leningrad, whose inventory numbers are included. The details of artists' education and exhibitions (exh) are selective.

NATAN ISAEVICH ALTMAN

1889 (Vinnitsa, Ukraine)-1970 (Leningrad)

Studied at Odessa Art School (1901-7) and Académie Russe de Marie Vasilieff, Paris (1910-11). Exh: Union of Youth (1913-14); World of Art (1913-16); 0.10 (1915-16); Jack of Diamonds (1916-17). Lived in St Petersburg-Leningrad, also Paris (1909-11, 1928-35) and Moscow (1921-28). Taught at Petrograd Svomas (1918-20). Member of Fine Arts Board, Narkompros (1918-21). Decorated Palace Square, Petrograd, in 1918 (see **4.8-11**).

1.1 Portrait of an Unknown Man 1908 (1909?)

Oil on canvas, 111 x 75.5; inv. Zh-9379
Acquired in 1977 from the family of P.P. Kazachkov, Leningrad.

An early work done just before Altman's first trip to Paris and adoption of Cubist forms, 1.1 already shows the mastery of colour and psychology in Altman's *Portrait of Anna Akhmatova*, 1914 (State Russian Museum).

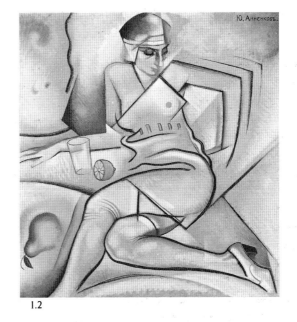

1.2

IURII PAVLOVICH ANNENKOV
1897 (Petropavlovsk, Kazakhstan)-1974 (Paris)

Studied in St Petersburg (1908-11) and in Paris with Maurice Denis and Félix Vallotton (1911-12). Exh: World of Art (1922), abroad. Lived in Petrograd. Designed mass festivals, 1920-21. From 1924, lived in Paris.

1.2 Portrait of Elena Annenkova 1917

Oil on canvas, 84 x 82; inv. ZhB-1227
Signed tr: 'Iu. Annenkov'.
Acquired in 1920 from A.A. Korovir..

The sitter is the artist's wife, born Galperina (1897-1980). Annenkov's talent for caricature can be felt also in his portraits. The exaggerations here are expressive; the extravagant character of the model is emphasised by the unusual composition.

VLADIMIR DAVIDOVICH BARANOV-ROSSINÉ (Volf Davidovich Baranov Shulim)
1888 (Bolshaia Lepatikha, Tavrida Province)-1942 (Germany)

Studied at Odessa Art School (1903-8), Academy of Arts, St Petersburg (1908-9) and in Paris. Exh: Salon d'Automne, Paris (1910-13), Salon des Indépendants, Paris (1911-14, 1925-42), First State Free Art Exh (1919), First Russian Art Exh, Van Diemen Gallery, Berlin (1922). Lived in St Petersburg-Petrograd (1908-9, 1917-19), Paris (1910-14, from 1925), Christiania (Oslo) (1915-17), Moscow (1919-25). Died in a concentration camp. In Paris known as Daniel Rossiné. Taught at Svomas (1918-19). Member of the Fine Art Board, Narkompros (1918). Decorated Petrograd, November 1918 (see **4.27-8**).

1.3 Woman in a Shawl* c 1917

Oil on canvas, 107 x 71.5; inv. ZhB-1416
Signed lc: 'Rossiné' (Latin alphabet).
Acquired in 1926 from Museum of Artistic Culture, Leningrad.

About 1917, after experiments with Futurism and Non-Objective Creation, the artist returned to a realistic style, enriched with the techniques of the new art.

1.28 Pëtr Miturich, *Portrait of the Composer Lourié*, 1915

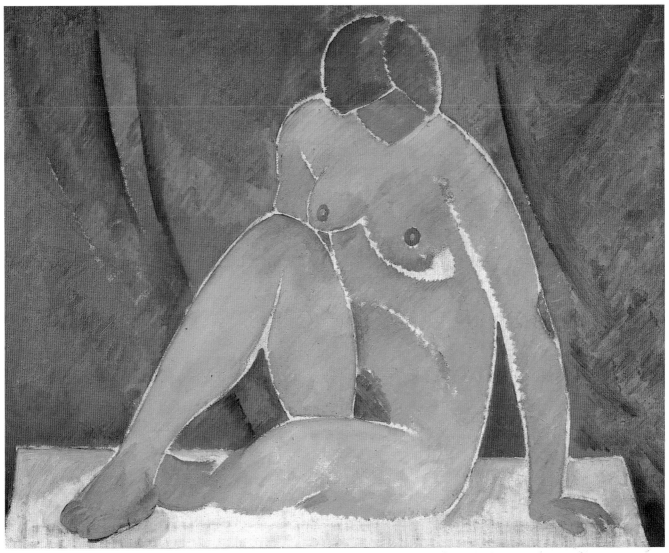

1.55 Vladimir Tatlin, *Model*, 1913

1.3

FËDOR SEMËNOVICH BOGORODSKII
1895 (Nizhnii Novgorod)-1959 (Moscow).
Studied law at Moscow University (1914-16), art in Moscow studios (from 1914), Vkhutemas, Moscow (1922-4), with Abram Arkhipov. Member of Bytie (1924), AKhRR-AKhR (1924). Exh: from 1916. Lived in Nizhnii Novgorod and (from 1922) Moscow. Travelled to Germany and Italy (1928-30). Taught at All-Union Institute of Cinematography (1938-59).

1.4 Red Navy Sailor-Poet* 1931
Oil on canvas, 78 x 58; inv. Zh-8919
Signed ll: 'F. Bogorodskii Batum': note on stretcher: 'Portrait of Reshetnikov'.
Acquired in 1973 from USSR Union of Artists.

1.5 Youth (Sailors)** 1932
Oil on canvas, 110 x 83; inv. Zh-4418
Signed lc: 'F. Bogorodskii, Moskva, 1932'.
Acquired from Leningrad City Soviet, 1933.

Bogorodskii made heroic-dramatic paintings, including his strongly felt portraits of homeless orphans of the 20s, 'Besprizorniki'. 1.5 belongs to Bogorodskii's more optimistic documentary pictures of the early 1930s, as does 1.4 and a series showing sailors and their families at the photographers. The artist presents his sitters directly, with their energy and intensity remaining fresh and immediate.

LEV ALEKSANDROVICH BRUNI
1894 (Malaia Vishera, Novgorod)-1948 (Moscow)
Son of the architect Bruni, the artist studied in St Petersburg (1904-12), and with J.-P. Laurens at Académie Julian, Paris. Exh: World of Art (1915-16, 1918), Petrograd Artists of All Trends (1923), Makovets (1924-5), Four Arts (1925-9). Lived in St Petersburg-Petrograd and (from 1923) Moscow; visited Paris (1912-13), Georgia (1915). Inspector in Fine Art Section, Narkompros (1920), Petrograd; taught at Vkhutemas-Vkhutein (1923-30) and Institute of Fine Art (1931-8), Moscow. Headed Studio of Monumental Painting of USSR Academy of Architecture (1935-48).

1.6 Peasant Girl 1916
Oil on canvas, 68 x 61; inv. ZhB-1346
Signed lc: 'Lev Bruni'.
Acquired in 1926 from Museum of Artistic Culture, Leningrad.

Bruni completed this confident work at the age of 22. The image combines seriousness and intelligence, severity and shyness.

1.6

MARC ZAKHAROVICH CHAGALL
1887 (Liozno, near Vitebsk)-1985 (Saint-Paul, Alpes Maritimes, France)
Studied in Vitebsk (1906) and St Petersburg at Drawing School of the Society for the Encouragement of the Arts (1907-8), Zaidenberg's studio (1908), and with Bakst and Dobuzhinskii at Zvantseva's school (1908-10). Exh: World of Art (1912), Donkey's Tail (1912), The Target (1913), Jack of Diamonds (1916); member of Union of Youth (1910-12). Many foreign exhibitions. Lived in Vitebsk (to 1907, 1914-15, 1917-20),Paris (1910-14), Petrograd and Moscow (1921-2), Germany, France, USA, and (from 1948) Paris.

1.7 Red Jew,** 1915
Oil on board, 100 x 80.5; inv. ZhB-1708
Signed lc: 'Chagall'; on reverse: 'Chagall 915'.

Acquired in 1926 from Museum of Artistic Culture, Leningrad. The picture is one of the most dramatic of the cycle painted in 1914-15 in Vitebsk showing typical inhabitants of a small town of the Jewish Pale of Settlement. In Chagall's pictures the poor, elderly Jews are transformed into allegorical figures of inner power. The background incorporates texts from Hebrew Scriptures.

ALEKSANDR ALEKSANDROVICH DEINEKA
1899 (Kursk)-1969 (Moscow)

Studied at Kharkov Art School (1915-17), and with Favorskii and Nivinskii in Print Faculty, Vkhutemas (1921-5). Founder-member, OST (1925-8), October (1928-30); member of RAPKh (1931-2). Exh: First Discussional Exh of Associations of Active Revolutionary Art, as part of the Union of Three. Served in the Red Army at the defence of Kursk (1919-20). Lived in Moscow from 1920. Travelled to France and Italy (1925-36), USA (1935), Germany (1945), Austria (1947), Italy (1965). Taught at Vkhutein (1928-30), Poligraphic Institute (1928-34), Institute of Fine Art-Art Institute (1934-46; 1957-63), Institute of Applied and Decorative Art (1945-53) and Architectural Institute (1953-7), all in Moscow.

1.8 Midday** 1932

Early version-sketch for *Midday Break on the Donbass* (1935), 149.8 x 248.5, Latvian State Art Museum, Riga

Oil on canvas, 59.5 x 80; *inv.* ZhB-1816

Signed *lr:* 'A. Deineka 32g' (g = year).

Acquired in 1934 from All-Russian Committee of Artists.

1.9 White HQ: Interrogation** 1933

Oil on canvas, 130 x 200; *inv.* Zh-7710

Signed *lr:* 'A. Deineka 33g'.

Acquired in 1962 from Central Museum of the Soviet Army, Moscow.

1.10 Air Ace Shot Down** 1943

Oil on canvas, 283 x 188; *inv.* Zh-7018

Acquired in 1960 from USSR Ministry of Culture.

1.11 Freedom of the Open Spaces** 1944

Oil on canvas, 204 x 300; *inv.* Zh-4500

Acquired in 1949 from Arts Committee of USSR Council of Ministers.

The many-sided talent of Deineka revealed itself in different subjects and forms of art. As well as the epic approach, his work showed a lyrical perception of the world, expressed in 1.8, a scene in the industrial Donbass. The design, precise and economical, yet suggestive of freedom, gives it an individual, poetic character.

The theme of revolutionary history is important for Deineka. In 1.9 the artist organises his canvas in sharply opposed black and white, concentrating on the energy of the silhouetted figures. In the tough confrontation of the captive communist and the White officers, who are caricatured, the artist points to the irreconcilable gulf between the opposed sides during the Russian Civil War.

In 1.10 the German pilot is shown with complex foreshortening, as if in slow motion, as he falls inexorably towards the anti-tank defences of the battered city: the fall is perceived in real terms, but also as a metaphor. It is both a possible scene of wartime, but also an original image of retribution.

1.11 was painted at the very end of the Second World War, uniting peace-time memories of the artist with an assertion that suffering will not break the spirit of the people. After a series of tragic images of the events of the war, Deineka expressed here his feeling for his homeland and his confidence in the coming victory. The epic treatment of the spaciousness of Russia and the expressiveness of the girls' outlook made it an original symbol for the affirmation of life. The river probably represents a synthesised Russian scene.

1.12

NIKOLAI IVANOVICH DORMIDONTOV
1898 (St Petersburg)-1962 (Leningrad)

Studied at Drawing School of the Society for the Encouragement of the Arts (1914-18), and with Kardovskii, Petrov-Vodkin and Vasilii Shukhaev at Svomas (1918-22), both in Petrograd. Founder-member of AKhRR-AKhR (1922-32). Lived in St Petersburg-Leningrad. Taught at Leningrad Industrial Art Technical College (1923-9).

1.12 Street Musicians 1931-4

Oil on canvas, 60 x 76; *inv.* Zh-8297

Signed *ll:* 'N. Dormidontov 931-34'.

Acquired in 1967 from T. P Dormidontova, artist's widow, Leningrad.

Cityscape is one of Dormidontov's favourite early subjects: he was attracted not to the ceremonial, official aspect of the city, but to its outskirts, to dilapidated, run-down buildings, courtyards strewn with rubbish and rickety fences. Here the sad figures of beggar-buskers are shown against such a background.

1.7 Marc Chagall, *Red Jew*, 1915

1.15 Boris Grigorev, *Girl with a Milk-can*, 1917

ROBERT RAFAILOVICH FALK
1886 (Moscow)-1958 (Moscow)
Studied at Konstantin Iuon and Ivan Dudin's school of drawing and painting (1904-5), in Mashkov's studio, and with Serov and Korovin at Moscow School of Art, Sculpture and Architecture (1905-12). Exh: Golden Fleece (1909-10), Jack of Diamonds (1910-17), World of Art (1910, 1917, 1921-22), Moscow Painters (1925), AKhRR (1926-8, member from 1926), Society of Moscow Artists (1928). Lived in Moscow and Paris (1928-37). Member of Fine Art Board, Narkompros (1918-21), on staff at Inkhuk (1920). Taught at first Svomas (1918-20), at Vkhutemas-Vkhutein (1920-28).

1.13 Portrait of an Unknown Man 1910s
Oil on canvas, 137 x 114; inv. ZhB-1505
Acquired in 1926 from Museum of Artistic Culture, Leningrad.

Falk's meditative art in 1915-17 is known as 'lyrical Cubism'. The Cézanne-influenced forms and sombre colours are expressive. Falk wrote later that he used 'dislocations of form to accentuate emotion'.

SERGEI VASILEVICH GERASIMOV
1885 (Mozhaisk, Moscow)-1964 (Moscow)
Studied at Stroganov School of Applied Art (1901-7) and School of Painting, Sculpture and Architecture (1907-11), both Moscow. Member of World of Art (1921), Makovets (1922-5), OMKh (1926-9), AKhR (1930-32). Exh: from 1906. Lived in Moscow, spending World War Two in Samarkand. Visited Italy, Greece, Turkey (1925), Western Europe (1950s and 60s). Taught in art school at Sytin Press (see p70) (1912-14) and at IZO State School of Printing at First Model Press (1918-23), in Vkhutemas-Vkhutein, Moscow (1920-29), in Printing Institute (1930-36), Institute of Fine Art-Art Institute (1936-50) and Higher Applied Art School (1950-64), all Moscow. Decorated Moscow in November 1918.

1.14 Mother of the Partisan, study 1943
Study for main figure in large painting of same title (1943-6), State Tretiakov Gallery.
Oil on canvas, 113 x 84.5; inv. Zh-4414
Signed ll: 'Sergei Gerasimov 43'; and on stretcher 'Sergei Gerasimov'.
Acquired in 1948 from Art Committee of RSFSR Council of Ministers.

The artist described his theme as 'the life of the Russian people'. The subject of this study appears full-length in the large composition of the same name, showing a Russian peasant woman stubbornly defying an inquisitorial German officer. The image affirms the power of the individual and represented at this point an emblem for the land itself, the Soviet people who would not submit to fascism.

BORIS DMITRIEVICH GRIGOREV
1886 (Rybinsk)-1939 (Cannes)
Studied at Stroganov School of Applied Art (1903-7) and Academy of Arts, St Petersburg (1907-12). Lived in St Petersburg-Petrograd, Paris (1912-14), and (after 1919) in Finland, Germany and France. Exh: World of Art (1913, 1915-18, a member from 1918); took part in decoration of Petrograd, November 1918, painting a portrait of Whitman. Taught at 1st State Svomas, Moscow (1918-19).

1.15 Girl with a Milk-can** 1917
Oil on canvas, 71 x 62; inv. Zh-11143
Signed lr: 'Boris Grigorev 917'.
Received in 1984 from B.N. Okunev, as a legacy.

1.16 Countryside** 1918
Oil on canvas, 80.5 x 97.5; inv. ZhB-1686
Signed ll: 'Boris Grigorev 918'.
Acquired from the artist in 1918.

Like many Russian artists of his generation, Grigorev painted the life of peasants. But instead of the lyricism of typical pictures, Grigorev's works underline darker intonations. His ambivalence was clear in the series of drawings and paintings *Raseia* (a title which is a primitive form of 'Russia'), made in 1917-18, to which the closely-related pictures here belong. Addressing the theme of childhood and deprivation, the loneliness of a child in a harsh world, Grigorev is close to Dostoevsky's belief that the pursuit of even a virtuous cause does not justify the suffering of the innocent. Grigorev also painted sophisticated portraits of the St Petersburg cultural world, most notably in his *Portrait of Meyerhold* (State Russian Museum).

1.14

ALEKSEI VASILEVICH GRISHCHENKO
1883 (Krolevets, Chernigov Province, Ukraine)-1977 (Paris)
Studied philosophy at Kiev and Moscow universities (1905-12), painting in Kiev (1905) and in Iuon and Mashkov's studios in Moscow (1910-11). Exh: Jack of Diamonds (1912), Union of Youth (1913-14), World of Art (1917). Taught at Svomas, Moscow, 1919. Lived in France from 1923.

1.17 Female Portrait 1918
Oil on canvas, 60.5 x 52; ZhB-1375
Signed in image on collar: 'A.G. 18'; and, l, 18'.
Acquired in 1926 from Museum of Artistic Culture, Leningrad.

The artist is drawn to several traditions of the immediate past being explored at this time; he combines elements of simplified Cubism in a decorative way with geometric schematisation and Impressionist brushstrokes.

PËTR PETROVICH KONCHALOVSKII
1876 (Slaviansk, Ukraine)-1956 (Moscow)
Studied at evening classes at Stroganov Central School of Applied Art, Moscow, in Paris (1897-8), and at Academy of Arts, St Petersburg (1898-1907). A founder of Jack of Diamonds (1910). Exh: Union of Youth (1911), World of Art (1911-22 *passim*), Bytie (1926-7), AKhRR (1928). Lived in Moscow. Taught at Svomas (1918-21) and Vkhutemas-Vkhutein (1926-9). People's Artist of RSFSR, 1946; member of USSR Academy of Arts, 1947.

1.18 Portrait of Iu.P. Denike and A.D. Pokrovskii* 1913
Oil on canvas, 160 x 132; inv. ZhB-1902
Signed ur: 'P. Konchalovskii 1913'.
Acquired in 1926 from Museum of Artistic Culture, Leningrad.

1.19 Portrait of S.P. Konchalovskaia and her Daughter Tatiana* 1916
Oil on canvas, 199 x 200; inv. ZhB-1903
Acquired in 1929 from State Tretiakov Gallery.

Cézanne was influential on Konchalovskii, especially in his early works and portraits. The artist rejects psychological refinements, revealing and emphasising only certain basic features, expressed in silhouette and the thick, rough paintwork. The second work interprets the portrait as still-life, the colour and form rendered summarily, without spatial depth. The subjects of 1.18 were friends of the artist, and of 1.19, his sister, Sofia, and niece (b.1904).

KONSTANTIN ALEKSEEVICH KOROVIN
1861 (Moscow)-1939 (Paris)
Korovin studied at Moscow School of Painting, Sculpture and Architecture (1875-86), and Academy of Arts, St Petersburg (1882), academician 1905. A member of Abramtsevo circle from 1885. Exh: Itinerants (1889, 1891, 1893-9), World of Art (1899-1903, 1906, 1921-2, member 1899), Union of Russian Artists (1903-18, 1922, 1923, member 1903), Exposition Universelle, Paris (1900), international shows in Munich (1898), Vienna (1902), Venice (1907), Rome (1911). Lived in Moscow and (from 1923) Paris. Travelled in the West from 1888. Taught at Moscow School of Painting, Sculpture and Architecture (1901-18). Also prolific theatre designer.

1.20 Landing-stage at Gurzuf 1914.
Oil on canvas, 89 x 121; inv. Zh-2005
Signed ll: Konst. Korovin 1914'.
Acquired in 1915 from Union of Russian Artists exh.

Among the most popular and successful Russian painters of the early 20th century, Korovin was always true to Impressionism. This picture shows a spa town in the Crimea, a sparkling, sunny world in a mood of cloudless optimism. At the emotional and compositional centre of the picture is the artist's favourite model, the actress Nadezhda Komarovskaia (1889-1967).

1.20

BORIS MIKHAILOVICH KUSTODIEV
1878 (Astrakhan)-1927 (Leningrad)
Kustodiev studied in Astrakhan (1893-6) and with Savinskii and Repin at Higher School of Art attached to Academy of Arts, St Petersburg (1896-1903), where he also studied sculpture. An organiser of New Society of Artists (1904-8), member of Union of Russian Artists (1907-10), World of Art (from 1911). Exh: include AKhRR (from 1923). Lived in St Petersburg-Leningrad from 1896. Bursary to visit France and Spain (1904), travelled in Italy (1907, 1913), Austria, France (1909, 1917), Germany (1909), Switzerland (1911, 1912) and Finland (1917). Taught in New Art Studio, St Petersburg, 1913. Decorated Petrograd, November 1918 **(4.16-18)**.

1.21 Merchant's Wife at the Mirror** 1920
Oil on canvas, 142 x 102; inv. Zh-7654
Signed ll: 'B. Kustodiev 1920'.
Acquired in 1962 from Dzerzhinskii club of Interior Ministry, Leningrad.

1.22 Festivities in Uritskii Square on the Opening Day of the Second Congress of the Comintern in July 1920** 1921
Oil on canvas, 133 x 268; inv. Zh-6148
Signed ll: '19-B-21 Kustodiev'; on the reverse is inscription: '3366 pr. M.R. rab. B. Kustodieva "Demonstratsiia I-go maia 1920g. na pl. Uritskogo'".
Acquired in 1955 from Central Lenin Museum

1.16 Boris Grigorev, *Countryside*, 1918

1.21 Boris Kustodiev, *Merchant's Wife at the Mirror*, 1920

45

1.23

1.25

1.23 Portrait of the Architect Isidor Samoilovich Zolotarevskii 1922

Oil on canvas, 98.5 x 111.5; inv. Zh-6421
Signed *ll*: 'B Kustodiev 1922'.

1.21 is an example of the artist's more traditional works centred on recollections of his Astrakhan childhood and the life of Russian merchants. The image of the merchant's wife is especially typical of these pictures, as are the attention to descriptive detail and the richness of colour. The muffled tones of this picture are more sombre than in the outdoor, festive compositions of this kind, which are full of nostalgia evoked in bright, high-keyed colour.

1.22 conveys the celebratory atmosphere of the popular revolutionary festivals, precisely observed in the details and powerful and elegaic in colour. Kustodiev was ill from 1909 and lost the use of his legs in 1917: he was lent a car in July 1920 to view the Petrograd celebrations. He wrote of such works 'A picture should be a document for our descendants'.

In 1.23 the artist combines the image of the sitter in an interior with the cityscape beyond the frosty window; the device matches the aesthetic milieu and character of the sitter with the world of his work outside.

ARISTARKH VASILEVICH LENTULOV
1882 (Vorona, Penza Province)-1943 (Moscow)

Lentulov studied in Penza (1898-1900), Kiev (1900-1905) and in St Petersburg with Kardovskii (1906-7). Worked with Henri Le Fauconnier and Jean Metzinger at Académie La Palette, Paris, 1911. Exh: World of Art (1912, 1922, *passim*). Founder member of Jack of Diamonds (1910), member, Obmokhu (1919-21), AKhRR (1926-8), Society of Moscow Artists (1928-32, chairman); member, Fine Art Board, Narkompros (1918). On staff of Inkhuk (from 1920). Lived in Moscow from 1910. Taught in State Svomas, Moscow Institute of Fine Art-Moscow Art Institute (1918-43). Took part in setting up Kafé Pittoresk and the literary cabaret Kafé Poetov in 1917.

1.24 Self-portrait** 1913

Oil on canvas, 83 x 83; inv. Zh-8240
Acquired from artist in 1920 via Fine Art Section, Narkompros.

Like other Russian artists of his generation, Lentulov was influenced by peasant art: toys, printed textiles and other cottage industry work. He is known for his brightly coloured canvases with their unexpected rhythms. 1.24 is typical of the Jack of Diamonds group in its French fauvist colour. The artist is attempting here to give easel painting a sculptural quality.

NADEZHDA VLADIMIROVNA LERMONTOVA
1885 (St Petersburg)-1921 (Petrograd)

The artist, of the family of the poet Mikhail Lermontov (1814-41), and daughter of a St Petersburg University professor, was a graduate of the Bestuzhev Higher Courses for Women (see 6.78). Studied under Bakst at Zvantseva's School, St Petersburg (1907-10). Exh: World of Art (1911-12, 1916-17), Union of Youth (1912-13). Lived in St Petersburg; visited Germany (1907), Crimea (1911, 1915), Scandinavia (1912), Samarkand (1915-16). Painted frescoes in church of Vasilii Zlatoverkhii in Ovruch, Ukraine, 1910. Published drawings in journal *Bogem* (Bohemian); made sets for Petrograd Puppet Theatre.

1.25 On the Sofa. Self-portrait 1910s

Oil on canvas, 106.8 x 124.5; inv. Zh-11720
Acquired in 1988 from M.V. Fok, Moscow.

After Chagall, Lermontova was considered the most talented pupil of Bakst. This painting is one of the best to have survived, showing her gift for colour. The model's despair, the brittle drawing of her figure and the melancholy but resonant range of refined colours give a dramatic representation of Lermontova's character.

ILIA IVANOVICH MASHKOV
1881 (Mikhailovka, now in Volgograd Region)-1944 (Moscow)
Studied with Arkhipov, Leonid Pasternak, Korovin and Serov at Moscow School of Painting, Sculpture and Architecture (1900-09). A founder of Jack of Diamonds, 1910; member and exhibitor, *passim*, World of Art (1911-17), member AKhRR (from 1924) and Society of Moscow Artists (1927-8). Lived in Moscow, teaching at his studio 1904-17; taught at Svomas-Vkhutein, 1918-30; head of central studio of AKhRR, 1925-9. Honoured Artist of RSFSR, 1928.

1.26 Portrait of a Woman With Pheasants** 1911
Oil on canvas, 177 x 133; inv. ZhB-1240
Signed lr: 'Ilia Mashkov'.
Acquired in 1920 from Fine Art Section, Narkompros, Moscow.

1.27 Portrait of Z.D.P. (Woman in Blue)* 1927
Oil on canvas, 184 x 132; inv. Zh-11312
Acquired in 1985 from A.G. Khailova, Moscow.

The heightened colour, vigorous brushstrokes, contrast between intensely coloured and pale areas, and the eyecatching character of the scene, are all typical of the Jack of Diamonds group, of which Mashkov was a leading member. This is an early work, in which exaggeration, decorative and expressive colour, and a certain stylisation in the manner of popular prints (see pp 61-96) are basic elements. Mashkov presents a generalised image: a well-groomed upper middle-class woman in an elegant gown and jewellery, unexpectedly portrayed in bright, unnatural colours. She poses in front of two absurd stuffed birds, and, in the ironical view of the artist, becomes herself — like them — a piece of artifice. The model was F. Ia. Gesse, sister of the poet S. Ia. Rubanovich, himself close to the Jack of Diamonds group. In 1.27 Mashkov poses his striking model in a milieu of fine furniture and *objets d'art*. There is a sense of genuine admiration on the artist's part for the sitter and her elegant interior.

PËTR VASILEVICH MITURICH
1887 (St Petersburg)-1956 (Moscow)
Studied at Kiev Art School (1906-9) and Academy of Arts, St Petersburg (1909-16). Lived in Moscow from 1922. Member of World of Art from 1915 and Four Arts from 1925. Taught at Vkhutemas-Vkhutein (1923-30) and Moscow Institute for Raising the Qualifications of Artists (1930-37). Made innovatory 'space paintings' and 'space graphics'.

1.28 Portrait of the Composer Artur Sergeevich Lourié** 1915
Oil on canvas, 102 x 101.5; inv. ZhB-1714
Signed ll: '15 g P. Miturich'.
Acquired in 1920 from S.K. Isakov.

A gifted draughtsman, Miturich carried the sharpness and economy of his drawings over into painting. A contemporary recalled that he painted this portrait in one and a half hours in the studio of Lev Bruni (1.6), where the *avant-garde* composer (1892-1966) was posing for a portrait that is also in the State Russian Museum. Although painted quickly the work conveys both a likeness of Lourié and the character of the musical-Futurist; the dislocation between the graphic lines and the colour reflects contemporary artists' interest in similar effects in popular prints (see **2.85**).

MIKHAIL VASILEVICH NESTEROV
1862 (Ufa)-1942 (Moscow)
Studied at Moscow School of Painting, Sculpture and Architecture (1877-81, 1884-6) and Academy of Arts, St. Petersburg (1881-4), academician, 1898. Exh: Itinerants (1889-1901, member 1896), World of Art (1899-1901), Artists of the RSFSR After 15 years (1932), Exposition Universelle, Paris (1900); other international shows in Munich (1898, 1909), Rome (1911) etc. Lived in Moscow (from 1874) and Kiev (1890-1910). Decorated interior of Vladimir cathedral in Kiev, Resurrection church in St Petersburg, and Convent of Martha and Mary in Moscow. Visited Italy, France, Austria, Germany, Greece and Turkey. Honoured Artist of RSFSR, USSR State prizewinner.

1.29 Self-portrait* 1915
Oil on wood, 94 x 100; inv. Zh-4340
Signed lr: 'Mikh. Nesterov 1915'.
Acquired in 1945 from Arts Administration of RSFSR Council of People's Commissars.

1.30 Portrait of the Surgeon Sergei Sergeevich Iudin* 1933
Oil on canvas, 99 x 80; inv. Zh-1855
Signed lr: 'Mikhail Nesterov. 1933'.
Acquired in 1939 from Leningrad Purchasing Committee.

Nesterov was formerly a painter of poetic mystical works, based on themes from the mythology attached to Orthodox Church history. After the revolution he concentrated on portraits. At the time of 1.29 the artist was working on the philosophic painting In Rus (*Spirit of the People*), influenced by the events of the First World War; the severe Urals landscape behind him echoes his sombre thoughts.
  Nesterov painted several portraits of Professor Iudin (1891-1954), to whom he was attracted by the surgeon's love of his work, but also his unusual appearance and expressive gestures.

IAROSLAV SERGEEVICH NIKOLAEV
1899 (Shauliai, Kaunas, Lithuania)-1978 (Leningrad)
Studied at Tomsk School of Painting (1915-17), at Tomsk and Irkutsk universities (1917-20), and in East Siberia Art Studios (1925-8). Member of Society of Irkutsk Artists (1920-29) and AKhRR (from 1930-32); exhibited from 1927. Lived in Leningrad from 1930. Travelled in Mongolia, 1927. Taught in East Siberia studios, 1928-30.

1.31 Self-portrait* 1942
Oil on canvas, 61 x 48; Zh-7940
Acquired in 1964 from Culture Administration of Leningrad Soviet.

The portrait is a harsh document of suffering during the blockade of Leningrad, showing an emaciated, exhausted figure, the pallor of the thin face emphasised by the bright scarf.

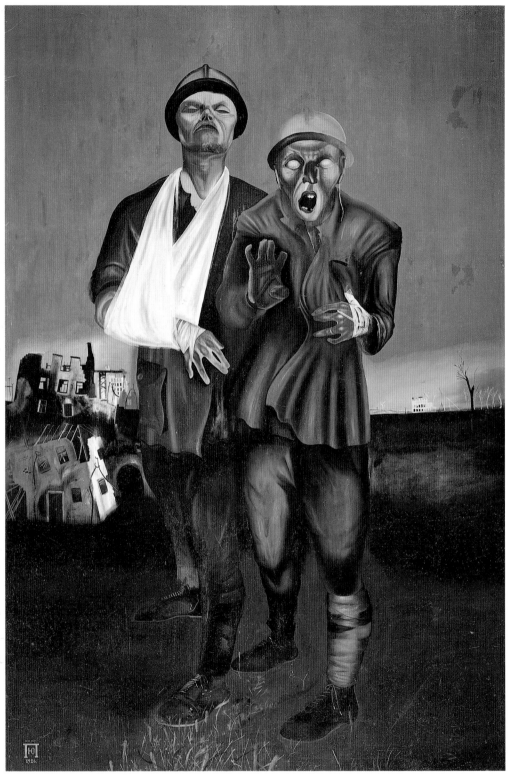

1.39 Iurii Pimenov, *Disabled War Veterans*, 1926

1.5 Fëdor Bogorodskii, *Youth (Sailors)*, 1932

1.31

PĒTR ALEKSEEVICH OSOLODKOV
1898 (Rybinsk)-1942 (Leningrad)

Studied in Omsk, in art studios of the Fifth Army and at Applied Art Technical College (1920-24), and in Leningrad at Vkhutemas-Vkhutein (1924-9), Institute of Painting, Sculpture and Architecture (1932-4) and All-Russia Academy of Arts (1934-6). Member of the Circle of Artists (1927-32). Exh: from 1927. Lived in Leningrad from 1924, where he died during the wartime blockade.

1.32 Portrait of a Miner* 1933-4

Oil on canvas, 119 x 85.6; inv. ZhB-1797
Inscribed on reverse: 'Petr Osolodkov/1933-1934'.
Acquired in 1934 from the artist, Leningrad.

The choice of model and interpretation are typical of this artist, who painted ordinary people without deliberation or calculated pose. The image has moral strength and is depicted tersely, with its own epic character.

KUZMA SERGEEVICH PETROV-VODKIN
1878 (Khvalynsk, Saratov Province)-1939 (Leningrad)

Petrov-Vodkin studied with Arkhipov and Serov at Moscow School of Painting, Sculpture and Architecture (1897-1904), at Anton Azbé's school, Munich (1901), and in Paris (1905-8). Exh: Salon d'Automne, Paris (1906-8), World of Art (1911-24), AKhRR (1923, 1928), Four Arts (1925-8). Lived in St Petersburg-Leningrad (from 1908), in Paris (1924-6). Taught in Svomas (1918-21), All-Russia Academy of Arts (1921-38). Decorated Petrograd, November 1918 **(4.19-20).** First chairman of the Leningrad branch of USSR Union of Artists. Honoured Artist of the RSFSR, 1930.

1.33 Dream** 1910

Oil on canvas, 161 x 187; inv. ZhB-1242
Signed lr: 'K. Petrov-Vodkin 1910'.
Acquired in 1921 from Society for the Encouragement of the Arts, Petrograd.

1.34 Thirsty Warrior** 1915

Oil on canvas, 65 x 105; inv. Zh-8013
Signed lr with monogram: 'KPV 1915'.
Acquired in 1964 from the State Hermitage.

1.35 Midday** 1917

Oil on canvas, 89 x 128.5; inv. ZhB-1263
Signed lr; 'KPV 1917'.
Acquired in 1926 from Museum of Artistic Culture, Leningrad.

1.36 Morning* 1917

Oil on canvas, 161 x 129; inv. ZhB-1261
Signed lr: 'KPV 1917'.
Acquired in 1920 from the artist.

1.37 Death of the Commissar** 1928

Oil on canvas, 196 x 248; inv. Zh-7685
Signed lr: 'KPV 28'.
Acquired in 1962 from Central Museum of the Armed Forces of the USSR, Moscow.

1.38 1919. The Alert** 1934

Oil on canvas, 169 x 159; inv. ZhB-1269.
Signed lr: 'KPV 1934'.
Acquired in 1940 from Leningrad City Soviet.

Petrov-Vodkin's early work is influenced by French Symbolism, while the importance for him of early Renaissance art is clear from the sculptural, generalised forms, strictly rhythmic composition and crisp drawing. Alexandre Benois reported Petrov-Vodkin saying of 1.33 'Asleep on a renascent earth is human genius. . . . Standing guard over its awakening are the two goddesses who always attend creative effort. The pink, timid, frail Beauty, and strong, swarthy Ugliness. In their embrace genius will discover full understanding of life and the meaning of things.'

1.34 is very close to *Bathing the Red Horse* (State Tretiakov Gallery), the major work of 1912 in which Petrov-Vodkin was influenced by Russian fresco and icon painting in creating a compelling image of renewal. 1.34 unites an 'icon' character with Classicism in a modern way: sculptural images with Symbolist overtones are portrayed in approximations to the three primary colours favoured by Petrov-Vodkin's colour theory, derived from the icon tradition. The picture's dynamic comes from this interplay, as well as polarities of movement and stillness, flatness and deep space, emotion and strict composition.

1.36 and 1.35 were both painted in the year the artist's father died, and reflect on the cycle of life and death. In 1.36 the mother and child are portrayed as part of an everyday scene, but are frozen and isolated in a way that gives them a solemn, ritual character. In 1.35 the high viewpoint Petrov-Vodkin often chose allows the cycle of life to be portrayed in different parts of the landscape, a device common in the early Renaissance paintings the artist was influenced by. This 'spherical' or 'inclined' perspective was adopted by Petrov-Vodkin to link the perceived scene to the expanse of the larger world. The location is specific — Volga countryside near the artist's childhood home. But, especially in 1.36, the grass is both realistic and at the same time a landscape of hills and valleys, a representation of the entire land.

The same is true of 1.37. The artist portrays the theme of sacrifice with depth and heroism, the 'planetary' perspective giving the individual death wider significance. The idea for 1.38 was first worked on at almost the same time as 1.37, but from 1926 Petrov-Vodkin suffered increasingly from tuberculosis and virtually abandoned oil painting. The Petrograd newspaper in the picture is dated October 1919, the time of an advance by a Civil War White army that threatened the city.

IURII IVANOVICH PIMENOV
1903 (Moscow)-1977 (Moscow)

Studied at Moscow Vkhutemas (1920-25). Founder member, OST, member IZO brigades (from 1931). Exh: from 1924, including First Discussional Exhibition of Associations of Active Revolutionary Art, as part of the Group of Three (1924). Lived and worked in Moscow. Visited Italy (1928, 1958), Germany (1928), Greece (1958), France (1958), England (1961), India (1962), USA and Japan (1970s). Taught at Institute for Raising the Qualifications of Artists, Moscow (1936-7), and All-Union Institute of Cinematography (1945-72).

1.39 Disabled War Veterans** 1926

Oil on canvas, 265.6 x 177.7; inv. ZhB-994
Signed ll with monogram: 'IuP 1926'.
Acquired in 1929 from State Tretiakov Gallery.

1.40 Station in Autumn 1945

Oil on canvas, 105.5 x 141.8; inv. Zh-4417.
Acquired in 1947 from Moscow Purchasing Committee.

1.39 dates from the period when the artist belonged to OST. The expressive colour and intense images of the maimed First World War soldiers make a concentrated composition. The terrible subject is interpreted realistically and as a symbol of the destructive power of war. In a far gentler way, 1.40 also reflects on war, the dislocation it brings to people's lives. Painted at the end of the Second World War, this work emphasises the woman's loneliness: in a station where the expectation is of meeting and reunion.

1.40

IVAN ALBERTOVICH PUNI
1894 (Kuokkala, near St Petersburg)-1956 (Paris)

Studied at Académie Julian, Paris (1910). Exh: Union of Youth (1912-14), Association of the Independents (1914-16), Tramway V (1915), 0.10 (1915-16), Jack of Diamonds (1916-17), First State Exhibition of Free Works of Art (1919). Lived in St Petersburg-Petrograd (to 1919), Paris (1909-12, 1914, from 1923), Vitebsk (1919), and Berlin (1920-23). Visited Italy (1912), etc. Participated in the Futurist almanac *Roaring Parnassus* (1914), organiser of Tramway V and 0.10. Decorated Petrograd, November 1918 (4.44-5). The artist is also known as Jean Pougny.

1.41 Portrait of the Artist's Wife 1914

Oil on canvas, 89 x 62.5; inv. ZhB-1627
Signed ll: '1914 g. Puni'.
Acquired in 1926 from Museum of Artistic Culture, Leningrad.

1.41 realises in a lyrical key the ideas of Russian Cubo-Futurism. Intersecting colour planes and slender lines create a metaphorical portrait of Puni's wife, the artist Kseniia Boguslavskaia **(see 3.67)**, to whom he was married the previous year.

1.8 Aleksandr Deineka, *Midday*, 1932

1.46 Aleksandr Samokhvalov, *Repairing a Locomotive*, 1931

1.43

1.44

ILIA EFIMOVICH REPIN
1844 (Chuguev, Kharkov, Ukraine)-1930 (Kuokkala, now Repino, near Leningrad)

Studied in St Petersburg at school of Society for the Encouragement of the Arts (1863) and at Academy of Arts (1864-71). Academy bursary to visit Italy and France (1873-6), academician 1876. Exhibiting member, Itinerants (1878). Exh: Academy of Arts, Society for the Encouragement of the Arts, World of Art. Lived in St Petersburg (from 1882), Kuokkala (from 1900). Travelled widely in Russia and Western Europe. Taught as professor in charge of the studio of historical paintings in Academy of Arts, and at Tenisheva's school.

1.42 Portrait of Vladimir Mikhailovich Bekhterev* 1913

Oil on canvas, 107 x 78; inv. Zh-6545
Signed lr: 'Il. Repin 1913'.
Acquired in 1956 from Pavlov Institute of Physiology, USSR Academy of Sciences.

Repin was a renowned portraitist, providing a glittering record of his cultural contemporaries. His directness and psychological insight is evident. Bekhterev (1857-1927) was the neuropathologist and psychiatrist who in 1918 became head of the Petrograd institute that today bears his name. Repin's famous subject paintings include *The Volga Boatmen* (1870-73) and *Religious Procession in Kursk Province* (1880-83: see p 23).

GEORGII GEORGIEVICH RIAZHSKII
1895 (Ignatevo, Moscow Province)-1952 (Moscow)

Studied drawing at Prechistenskie (workers) evening courses, Moscow (1910-15), then in various studios (1912-14, 1917) and at Moscow Svomas (1918-20), under Malevich. Organiser, NOZh (1922); member of AKhRR-AKhR (1923-30), RAPKh (from 1931). Exh: from 1918. Lived in Moscow from 1910. Visited Italy, Germany (1928, 1929). Taught at Moscow Vkhutein (1929-31), and Moscow School of Fine Art-Moscow Surikov Art Institute (1934-52).

1.43 Self-portrait 1928

Oil on canvas, 53 x 44; inv. Zh-5677
Acquired in 1933 from the artist, Moscow.

1.44 The Letter 1939

Oil on canvas, 100 x 79; inv. Zh-5676
Signed lr: 'G. Riazhskii 1939 g'.

The features of Riazhskii's work — realism, social specificness and clarity — are present in 1.43. Although the image is individualised it also represents a type often found in the art of the late 1920s, confident, straightforward and open. Riazhskii's portraits of the 1930s, such as 1.44 are more lyrical and pensive.

ALEKSANDR NIKOLAEVICH SAMOKHVALOV
1894 (Bezhetsk, Tver (Kalinin) Province)-1971 (Leningrad)
Studied at Higher Art School at Academy of Arts, St Petersburg (1914-17), and with Petrov-Vodkin, Kardovskii and Rylov at Petrograd Svomas-Vkhutemas. Exhibiting member, World of Art (1917), Circle of Artists (1927-9), October (from 1930). Lived in Petrograd-Leningrad. Samokhvalov was also a poster artist (see **3.37** and **58**) and took part in decoration for mass festivals.

1.45 Hairwashing* 1922-3
Oil and tempera on canvas, 132 x 97; inv. Zh-9185
Signed ll: 'A. Samokhvalov 1922-23'.
Acquired in 1976 from M.A. Kleshchar-Samokhvalova, artist's widow, Leningrad.

1.46 Repairing a Locomotive** 1931
Oil on canvas, 82.5 x 86; inv. Zh-9324
Signed ll: 'A. SA. 31'; inscribed on stretcher: 'A.S.'
Acquired in 1977 from RSFSR Ministry of Culture.

1.45 shows the influence of Petrov-Vodkin, who was one of Samokhvalov's teachers: in the clarity of the complicated forms, the fresco-like colour, and decorative surface, which endow the everyday event with ritual significance. Samokhvalov made several paintings of industrial subjects. In 1.46 the expressive pattern of the figures is emphasised by the rhythm of line and colour.

ZINAIDA EVGENEVNA SEREBRIAKOVA
1884 (Neskuchnoe, near Kharkov, Ukraine)-1967 (Paris)
Daughter of sculptor Evgenii Lanseray, sister of artist of same name, and niece of Alexandre Benois, Serebriakova studied in St Petersburg at Tenisheva's school (1901) and Braz's studio (1903-5), and in Paris (1905). Member, World of Art (1911). Exh: World of Art (1911-13, 1915-16, 1922, 1924), travelling Russian exh in USA (1924-5) and Japan (1926-7), private galleries in Paris (1927-41). Lived in St Petersburg and Neskuchnoe, Kharkov (1918-20), and Paris (from 1924). Made several trips to Italy (from 1902), Germany (from 1903), Switzerland (from 1914), England (from 1925), Belgium (from 1927), Morocco (1928 and 1932).

1.47 Bather** 1911
Oil on canvas, 98 x 89; inv. Zh-1903
Signed lr: 'Z. Serebriakova 1911'.
Acquired in 1912 from World of Art exh.

1.48 The Bath-house, study** 1912
Study for painting of same title (1913) also in State Russian Museum, with variant composition
Oil on canvas, 102 x 82.5; inv. Zh-1909
Signed ll: '1912 Serebriakova'.
Acquired in 1946 from Evgenii Serebriakov, artist's son.

1.49 Peasants* 1914.
Oil on canvas, 123.5 x 98; inv. Zh-4362
Signed ll: 'Serebriakova 1914'.
Acquired in 1920 from A.A. Korovin.

1.50 House of Cards** 1919
Oil on canvas, 65 x 75.5; inv. Zh-6634
Acquired in 1957 from Evgenii Serebriakov, artist's son.

1.51

1.51 Self-portrait 1922
Oil on canvas, 69 x 56; inv. Zh-6708.
Acquired in 1957 from Evgenii Serebriakov, artist's son.

From the early 1.47, a self-portrait, Serebriakova painted female nudes. The painting's closeness to the West European Classical tradition expresses itself in the composition, pose and treatment of the body. Serebriakova made many studies of the female form, with particular success in 1.48, painted at Neskuchnoe. This picture also shows the artist's delight in mysterious effects of lighting, especially candle-light.

In 1.49, one of many works on this theme painted at Neskuchnoe, Serebriakova uses devices of Classical art to monumentalise her subjects: well proportioned figures, clarity of outline, and resonant local colour. The inner harmony and physical perfection of the figures makes this the most sublime painting of peasants in Russian art of the early 20th century.

1.50, one of the many paintings Serebriakova made of her children, was done in the year their father died of typhus. It shows Evgenii (b.1906), Ekaterina (b.1913), Aleksandr (b.1907) and Tatiana (1912-89). In 1924 the artist went to Paris, planning to earn some money and return. She did not meet with the success she had expected, but remained hoping things would improve. Ekaterina and Aleksandr soon joined her, but Evgenii and Tatiana remained in Leningrad with Serebriakova's mother. All were successful in artistic life, Ekaterina and Aleksandr as painters, Evgenii as an architect. Tatiana, a designer for the Moscow Art Theatre, became an Honoured Artist of the RSFSR. Serebriakova's later self-portrait, in contrast to the radiant young woman of 1.47, is tired and worn.

1.50 Zinaida Serebriakova, *House of Cards*, 1919

ALEKSANDR VASILEVICH SHEVCHENKO
1883 (Kharkov, Ukraine)-1948 (Moscow)

Studied at Stroganov Central School of Technical Drawing (1899-1905, 1907) and Moscow School of Painting, Sculpture and Architecture (1907-10). Worked in paris in Carrière's studio and with J.-P. Laurens at Académie Julian (1905-6). Exh: World of Art (1904-13, 1917, 1921), Donkey's Tail (1912), Union of Youth (1912-13), Makovets (1922-5), Artists' Workshop (1926-30, organiser), Society of Moscow Artists (1928-9), one-man shows in Moscow and Leningrad. Lived in Moscow from 1898. Taught in higher-level schools of Moscow (1918-29, 1940-48), Ukraine (1921), and Leningrad (1930).

1.52 Musicians 1913

Oil on canvas, 114 x 104.5; inv. ZhB-1704
Signed ll: 'A. Sh. 13'.
Acquired from Museum of Artistic Culture, Leningrad.

Like other artists of his generation, Shevchenko moved to modernism through Impressionism and Post-Impressionism, learning from French painting, and mastering the Russian traditions: icons, lubok (see pp 61-96) and signboards. His own style uses elements of Cubism and Futurism in the displacement and dislocation of contours and the repetition of lines and forms to convey motion.

KONSTANTIN ANDREEVICH SOMOV
1869 (St Petersburg)-1939 (Paris)

Studied at Academy of Arts, St Petersburg (1888-97), from 1894 under Repin, and at Colarossi's studio in Paris (1897-9); academician, 1914. A founder of and exhibitor at World of Art (1899, 1900-02, 1906, 1911-12, 1915), member of and exhibitor at the Union of Russian Artists (1903-4, 1907-10). Exh: Russian art in Paris and Berlin (1906), and USA (1923). Lived in St Petersburg-Petrograd, New York, Paris (from 1925).

1.53 Portrait of the Composer S.V. Rakhmaninov* 1925

Oil on board, 63.7 x 51.6; inv. Zh-8043
Signed ul: 'C. Somoff 1925. Chateau de Corbeville d'Orsay' (Latin alphabet).
Acquired in 1964 via USSR Ministry of Culture from M.V. and S.A. Braikevitch, London.

A leading member of World of Art, Somov was known for his genre scenes and was also an important portraitist. The painting of Rakhmaninov (1873-1943) shows the artist's characteristic directness, learned from Repin. The work is a study for a large portrait commissioned by Steinway now in Carnegie Hall, New York; Somov worked on it at the chateau at Orsay where Rakhmaninov lived.

1.52

1.54

VASILII IVANOVICH SURIKOV
1848 (Krasnoiarsk)-1916 (Moscow)

Studied at Academy of Arts, St Petersburg (1869-75), academician 1895. Member of Itinerants (1881), Union of Russian Artists (1907). Lived in St Petersburg (1869-76) and Moscow. Travelled in Russia and most countries of Western Europe.

1.54 Portrait of an Unknown Woman on a Yellow Ground* 1911

Oil on canvas, 51 x 44; inv. Zh-4243
Signed *ul*: 'V. Surikov 1911 g.'
Acquired in 1926 from O.V. Konchalovskaia.

Surikov was best known for his large canvases on themes from Russian history, like *The Morning of the Execution of the Streltsy* and *The Boyaryna Morozova*, in which he created convincingly arresting faces for the historical figures. This is a rare portrait, an example of Surikov's interest in Russian faces of a particular, traditional beauty, here characterised by comely modesty, health and purity.

VLADIMIR EVGRAFOVICH TATLIN
1885 (Moscow)-1953 (Moscow)

Studied at Seliverstov Art School in Penza (1904-10) and with Serov and Korovin at Moscow School of Painting, Sculpture and Architecture (1902-3, 1909-10). Lived in Moscow, visiting Berlin and Paris in 1913. Exh: Donkey's Tail (1912), Jack of Diamonds (1913), World of Art (1913), Union of Youth (1911-14), Tramway V (1915), 0.10 (1915-16). Member, Association of New Trends in Art (1921-3). An important teacher and an initiator of Petrograd Inkhuk, Tatlin was also a sculptor of reliefs and counter-reliefs, painter, graphic artist, theatre designer, designer of architectural and engineering projects.

1.55 Model** 1913

Oil on canvas, 104.5 x 130.5; inv. ZhB-1330
Acquired in 1920 from the artist.
Paintings by Tatlin are rare, and 1.55 is one of the most important. Tatlin has given priority to clarity of design and created a precise series of graceful, interlocking rhythms, minimising detail and eliminating facial features. Nonetheless, the painting is sensuous and deeply felt. The elegant curved forms in early Russian painting are an influence.

Glossary

AKhR. Association of Artists of the Revolution. See AKhRR.

AKhRR. Artists of Revolutionary Russia. Founded 1922, large and very influential group which laid the foundations of Socialist Realism. Name changed in 1928 to AKhR.

Blue Rose Group. A group with a Symbolist orientation that had one exhibition in Moscow in 1907.

Bytie. Objective Reality. Founded 1921, the group stood for the renewal of realism in easel painting.

Circle of Artists. A group of young Leningrad artists dedicated to realism who came together in 1925 and exhibited frequently during the later 20s.

Donkey's Tail. Founded in 1911 by the more radical members of Jack of Diamonds, it stood for an independent, innovative Russian art and held an exhibition in Moscow in 1912.

'The First Russian Art Exhibition'. Held under the auspices of Narkompros, at the Van Diemen Gallery, Berlin, in 1922, this key exhibition was in effect a history of Russian modernism since the World of Art. The only comprehensive contemporary presentation of Russian modernism in Western Europe.

Four Arts Society. Founded in 1924, it was a large and varied group including many major innovative artists; emphasised formal problems in art and opposed exclusive preoccupation with subject.

Golden Fleece. A periodical, a group of artists and a series of three exhibitions, 1906-9, it was strongly oriented towards French modernism and was a key link between Symbolism and the growth of modern art in Russia.

Group of Three. Founded by Deineka, Pimenov and Andrei Goncharov in 1924. Organised 'First Discussional Exhibition of Active Revolutionary Art' the same year.

Inkhuk. Institute of Artistic Culture. Avant-garde research 'laboratory', set up in Leningrad in 1924, based on the Petrograd Museum of Artistic Culture (founded 1919). Inkhuk properly became Ginkhuk in 1925 (State Institute of Artistic Culture). In spring 1926 its museum department was shut down and its art collection transferred to the State Russian Museum; the whole Institute was dismantled later that year. Inkhuk also existed in Moscow, conducting similar research, 1920-24.

Itinerants. Established 1870 out of a group of rebels (in 1863) from the St Petersburg Academy of Arts, the Itinerants were socially motivated, believed art should be concerned with everyday life, and took travelling exhibitions to many towns. Very influential to c.1880 but continued to show as a group to 1922.

IZO. Visual Arts Section of Narkompros. Organised numerous State Free Exhibitions (no juries), was responsible for May Day and revolutionary festivities, promotion of design and art for production.

Jack of Diamonds. Founded in 1910, the group had regular exhibitions to 1917 of work influenced by Cézanne and Cubism. Very important at first, in mid-20s members joined Bytie and AKhRR.

LEF. Left Front of the Arts. A periodical published from 1923-5 and, as Novii Lef, from 1927-8, strongly supporting Constructivism and the avant-garde.

Makovets. Named after the site of a monastery in Zagorsk and affirming the spiritual in art, continuity with the past and a restrained modernism, Makovets, founded 1921, organised exhibitions to 1926 and published a journal.

Museum of Artistic Culture, see Inkhuk.

Narkompros. People's Commissariat for Enlightenment. Established in November 1917 under Anatolii Lunacharskii, the dominant figure in early Soviet educational and arts administration and a skilful and tenacious defender of artistic pluralism till his departure in 1929.

NEP. New Economic Policy. Current from 1921 to 1925-6, NEP introduced a limited free market in goods and permitted the reintroduction of a private market in the arts.

NOZh. New Society of Artists. Established in 1922 and dedicated to a return to objectivity and realism in painting in opposition to Constructivism. Influential to 1924 when many members joined Bytie.

Obmokhu. Society of Young Artists. Founded 1919, their aesthetic was collective, anonymous and oriented to the use of modern materials and tools in workshops. Close relations with Inkhuk. Held important exhibitions 1919-21.

October. Set up in 1928, October group had a single exhibition in 1930. It supported a middle way between abstraction (regarded as incomprehensible to the masses) and Socialist Realism (seen as academic and propagandist).

'O.10. The Last Futurist Painting Exhibition'. Major avant-garde show in 1915, and successor to Tramway V, it showed revolutionary developments in work of Malevich and Tatlin.

OMKh. Society of Moscow Artists. Formed in 1927, it included the founding group of the Jack of Diamonds who, after that group's dissolution, joined AKhRR, but were quickly disenchanted. Held three exhibitions, 1928-9.

OST. Society of Easel Painters. Established 1925, a very important group rejecting both abstraction and old fashioned realism in favour of a modern figurative painting. Influential exhibitions to 1930.

Proletkult. Proletarian Cultural Organisation. Founded on ideas formulated by Bolsheviks in exile as early as 1906, Proletkult was a widespread popular movement for mass education and cultural development. Officially established in October 1917, it remained independent until subsumed within Narkompros in 1920. Artists of different orientations contributed.

RAPKh. Russian Association of Proletarian Artists. An important organ up to 1932 for the nurturing and dissemination of proletarian art.

ROSTA. Russian Telegraph Agency. Published 'ROSTA windows', propaganda posters for display in shop fronts.

Socialist Realism. Though its origins belong with AKhRR and RAPKh, it was only formalised at the First All-Union Congress of Soviet Writers, 1934. It stood, in the words of Zhdanov, for 'realism in its revolutionary development', *ie* — in so far as it promoted progress, optimism, and the achievement of national goals.

Svomas. Free State Art Studios. Set up in Moscow and Petrograd in 1918 to replace the Academies, Svomas had teachers elected by students and provided for a wide range of interests. Developed into Vkhutemas in 1920.

The Target. Successor exhibition, 1913, of the Donkey's Tail.

'Tramway V. The First Futurist Painting Exhibition'. 1915. Important in bringing all leading future abstract artists together. See 0.10.

Union of New Trends in Art. Initiated by Tatlin in 1921, its members participated in the *Exhibition of paintings by Petrograd Artists of Every Trend* 1918-1923.

Union of Russian Artists. Founded 1903 at the Stroganov School, Moscow, a moderate exhibiting society continuing to 1923.

Union of Youth. Founded 1910, had regular exhibitions and a publication to 1913. Group revived 1917. Members included a wide spectrum of the *avant-garde*.

Unovis. Union of Affirmers of the New Art. Formed 1919 by Malevich and students at Vitebsk Art School, and moved with Malevich to Petrograd in 1922.

Vkhutemas. Higher State Art-Technical Studios. Succeeded Svomas in 1920, dedicated to the fine arts, ideology and theory, and particularly to training designers. Name changed in 1928 to Vkhutein (Higher State Art Technical Institute). Dissolved, 1930, to be replaced with separate institutes for each discipline.

World of Art. Leading *avant-garde* group of 1890s and early 1900s. Led by Benois and St Petersburg-based, it was oriented to Symbolism and 'art for art's sake'; internationalist in outlook and closely linked with theatre. Published a journal from 1898 and held regular exhibitions, 1899-1906, which were later revived.

The Russian Lubok

Two Hundred Years of Popular Prints

Lubok prints, a traditional art form that flourished independently for two hundred years, have attracted attention for both their visual qualities and their subject-matter. The imaginative vision, involving fantasy and allegory, seems other-worldly to a Western audience. But — before the tradition was emasculated by censorship in the 19th century — it had a harder edge, accommodating biting political satire, crude humour and misogynist undercurrents. The prints' simplified forms, strange perspective effects and bold colouring were all influential on Russian painting and drawing of the early 20th century. The conceptual nature of many *lubki*, their perception of the world in terms of symbol and metaphor, helped Russian artists to break out of heavy 19th-century realism that imitated life into a dynamic modern art.

In the earlier period, the term 'popular' referred to the images produced using woodcuts, which were necessarily simplified and very expressive. The term also describes the location of this art form at the heart of popular culture. With the introduction of increasingly sophisticated printing techniques the works were able to reach a wider and more numerous audience. The direct appeal of *lubok* style and the prints' place in people's lives made them of relevance this century in the evolution of visual propaganda in war and revolution.

Mirror of a Traditional World

by Natalia Rudakova, senior keeper of lubok prints, Saltykov-Shchedrin State Public Library, Leningrad

Lubki, popular prints sold at fairs and markets, were known in Russia from the second half of the 17th century. There are several theories about the origin of the term '*lubok*', but the most convincing is that connecting it with the word *lub* (bast), meaning the layer of wood found under the bark of the lime tree. This material was widely used in peasant Russia, for purposes as varied as footwear, roofing, basket-making, and also for writing on. The expression *lubochnyi* (*lub*-like) was employed in the 19th century in a disparaging way, to signify anything crudely made, but it was also used in the specialist literature to describe a popular print.

Lubki were printed in black ink on white paper, and were coloured by hand. In the 19th century the colouring was a handicraft cottage trade carried out by people living in the villages around Moscow and Mstëra, a small country town in Vladimir province. Colours were made to personal recipes, mixing honey, milk and eggs. *Lubki* were sold in Moscow and at provincial fairs (see **2.89**), being taken round the villages by pedlars (see **2.88**). The prints were the main decoration on the walls of peasants' huts, taverns and coaching inns, but could also be seen in the houses of merchants and small traders. In the early period, they were bought by grand boyar (noble) families and even displayed in the palaces of Peter the Great and his father, Tsar Aleksei Mikhailovich.

The earliest *lubki* were printed from wooden blocks and were distinguished by the high quality of execution and colouring. The

2.88 *Moscow Mead Vendor and Picture Pedlar*, 1858

2.89 *Peepshow*, 1858

appearance of the *lubok* was dictated by the technique of production. On a block made from soft wood split lengthwise a picture was drawn, the wood surrounding the main outline was cut away, and an impression was printed from it. The 'resistance' of the material, the difficulty of carving the wood, compelled the craftsmen to simplify designs and determined the laconic style. Colour was added to elaborate and decorate the image. A distinctive feature of *lubok* prints was the inclusion of a text.

Lubok prints were rarely dated and almost always anonymous. Only one case of signed work of the early period survives, the illustrations to the Book of Genesis and the Apocalypse of Vasilii Koren, with both text and illustrations printed from wooden blocks, made in 1692-6. Religious subjects were common in the *lubok* woodcuts of the 17th and early 18th centuries. Depictions of Christ, the Virgin Mary and saints, together with the illustrated texts of prayers, would be placed in the corner of a dwelling reserved for icons. However, the Church authorities repeatedly banned publication of religious *lubki* (see **2.1**), considering that the pictures departed too often from canonical norms (see **2.1**), and most surviving prints of this period show secular subjects.

Alongside Church culture, alternative traditions of songs and tales passed on orally from generation to generation had existed since the time of Kievan Russia. Secular rituals and customs were an important part of everyday life and found their way into popular tales and sayings, while a decorative tradition involving the ornamentation of objects in daily use was also well established. Thus heroes of knightly romances, genre scenes, and real and imaginary birds and beasts were the subject of secular *lubki* . Especially popular were the characters of the 'world of laughter' (*smekhovoi mir*), in which jokes, irony and satire, caricature and ridicule poked fun at serious aspects of life, exposed unfairness and showed up human failings and weaknesses. Humorous stories were written down and distributed in manuscript books from the 17th century, providing subjects for *lubki*, although some folklore tales were first published as *lubok* pictures, without being previously written down.

Typically the targets of satire were mocked by the breaking of conventions or proprieties: the events portrayed in a picture would be transferred to the animal world, for example in *The Tale of the Cock and the Fox* (2.23), or the world depicted would be 'turned upside down', as in *The Mice Bury the Cat* **(2.12)**. The inclusion of a text beside the image in *lubki* also gave opportunities for irony and satire: in *The Cat of Kazan* (2.13), for example, the grandiloquent inscription with references to the grand titles of Russian

2.1 *The Dreadful Parable of the 'Great Mirror'*, second half 17th century

rulers is undermined by the accompanying picture of the cat. The world of laughter also provided overtly comic personages, like the recurring buffoons Foma and Erëma (**2.52-4**).

From the earliest times *lubok* pictures kept a widely dispersed population in touch with contemporary life, describing current events and (in the 19th century) familiarising people with the works of living writers. As time went by the *lubok* was absorbed and enriched by innovations from the field of fine art. However, all change was subject to popular demand, which determined both the theme and the way it was presented.

During the second half of the 18th century *lubok* woodcuts deteriorated in quality. They became less original, many being copied from French engravings; all the best examples of this period are engraved on copper. The bulk of *lubok* production at this time came from the big workshop of Ilia Akhmetev, which had 20 printing presses. Plates were commissioned from two sources. Firstly, from etchers who worked in a fine-art tradition, and who used Western prints as their inspiration. These etchings, more sophisticated in their approach and elevated in their subject-

2.53 *Foma the Musician and Erëma. Prokhor and Boris* (detail), second half 18th century

matter, are not now considered part of the *lubok* tradition. Secondly, the plates came from copper engravers working in small workshops, whose craft skills were passed on from one generation to another. The prints produced by the latter were made using a graving tool on polished copper and incising deep lines which would not be worn down quickly by the printing press. By the end of the 18th century some of the peasant *lubok* engravers had become masters of their own workshops. One, Ivan Loginov, took over Akhmetev's business.

The repertoire of the copperplate *lubok* was considerably more extensive than that of the woodcut. Many *lubki* with religious subjects were published: illustrations to the Bible, engraved icons of Christ and the Virgin, the Orthodox saints (see, for example, **2.5**), and pictures with a morally-improving content. But 'entertainment literature' in the form of books with both text and pictures engraved on the same plate was also now widespread. Tales, poems and knightly romances were borrowed for *lubki* from these printed anthologies, involving such popular heroes as Eruslan Lazarevich and Ilia Muromets; some of the illustrations from the books were enlarged and issued as separate sheets. Love scenes were also successful. 'Just One Kiss, Blackeyes' **(2.37)**, for example, was still being re-engraved in the 1820s and 30s.

Contemporary events also entered the repertoire. Besides scenes from wars, publishers liked to show wonders such as earthquakes and monsters, both real and imaginary (2.73-8). Although there were references to the newspapers, the inscriptions and images on these prints most often tended towards the 'world of laughter'. (2.74) At the same time other copperplate prints such as *The Pancake Vendor, Taras the Bald* (2.55) *or The Most Unbelievable Story* are recreations of woodcut *lubki*, and favourite copperengraved *lubki* were repeated. As the copper plates used for popular images wore out, some of the most worn lines could be re-cut, but if plates became completely useless, copies would be made from them, some introducing the stylistic features of the newer age. Dmitrii Rovinskii, author of the standard work on *lubok* was the first to notice that towards the end of the 18th century the style of the *lubok* showed a marked influence of icon painting for example in the slightly later *Saints Zosima and Sabbas* (2.7). Rovinskii explained this by suggesting that production of these prints had fallen into the hands of Old Believers, religious schismatics who risked persecution by adhering to rituals outlawed by reforms

2.37 'Just One Kiss, Blackeyes', mid 18th century

2.12 *The Mice Bury the Cat*, first half 18th century

of 1667. But while it is true that many Moscow industrialists and merchants were of the old faith, the engraved *lubki* with religious subjects do not show the distinctive features of the Old Believer spiritual culture. A more likely explanation for the new stylistic feature is that, as the copperplate *lubok* became more widely disseminated among the people, its style changed to appeal to the taste of consumers who were used to religious books in the unreformed Cyrillic script and to old icons. These people preferred single-sheet prints and engraved booklets which were in tune with the established traditions now made old-fashioned, even heretical, by the new Western-oriented and secular culture of Petrine and post-Petrine Russia. This 'icon' style gradually grew increasingly schematic and dull, but continued to be used right down to the 1840s.

Lubki of the second half of the 19th century differ in both subject and style from that of the first half. Art historians argue that the change resulted from the tightening up of censorship at the end of the reign of Nicholas I. The Governor of Moscow decreed that all published prints be subject to the censor, and plates from which banned prints had been taken were destroyed. However, this action merely accelerated a natural process in the evolution of the *lubok* already under way. Fresh subjects and different methods of depiction had appeared in the 1840s, before strict censorship began. Arkhip Beliankin had begun to publish prints with the texts of songs and romances written by Russian authors, subjects not previously found in *lubki*. A decade later the sheets he issued served as prototypes for pictures that were published

in huge quantities for sale in country districts (see **2.72**). On the other hand, not all the forbidden engraved plates were actually destroyed, and from the early 1860s these plates were re-printed for those who preferred the old images. Such prints were sometimes accompanied by inscriptions identifying them as *lubok* pictures 'from an earlier period' (*lubochnaia prezhniaia kartinka*).

A further change came at the end of the 1860s with the introduction of aniline colours, which soon became widespread. The chemical dyes were brighter, more saturated and intense, and they were often applied in broad strokes, paying little respect to the lines beneath (**2.85**).

During the 1840s and 1850s a small number of workshop-masters and publishers decided what the repertoire and style of *lubki* would be. These were Aleksandr Loginov, who inherited his enterprise from his father; the publisher Arkhip Beliankin, whose *lubok* work was printed by Grigorii Chuksin; Vasilii Sharapov, who soon handed his business over to his brother Pëtr, later one of the most important publishers of the 19th century; and the copperplate workshop of Evdokiia Lavrenteva, which borrowed many subjects and compositions from Beliankin, but adapted them to the taste of the rural consumer, for whom they were bought by the Mstëra trader Aleksandr Golyshev.

From 1853-4 many workshop-masters, trying to prolong the life of their copperplates, began to employ the technique of lithographic transfer (see **2.70**). A print was made on paper from a copper plate, then transferred to a lithographic stone, from which impressions were printed. Towards the end of the 1850s virtually

2.72 *'Don't Awake the Pretty Maiden'*, 1868

2.70 *The Peasant and Death*, 1865

2.67 *The Slanderer and the Serpent*, 1873

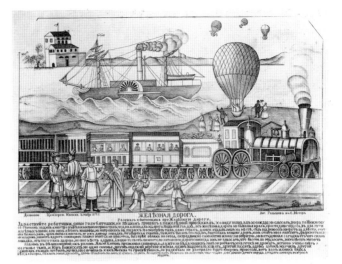

2.81 *The Railway*, 1874

all the workshops began to print their images lithographically rather than from copper plates, although some craftsmen were forced to give up printing and place work outside, with specialist lithographic printers, In the 1860s and 1870s the production of *lubki* was thus concentrated in a few large-scale workshops. Efim Iakovlev became the owner of a lithographic enterprise where he printed transfers from his own plates and from Sharapov plates. Anton Abramov was a publisher with his own printing works, using plates of the former copperplate workshop of Lavrenteva; in 1867 Andrei Abramov took over, using mainly these.

The workshops began to produce lithographs of a more up-market nature, borrowed from foreign pictures and intended for the drawing rooms of townspeople. Their subjects were images of romance and sentimentality, portrait heads of women and children, and hunting scenes. However, images of a more traditional *lubok* appearance, made by lithographic transfer from copper plates, continued to be more popular in the countryside. Transfers from plates engraved in the 1850s were still being published in the 1880s and throughout all these years some favourite subjects enjoyed unchanged success: *The Mice Bury the Cat*, *Eruslan Lazarevich*, and *Ilia Muromets*.

Lubki illustrating Russian songs were extensively sold now, using texts taken from printed anthologies; only works that were truly 'popular' were chosen, as being appropriate to *lubok* conventions. However, in the area of works for moral improvement, the familiar group of parables used in the 18th century were replaced by edifying literary fables and verses by recent Russian poets: *The Slanderer and the Serpent* **(2.67)** and *The Industrious Bear*

(2.25), by Ivan Krylov, *Why Are You Sleeping Peasant?* **(2.71)**, by Aleksei Koltsov.

From 1858 Moscow, which supplied pictures to all Russia, faced competition from the lithographic works in Mstëra, in Vladimir province. Its owner Ivan Golyshev (1836-96), son of Aleksandr Golyshev the Mstëra peasant and *lubki*-seller, studied at Count Stroganov's school of applied art in Moscow and went on to Lavrenteva's enterprise and Efimov's lithographic works for practical training in printing and publishing, Unlike the *lubki* produced in Moscow, which were transferred from copper plates, those from Mstëra were drawn directly onto the lithographic stone. Golyshev himself worked on the stones, along with pupils from among the local icon-painters. As well as publishing the most popular of the Moscow *lubki*, this workshop also issued original sheets, including *Pantiushka and Sidorka See the Sights of Moscow* (2.59) *and The Railway* **(2.81)**. If, with time, the images from which the most popular subjects were printed lost clarity, the surface of the stones could be ground down and the image redrawn. Lithography could nevertheless produce many more impressions than copper engraving, as well as being a cheaper process.

After the 1880s Golyshev's output of *lubki* began to diminish, because the workshop could not compete with the printers in Moscow now equipped to use the new chromo-lithography printing technique (see **2.47** in Catalogue). Chromo-lithography made possible far higher output than hand colouring. The character of the prints now altered, as publishers increasingly catered for the tastes of the urban petty bourgeoisie (see 2.18). Romances in a town setting and funny stories joined popular songs as new sub-

2.5 *The Holy Trinity*, 1820s or 30s

2.74 *'Satyr' Shown in Spain in 1760*, second half 18th century

Изд. Печ. Москва 11 Марта 1874 г. 1865 го. печ. въ Литографiи Андрея Абрамова на Нѣмецкой улицѣ въ Посадѣ, пер. въ домѣ Киселевой

А нутка Мишенька Иванычъ, родомъ бояричъ, ходи ну, похаживай говори, поговаривай, да изгнись дугой, словно мѣшокъ тугой да ну поборотись, развернись, добрымъ людямъ покажись! А нука, вотъ ну, какъ старыя старушки молодыя молодушки на барщину ходили до дыръ пяты сносили, А какъ теща прозятя блины пекла, да угорѣла головушка заболѣла! А вотъ ну какъ красные дѣвицы моются, билятся, румянятся, въ зеркальцо глядятся да изъ подрученьки женишковъ выглядываютъ. А вотъ ну какъ малые ребятишки горохъ воровали, тишкомъ танкомъ гдѣ сухо тамъ брюхомъ гдѣ мокро тамъ накольначкахъ. А вотъ ну ходи разходись во всемъ народѣ покажись А ну какъ конные драгуны во походъ ходили ружьемъ метали, артикулы выкидали а вотъ какъ съ порохомъ тѣма оттянула всѣ плеча, А нука вотъ ну какъ мужъ у жены кило воруетъ а холостой парень по чужой женѣ тоскуетъ, ходи не потыкайся впередъ подавайся разгуляйся! вались да катись бока незашиби самъ себя береги А ну жонка въ гости пошла съ собой взяла мужа прочь прогнала. А ну вотъ ну какъ наши бабёнки въ баню ходили винцо съ сокой носили на полокъ забирались, насциньей валялись вѣничкомъ махали животики протирали.

2.85 `Come On, Mishenka Ivanich', 1863

2.90 Kazimir Malevich, *Look, Oh Look, Near the Vistula*, 1914

Natalia Goncharova, *The Archangel Michael*, 1914

jects for *lubki*. For this public, the style of the chromo-lithographic *lubok* was influenced by easel painting, commercial advertisements and newspapers caricatures.

Outstanding among the many publishers of works using chromo-lithography was the well-known book-publisher and educationist Ivan Sytin (1851-1934). From 1866, when still a boy, he worked at the bookshop of the *lubok* publisher Pëtr Sharapov; in 1876 he started a lithographic workshop which bore Sharapov's name, but seven years later went into business on his own. Sytin employed only skilled draughtsmen who took serious account of the *lubok* tradition; his *lubki* promoted the work of Russian writers, while continuing also to illustrate folk songs. These works varied considerably in style, but Sytin valued the old repertoire, often publishing copies of pictures popular in the 1850s-70s.

During the Russo-Japanese war of 1905, and then again in the First World War, the *lubok* workshops were quick to issue sheets with texts taken from the newspapers, although these were often printed carelessly. One of the most interesting features of the wartime *lubok* was the output of a firm that called itself 'Today's Lubok'. In August 1914 a group of young artists tending to the 'left' in art — Vladimir Mayakovsky, Kazimir Malevich and Aristarkh Lentulov — began to design propagandist material in support of the

official war effort. While not imitating the *lubok* style, these achieved the unity of text and content that was characteristic of the traditional print **(2.90-4)**.

Painters and theatre designers of the early 20th century had already revived the *lubok* idiom as part of an intense preoccupation with Russian popular and traditional art. Influential in the succeeding period was the exhibition *Icon Originals and Lubok* organised in 1913 by Mikhail Larionov and Natalia Goncharova. Goncharova's series 'Mystical Images of War', for example T*he Archangel Michael* (**ill**), of 1914 reflects this interest, while the lithographically-printed books of Pavel Filonov and Olga Rozanova continued in their own way the traditions of the popular *lubok* books. *Lubok* influence can also be traced in the work of some of the artists of World of Art, for example Boris Kustodiev. Later it was important to for the work of Mashkov, Konchalovskii and Lentulov of the Jack of Diamonds group (see **1.26, 1.18**).

After the October Revolution, when it was necessary to tell the people about the tasks facing the Republic, poster artists had much recourse to the methods, forms and artistic language of the *lubok* for direct popular appeal (see pages 98-107). Even today many contemporary artist consciously make use of the themes, images and flexible language of the *lubok*.

Note on the origins of the Public Library's collection

We know how widely *lubki* were disseminated from references to them in memoirs and in the works of such writers as Pushkin and Gogol. But because of their cheapness they were not retained for long in everyday use, and over the years it is only thanks to the efforts of collectors that specimens have been preserved.

From as early as the 18th century, there were a few educated and enlightened people who valued *lubki* for their distinctive quality and aesthetic interest. During the 19th century historians and students of folklore began to collect the prints, not just as connoisseurs but in order to undertake more serious study. Perhaps the most important of the latter collectors was Dmitrii Rovinskii, who compiled a catalogue of his own works, adding descriptions of the *lubki* known to him; his book *Russian Folk Pictures*, published in 1881-93, is the standard work on the subject. The Saltykov-Shchedrin Public Library holds three of the most important collections of *lubki* , assembled between the 17th century and the second half of the 19th.

The collection of Senator Count Adam Olsufev was obtained by the library from the Princes Beloselskii-Belozerskii in 1915. It consists of *lubki* printed from both wooden blocks and copper plates. A godson of Peter the Great, Olsufev (1721-84) was considered by his contemporaries to be one of the best educated and cleverest men of his time. His whole life was spent at the Russian imperial court, where Catherine II made him a secretary of state. Olsufev kept out of court intrigues and did not try to make a career, preferring to occupy himself with literature and art. Of his collections, only the Russian section has survived, together one volume of reproductive prints after pictures by Watteau; the rest were apparently burnt during the war of 1812. The *lubok* sheets in his collection were not coloured, because Olsufev did not acquire prints in actual circulation but, in the 1770s, ordered impressions from wood and copper plates preserved by the publishers. These were then classified by subject and pasted to mounts; the spines of the volumes making up the collection were printed with the words 'Pictures from Moscow'. The care shown to achieve a complete collection, to ensure that different versions of a print and later copies were indicated, together with

notes on the condition of the plates, testifies to the collector's scholarly approach.

Olsufev's work was added to and continued by the historian Mikhail Pogodin (1800-75), the foundation of his collection being the earlier libraries of Iakov Shtelin (Jacob von Stählin) and Ivan Snegirev, which he acquired.

Shtelin (1712-85), a Swiss, was invited to Russia in 1735 as an expert in the making of fireworks and medals. When he later became director of the Academy of Arts in St Petersburg, he assembled prints made in the course of teaching and experiment. In his archives, acquired by Pogodin from Shtelin's heirs in 1844, there was a folder of *lubok* woodcuts with an inscription stating that he bought them in 1766 in Moscow on Spasskii Bridge, centre of the *lubok* trade.

In 1850 Pogodin supplemented his collection by acquiring that of Snegirev, mainly coloured *lubki* printed from copper plates dating from the 18th and early 19th centuries. A professor at Moscow University, Ivan Snegirev (1793-1868) was the first person to undertake research on *lubok* pictures. In his books and articles from 1822, he tried to trace the origin of the term 'lubok' and compiled a catalogue of the popular prints known to him. His knowledge of traditional festivals and customs, the oral inheritance of poems, sayings and stories, enabled him to establish the place occupied by *lubki* in Russian popular culture.

In 1852, the Public Library received as a gift the collection of *lubki* belonging to Vladimir Dahl (1801-72), writer, collector of proverbs, and compiler of the famous explanatory dictionary of the Russian language. Dahl's collection contains mainly hand-coloured *lubki* printed from engraved copper plates between the 1820s and 1840s, sometimes in a number of variants and copies of the same subject.

After 1851 all *lubok* pictures had be be submitted to the censor. Thus one (uncoloured) print of every published *lubok* was sent to the Public Library, marked with the date of approval, the censor's name, and the name and address of the workshop concerned. Coloured examples of individual 19th-century *lubki* were also either received or acquired by the library.

2.3 The Punishment of Money-Grubbers, late 18th–early 19th century

Святый Іоаннъ многострадальный у гроба Преп. Антонія помощь отъ страсти блудныя прія, и тридцать лѣтъ въ затвори пребылъ нагъ въ желѣзѣ вкопавшись въ землю до плечь въ великій постъ, бѣсъ со дна ямы ада огнемъ поджигалъ его; и змій огнен- ныи дыша хотелъ пожрати его; но молитва Святаго сжеге бывшаго во устахъ діавола: молнія отогнала діавола отъ святаго: и слышанъ былъ гласъ Господень укрѣпляющъ: Іоанне, Іоанне, вотъ тебѣ помощь, но впротчемъ помни себѣ, чтобы не хуже тебѣ было въ будущемъ вѣкѣ. Это дается тебѣ по терпѣнію твоему.

2.8 *Saint Ioann (John), 1876*

Catalogue notes are by Greg Smith, assistant keeper (art) at the Whitworth Art Gallery, University of Manchester, and Natalia Rudakova, senior keeper (*lubki*) at the Saltykov-Shchedrin State Public Library, Leningrad. Where there are two dates, the first refers to the making of the block and the second, in brackets, to the date of printing. Measurements for woodcuts, lithographs (including lithographic transfers) and chromo-lithographs are of the image size including text; for copper engravings dimensions given relate to the visible plate mark. All works are from the Department of Prints at the Saltykov-Shchedrin Library; the inventory numbers are theirs; the prefixes 'Pog', 'Ols' and 'Dahl' indicate origin in the important collections of Mikhail Pogodin, Adam Olsufev and Vladimir Dahl.

Religious Scenes

The earliest *lubki*, dating from the second half of the 17th century, were religious subjects, paper icons to be pasted on the walls or iconostases of country churches and peasant houses. The first examples were produced in Kiev in an attempt by the Church to counter the challenge of Polish Catholicism. The ephemeral nature of these prints and the function they performed meant that few survive. An important exception to this is a group of woodcuts, many of religious subjects, which were confiscated in 1731 from a St Petersburg trader, Grigorii Chërnyi, and lay undisturbed in an archive until their discovery in 1980. Also exceptional are a group of 36 woodcuts (1692-6) by Vasilii Koren consisting of images from the Book of Genesis and the Apocalypse which together have been seen as the first printed Bible in pictures, aimed at the poor; many of the images were based on the work of Dürer. This is a unique example of a popular publication where we know the identity of both the engraver and the artist after whose drawings the engraver worked.

The Church's uneasy feelings towards this popular manifestation of faith was expressed by numerous attempts at censorship, the first dating from 1674. The Church was concerned in particular by the way in which the *lubok* artists went beyond the canonical images of the Byzantine tradition and freely interpreted biblical and holy images for commercial profit.

2.1 **The Dreadful Parable from the 'Great Mirror'** Second half 17th century (1820s)*
Woodcut, hand-coloured.
40.6 x 30.1; inv. Pog. 1-15.
The text tells how a young woman died without confessing the sins of the flesh. Her confessor prayed for her soul and she appeared to him in a vision sitting astride a fiery beast symbolising the untamed passions. Her hands are being gnawed by dogs, her breasts sucked by serpents, her eyes eaten by toads, her ears pierced by arrows and her lips burnt with fire. She explains to her confessor how each of the punishments reflects her life: the arrows pierce her ears because she has 'listened to the songs of devils', the dogs gnaw her hands because they have caressed the forbidden, and the serpents suck her breasts because of her lustful life. The subject is taken from *The Great Mirror*, a collection of moral tales.

2.2 **A Sinner's Mirror** Second half 18th century (1820s)
Copper engraving, hand-coloured.
37.1 x 53.7; inv 10764.
The subject, the vanity of everything on earth is found in popular prints throughout Europe. At the top are four scenes showing the three sons of Noah, Shem, Ham and Japhet, and also Death. Shem prays, Ham sows wheat and Japhet is shown as a ruler; Death, the final image, triumphs over all. *Below*, a well dressed man and woman engage in a witty dialogue, flanked by Death with his scythe and

a monster who guards the jaws of hell which is devouring a sinner. Between the figures there is an open grave with the caption 'For dust thou art, and unto dust thou shalt return'. The image is both a *memento mori*, a reminder of mortality, and a moral warning: 'Hell groans and sobs, takes sinners unto itself'. The mirror in the title suggests that the viewer is to see himself reflected in the image and thus take heed of the moral lesson.

2.3 **The Punishment of Money-Grubbers** Late 18th-early 19th century
Copper engraving, hand-coloured.**
31.2 x 26.5; inv Pog. 2120.
The subject is taken from the *The Great Mirror* (see 2.1). An angel explains to a pious monk the meaning of his vision: a man lying in flames with a tree growing from his stomach and figures hanging from the branches. The man is the father of all 'money-grubbers and bribe takers' and the figures hanging on the branches are his children and grandchildren. All are to be consumed by the giant hell mouth, *bottom right.*

2.4 **The Pure Soul** Second quarter 19th century
Copper engraving, hand-coloured.
38.7 x 31; inv. 8863.
The Pure Soul is personified as a beautiful young woman. She stands 'higher than the sun and the moon . . . before God'. She waters the flames of hell with her tears and tames the passions (symbolised by a lion and a dragon) with her meekness. The sinful soul, overcast by gloom, sits in a dark cave; a demon waits to pounce.

2.4

Изгна его господь богъ из
рая сладости дѣлати зе
млю ѿнеаже взатъ бысь
изрину адамъ ивсели егѡ
прамо рая сладости

2.6

2.5 The Holy Trinity 1820s or 30s**
Copper engraving, hand-coloured.
36.3 x 29.5; inv. Pog. 4-293.
The Holy Trinity is represented in Russian art, not by the image of God the Father, Christ and the Holy Spirit (symbolised by a dove), but instead by three angels sitting at a table. In the foreground a boy is slaughtering an ox for the meal.

2.6 The Creation Second quarter 19th century
Copper engraving, hand-coloured.
71 x 55.5; inv. Pog. 4-272.
The 20 scenes illustrate the first four chapters of the Book of Genesis including the Creation, the Fall and the Expulsion from the Garden of Eden which is the detail here. As in medieval Western art the traditional pattern for each scene was closely adhered to; in this case the print is a copy of a copper engraving of the second half of the 18th century. The earliest woodcut *lubki* of biblical scenes date from the end of the 17th century when new elements such as the depiction of Cain as a Russian peasant were introduced for the first time.

2.7 Saints Zosima and Sabbas of the Solovetskii Monastery 1820s or 30s
Copper engraving, hand-coloured.
41.8 x 32.5; inv. Pog. 4-289.
The monks Zosima and Sabbas founded the monastery on the Solovetskie Islands in the White Sea in the 15th century. The two saints are not differentiated. They are shown against a schematic representation of the monastery which was to become one of the most important in Russia. Christ is shown in a mandorla in the sky.

2.8 Saint Ioann (John) 1876**
Moscow, Andrei Abramov workshop
Lithographic transfer, hand-coloured.
29.5 x 29; inv. 12795.
Saint Ioann was a holy hermit from Kiev who died in 1160. He was known as 'the long-suffering', having lived for 30 years in a cave.

2.9 The Murder of the Tsarevich Dmitrii 1876
Moscow, Andrei Abramov workshop
Lithographic transfer, hand-coloured.
25 x 37; inv. 12171.
The Tsarevich Dmitrii (1582-91) was the son of Ivan the Terrible and his seventh wife, Marta. During the reign of his half-brother, Tsar Fëdor, the young Tsarevich was discovered in his palace at Uglich with stab wounds. His mother accused the regent Boris Godunov of having him murdered and, although he had probably stabbed himself in an epileptic fit, such was the climate of suspicion that she was widely believed. Some years later a number of false Dmitriis appeared and became the focus for popular uprisings. In order to discourage this, Dmitrii was canonised in 1606; numerous prints of his 'martyrdom' were produced from the 18th century onwards.

2.10 The Holy Martyr Agrippina 1878
Moscow, Petr Glushkov workshop
Lithographic transfer, hand-coloured.
39.5 x 32.5; inv. 12772.
Agrippina was the daughter of a noble family and dedicated her life to charitable works. She lived during the reign of the Emperor Valerian in the 3rd century and was persecuted and martyred.

2.11 The Holy Archangel Mikhail 1890
Moscow, Vasilii Vasilev workshop
Lithograph, hand-coloured.
40.5 32.5; inv. 12774.
Mikhail was one of the seven archangels of the Orthodox faith and the leader of the heavenly hosts against the forces of evil. The earliest *lubok* woodcut of the subject dates from 1688. In this version the archangel, dressed as a Christian knight, is shown triumphing over evil (a dragon) in a manner similar to Alexander the Great or other heroes of popular romances (see 2.26-31), but which ultimately derives from an icon.

2.20 A Merry Ride in a Mouse-drawn Carriage, 1820s or 30s

ЛЮДИ ДИВЫѦ НАИДЕННЫѦ ЦАРЕМЪ АЛЕКСАНДРОМЪ МКЕДОНСКИМЪ

Егда царь александръ макидонскїи своими грады плени-
ша тогда царствы мнози повираши востокъ изападъ
прохождаше сицевыхъ дивыхъ людеи вгорахъ вкустовыхъ
товыхъ нахождаше многихъ тамо живущихъ стра
шныхъ иужасныхъ людеи взимаще

Итщашаса ихъ вцарство свое провести нониединаго могу проiзве
сти соудивлениемъ люди нанихъ взирахꙋ ипищꙋ имъ подавахꙋ
нонне неприемше пищꙋ гладомъ помирахꙋ тогда иовъедино
мъ глазе единаго поима нотои потри его обманомъ обнима
кдивымъ людемъ идаша самже далече отнихъ обгаш

2.27 *Fantastic People Discovered by Alexander of Macedon*, 1820s

Satire, Political and Social

With the reign of Peter the Great (1682-1725) and the influx of foreigners and foreign prints the *lubok* tradition became increasingly secularised. The government censored images of the imperial family but this did not stop the production of images critical of Peter, whose reforms faced great opposition. *Lubok* publishers, in particular Old Believer religious schismatics, were forced to approach their subject in a more oblique way using all the disguises at the disposal of the satirist. Thus many images which we today read as quaint and fantastic originally had a more important function. The introduction of much stricter censorship in the early to mid 19th century put an end to a powerful outlet for popular discontent.

In addition to political comments many satirical prints are aimed at certain groups and classes. The folly of the merchant and middle classes was a popular subject, especially the fashionably dressed.

2.12 **The Mice Bury the Cat** First half 18th century (1760s)**

Woodcut, hand-coloured.

32 .8 x 57.3; inv. Pog. 9403.

The burial of the cat by its enemies the mice is one of the most popular *lubok* subjects and recurs in many versions, this being one of the earliest. The weak and injured mice are shown to triumph in the end over their implacable foe: to be on the safe side, however, they have tied his paws and bound him to the sledge. The subject has been interpreted as political satire, with the cat representing Peter the Great and the mice the Old Believers whom he persecuted. The interpretation is supported by a number of details: the sledge is pulled by eight mice, the number of horses in Peter's funeral procession; it is accompanied by musicians, when it was Peter who introduced music into funerals; one mouse is shown smoking a pipe, and tobacco had first been allowed to be sold openly during Peter's reign.

2.13 **The Cat of Kazan** First half 18th century (early 19th century)

Woodcut, hand-coloured.

33.6 x 26.9; inv. 8867.

This image originated as a satire on Peter the Great, parodying his appearance, with long moustache, and the pompous titles he assumed as a result of his military victories. The inscription reads: 'The Cat of Kazan, having the spirit of Astrakhan and the sense of Siberia, lived gloriously, ate agreeably and lived sweetly'. The compliments are meant ironically. The former khanates of Kazan, Astrakhan and Siberia all became part of Muscovite Russia in the late 16th century, during the reign of Ivan the Terrible, who is probably being linked to Peter as his only predecessor of comparable stature. The dead cat in 2.12 has a caption which also identifies him as the 'Cat of Kazan', underlying the political interpretation.

2.14 **The Barber Wants to Cut the Old Believer's Whiskers***

First half 18th century (1770s)

Woodcut.

36.4 x 30.5; inv. Ols. 6-1214.

The print illustrates one of the consequences of Peter the Great's attempts to westernise Russian society: the decree of 1705 which stated that all Russians must wear European costume and that all men, apart from peasants and priests, had to shave off their beards. The decree met with strong resistance since shaving was regarded by many Old Believers as heretical. In the print the barber is dressed in German costume and the victim, called a schismatic in the text, is resisting. There is evidence to suggest that the print was actually sanctioned by Peter himself.

2.15 **Pan Tryk and Khersonia** Mid 18th century (1770s)

Woodcut.

27.1 x 33.1; inv. Ols. 11-2296.

A comic dialogue between a courtesan and an officer. The text is a satire on the foreign officials and courtesans who flocked to Russia in the 17th century. It could refer to the huge expansion of Russia under the Catherine the Great, when eastern Poland (Pan is a Polish form of address) and ancient Kherson on the Black Sea became part of the Empire. In spite of this meaning the scene probably has as its inspiration a French engraving of the 17th century. The costumes are of the early 18th century, though the patches on the woman's face are typical of a later date. According to a contemporary text the patches could have a great significance — one on the left cheek indicating happiness, one between the eyebrows signifying a 'lover's meeting'.

2.16 **Cock-Rider** Late 18th or early 19th century

Copper engraving, hand-coloured.

32.9 x 30.2; inv. Pog. 3-209.

The image of the rider on a cock is a good example of imagery which has crossed both national boundaries and the centuries; it first occurs in Greek art of the fifth century BC. The *lubok* artists, however, derived the image from German folk pictures in the second half of the 18th century. The subject had a strong satirical element — the cuckolded husband — but later this meaning was gradually lost and, as elsewhere in *lubok*, the image became purely decorative and fanciful. In this case the text offers a warning to those men who think they are safe from similiar ignominy. A companion piece shows a woman riding on a hen.

2.13

2.21

2.17 The Wedding of Mishka Kosolapyi ('Clumsy Bear') 1860
Moscow, Pëtr Sharapov workshop
Lithographic transfer, hand-coloured.
32.3 x 41.7; *inv.* 39623.

Mishka Kosolapyi can be translated as the bear 'with pigeon toes'. The text tells how, at a wedding of one of their number, the bears ate plentifully, danced, declared their love for one another and remembered the day for many years. Although the subject-matter of *lubki* owes much to the free play of fantasy there is often a strong satirical element; here the bears parody the social mores of the merchant or petty bourgeois classes. The bears are dressed fashionably, their postures and movements parodying humans.

2.18 The Crinoline, or How, When the Opportunity Presents Itself, to Use It to Replace a Hot-Air Balloon* 1866
Moscow, Ivan Gavrilov workshop, published by Pëtr Sharapov
Lithographic transfer.
37.5 x 33.1; *inv.* 39611.

Many comic *lubki* took the extremes of fashion as their subject. In the text a merchant, a much ridiculed class in *lubok*, complains to an acquaintance that his wife in her fashionable crinoline dress has been carried away by the wind along with a young man who was trying to save her.

The World of Animals

Animals appear in many contexts in *lubok*. They may, as we have seen, perform a satirical function while another group, more fantastic in nature, aid or threaten the fate of the heroes of popular romances. The examples here all illustrate a tale or fable in which the animal exemplifies a moral of some kind. The animals often stand for man and by inverting the natural order draw attention to the moral point. The bear and his relationship to man was a particularly popular theme.

2.19 The Most Unbelievable Story 1876
Moscow, Andrei Abramov workshop
Lithographic transfer coloured.
32.1; *inv.* 1084.

This version of *The Mice Bury the Cat* was produced a hundred years later than 2.12, and shows the continuing popularity of the subject with all the big workshops producing their own versions well into the 20th century. The print parodies the conventions of the Baroque funeral procession print with layers of mourners stacked on top of each other. By this date the subject had lost its original satirical bite, illustrating instead the proverb that even 'mice take a cat to the churchyard'.

2.20 A Merry Ride in a Mouse-drawn Carriage 1820s or 30s**
Copper engraving, hand-coloured.
33.2 x 46.8; *inv. Dahl.* 4-5.

Like many *lubok* which include animals in the place of human figures, there is a moral point to this image of a tomcat in love - taking his partner for a ride in the country. The text records that 'The coachman is driving the team very hard, but the servant standing behind has a quaking heart, for if he angers his masters at all, he knows full well that his head will roll'. The helpless and dependent can thus expect no charity even from those who are in love.

2.21 The Bull That Didn't Want to be a Bull and Became a Butcher
Second half 18th century
Copper engraving.
37.1 x 29; *inv. Ols.* 6-1163.

The central scene is one of 14 on the theme of the world turned upside down. This comic and satirical device was common to many European folk traditions (for example at Epinal in France), having its origin in the medieval festival of Twelfth Night when masters and their servants swapped roles for the day. The text includes references to 'the women who gave the ass a treat, sat him in a carriage and trundled him down the street', 'the hunter hunted', and the 'sheep who sheared the shepherd'. This particular example was based, like so many 18th century *lubki*, on prints imported from France. (see *Le Monde á l'envers*, Le Mans 18th century **ill**).

2.22 About the Chameleon Beast First half 18th century (1770s)
Woodcut.
34.1 x 28.4; *inv. Ols.* 11-2320.

The print is an illustration to a collection of fables, *The Spectacle of Human Life*. The text describes the nature of the animal in a way similar to the medieval bestiary, partly observation and part fantasy. Thus the chameleon sustains itself from the air alone; it moves day and night without rest and can change its colour to match its surroundings. *Below* a moral: many people are like the chameleon, they change character according to the company they keep.

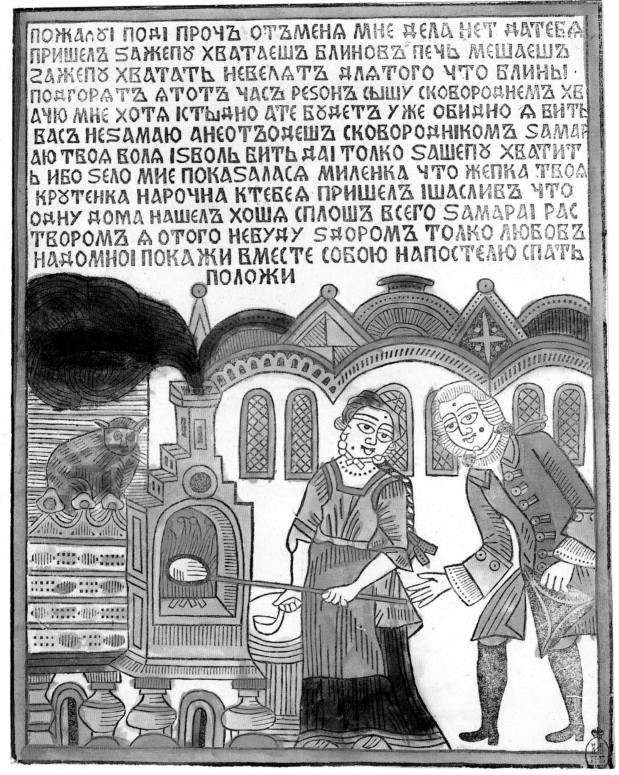

ПОЖАЛУІ ПОДІ ПРОЧЪ ОТЪМЕНА МНЕ ДЕЛА НЕТ ДАТЕБА
ПРИШЕЛЪ ЗАЖЕПУ ХВАТАЕШЪ БЛИНОВЪ ПЕЧЬ МЕШАЕШЪ
ЗАЖЕПУ ХВАТАТЬ НЕВЕЛАТЪ ДЛАТОГО ЧТО БЛИНЫ·
ПОДГОРАТЪ АТОТЪ ЧАСЪ РЕЗОНЪ СЫШУ СКОВОРОДНЕМЪ ХВ
АЧЮ МНЕ ХОТА КТЫАНО АТЕ БУДЕТЪ УЖЕ ОБИДНО А ВИТЬ
ВАСЪ НЕЗАМАЮ АНЕОТЪОДЕШЪ СКОВОРОДНИКОМЪ ЗАМАР
АЮ ТВОА ВОЛА ІЗВОЛЬ БИТЬ ДАІ ТОЛКО ЗАШЕПУ ХВАТИТ
Ь ИБО ЗЕЛО МИЕ ПОКАЗАЛАСА МИЛЕНКА ЧТО ЖЕПКА ТВОА
КРУТЕНКА НАРОЧНА КТЕБЕА ПРИШЕЛЪ ІШАСЛИВЪ ЧТО
ОДНУ ДОМА НАШЕЛЪ ХОША СПЛОШЪ ВСЕГО ЗАМАРАІ РАС
ТВОРОМЪ А ОТОГО НЕБУДУ ЗДОРОМЪ ТОЛКО ЛЮБОВЪ
НАДОМНОІ ПОКАЖИ ВМЕСТЕ СОБОЮ НАПОСТЕЛЮ СПАТЬ
ПОЛОЖИ

2.36 *The Pancake Vendor*, mid 18th century

МОСКОВСКИА ВЕДОМОСТИ ИО 58 ВПАТНИЦУ ИЮЛА . 21 . ДНА 1760 . ГОДА

огорода архангелскаго о 16 июна сотправленными исколь поморскому берегу сюда пришедшиии салдатами получено известие отаковомъ приключение которому подобнаго никто втамошнихъ местахъ неслыхалъ непаметуетъ аименно ввеломъ море видели кита потому изв естию несколко моржовыхъ промышланиковъ пошли въ 4 карвузахъ кмудюгеза 50 верстъ б сюда его искаты которого помн огимъ трудностамъ наконецъ удалосъ имъ наитить иопутать многии велужиеми неводами иотпали силу апотомъ острогами увили ннедалеко ô мутюги кберегу притащили еси иить длиною двенацати сажень атолшиною вдиаметредо трехъ сажень наодной голове 26 человевъ свободно стояли надеютса достать изнего до 700 пудовъ сала иио 60 пудовъ усовъ – – – – – – – –

2.77 News of a Whale Caught in the White Sea, second quarter 19th century

2.23 **The Tale of the Cock and the Fox** Early 19th century (1852)
Moscow, Aleksandr Loginov workshop
Copper engraving.
35.6 x 52.7; inv. 50937.

The scenes read from left to right. They illustrate a story from a 17th century manuscript which tells of the cock who, grief-stricken at the death of his hen, retires to a tree to devote himself to repentance and prepare for his own death. He is seen by a passing fox who lures him down and eats him. The fox in turn sits on a stump and mourns the cock, underlining the satirical intent of the print: an attack on hypocritical piety.

2.24 **The Bear and the Peasant Woman** 1820s or 30s
Copper engraving, hand-coloured.
27.1 x 33.7; inv. Pog. 3-240.

The text, in verse, tells how a woman gathering mushrooms in a forest meets a playful bear who offers to wrestle with her. She refuses saying the her 'fur' might get torn. She falls and the bear seeing her coat torn, goes to find bast (lime-tree bark) to repair it. A passing hare also goes to her aid, but the woman sets up such a commotion that both animals run away. The woman on returning home claims that she has frightened a bear and 'looked on the other beasts as mice'. As in many *lubki* with a narrative content, more than one part of the scene is shown in the same picture space. Both picture and text suggest an erotic meaning.

2.25 **The Industrious Bear** 1846
Moscow, Evdokiia Lavrenteva workshop
Copper engraving.
40.6 x 30; inv. 56327.

The text under the picture is in rhyme and was composed by the writer of Russian fables Ivan Krylov (1768-1844). It tells how a bear, trying to imitate man, attempts to make a yoke. Since he does not have the skills, or the patience to master them, he repeatedly breaks the wood with his brute strength. The peasant tells him that effort is not enough, one needs also to understand the techniques involved. Krylov's fables were very popular with *lubok* artists. In the world of *lubok* and folk tales the fierce bear is rendered as a placid and comic character.

2.25

Heroes

The popularity of tales of heroes such as Alexander the Great, as well as Russian figures like Ilia Muromets, was attested by the numerous *lubki* which portray their adventures, their appearance in block books, and by their survival well into the 20th century. The tales came from a rich oral tradition as well as increasingly from texts translated from foreign languages. Many were based on *byliny*, rhymes varying from one hundred to a thousand lines in length, chanted to music by travelling minstrels. These were being collected from the middle of the 18th century but had already entered the *lubok* tradition. The foreign tales were quickly russianised and took on many features of the oral stories.

Because the *lubok* artist could show only one scene from an often long and complex tale it is easy to forget their narrative context; they tended to portray the same scene and variations were not encouraged. Because the tales feature knights in armour a Western audience might be tempted to link them closely with medieval courtly romance. There is, however, an ambiguous morality to the tales and the air of the supernatural hangs too heavily over them for us to easily fit them into Western traditions.

2.26 **Tsar Alexander of Macedon (Alexander the Great)** First half 18th century (1770s).
Woodcut
32.6 x 29.9; inv. Ols. 6-1206.

The life of Alexander was the subject of numerous *lubki*. The source for many of the scenes was the Alexander romances, a collection of fantastic accounts of the hero's life and campaigns translated into many European languages and know in Russia from the 12th century. In this early woodcut Alexander is shown as a medieval knight and, apart from the title, there is nothing to distinguish him from any other hero.

2.27 **Fantastic People Discovered by Alexander of Macedon** 1820s or 30s**
Copper engraving, hand-coloured.
31.9 x 37.9; inv. Pog. 4-263.

The subject, from the Alexander romances, tells how Alexander, after conquering many kingdoms, met a race of 'horrifying and terrifying' people living in the mountains: strange mutants, part man, part beast. Alexander brought some of them back from the campaign but his attempt to introduce them into civilisation was not a success and 'the fantastic people took fright, rejected food and died of starvation'. The accumulation of fantastic tales around a historical figure proved an attractive source of imagery at a time when an uneducated audience still believed in aspects of the supernatural.

2.28 **The Glorious Battle Between Alexander of Macedon and Porus, King of India** Second quarter 19th century
Copper engraving, hand-coloured.
37.9 x 55.5; inv. 8866.

The word 'glorious' in the title is hardly suitable as Alexander is shown defeating Porus, King of India, by a far from sporting stratagem. The two kings rode out to meet each other in a personal duel to decide the outcome of the battle when Alexander, *left*, called out that the Indian army was following Porus. Porus, turning round to look, was killed by Alexander. This is not historically correct as Alexander actually showed the defeated king great clemency and returned his kingdom to him after the battle in 327 BC. This print is a repetition of an earlier woodcut version in which Alexander has a sword rather than, as here, a jousting lance.

2.29 The Glorious Knight Evdon Mid 18th century (1770s)
Woodcut.

24.5 x 27.5; inv. Ols. 6-1209.

The source of the tale of Evdon and his wife Berfa was a German story, translated into Russian in the 17th century. The two figures are often shown together, he the pattern of the dutiful knight, performing acts of bravery on behalf of his beloved, and she the perfect heroine, faithful, beautiful and virtuous with only a passive role to play. Such stories of idealised love were popular, especially with a class by definition distanced from the protagonists. There was also a fantastic element to the tale as the two lovers were helped and obstructed by magic forces and monsters. In this image the knight wears French clothes, underlying the story's foreign origin.

2.30 The Battle of Bova and Polkan the Centaur-Knight Second quarter 19th century
Copper engraving, hand-coloured.

28.9 x 36.7; inv. 4261.

Prince Bova and his wife Druzhnevna were the leading characters in a story known in Russia from the 16th century and soon became popular with all sections of society. Bova, having escaped from an attempt to poison him by his mother and her lover, undertook many adventures, aided by magic potions. At one point Bova was faced by an army of 300,000 sent by the Sultan Markabronn, which he duly defeated. The Sultan then despatched his bravest combatant, the centaur Polkan. Already tired, Bova fell but his horse came to his rescue and Polkan was forced to sue for peace. Polkan performed the role of guard for Bova's new bride and the two sons she bore him, while Bova pursued his enemy Dodon who, with his mother, had caused his exile.

2.31 The Mighty, Valiant Knight Ilia Muromets 1876
Moscow, Andrei Abramov workshop
Lithographic transfer, hand-coloured.

34.5 x 38.3; inv. 1036.

The story of Ilia Muromets was a popular one and a staple part of the oral tradition. Murom is an ancient Russian town on the Oka. In the 18th century publishers began to produce block books consisting of eight pictures and text, as well as *lubki* of this subject. The central scene was, as here, the conflict between Ilia Muromets and Solovei (Nightingale) the robber who lived in oak trees and who, from this vantage point, trapped wayfarers by his deafening whistling. Muromets is shown firing an arrow at the robber. The print is a good example of the common practice in *lubok* of showing more than one incident in the same scene; in the background the hero is dragging off the vanquished robber.

2.32 The Mighty, Valiant Hero Eruslan Lazarevich 1876**
Moscow, Andrei Abramov workshop
Lithographic transfer, hand-coloured.

27.5 x 38; inv. 1071.

The tale of Eruslan Lazarevich is possibly Persian or Serbian in origin and was one of the most popular tales of knights and chivalry; it circulated in oral form, as well as appearing in *lubki*. The print shows Eruslan's defeat of the three-headed monster living in a lake in the realm of King Vakhramei (here shown as the moat of the king's castle) and how, with the aid of a magic ring, he won the hand of the king's beautiful daughter Anastasia.

2.29

2.33 The Mighty, Glorious, Valiant Knight Ivan Tsarevich 1874
Moscow, Andrei Morozov workshop
Lithographic transfer, hand-coloured.

33.6 x 39; inv. 1074.

This print illustrates the successful outcome of the perilous adventures of Ivan Tsarevich, the youngest of the three sons of Tsar Vyslav Andronovich. The Tsar had a beautiful garden and in it an apple tree which produced golden fruit. Each night the Firebird visited the garden and stole some of the fruit. The king set his sons the task of capturing the bird with the promise of winning his kingdom. The tale tells of the youngest prince's adventures and the stratagems of the elder brothers to hinder him. Accompanied by Grey Wolf, who helped him capture the Firebird, the knight is shown with the rewards of his adventures: the golden-maned steed and Princess Elena the Beautiful, who was to become his bride.

2.34 The Mighty, Glorious, Valiant Knight Ivan Tsarevich 1894
Moscow, Ivan Sytin cooperative workshop
Chromo-lithograph.

29 x 38.5; inv. 50803.

This chromo-lithographic repetition was produced 20 years after 2.33 and testifies to the continuing popularity of the subject. As in medieval religious art a pattern was re-used over a long period with no attempt at origninality or new interpretation although, as here, there are differences of detail, in particular the costume which was updated in the interests of fashion. The technique is also relevant; recently introduced chromo-lithography colour printing allowed a more detailed approach and the elimination of hand-colouring, but to the modern eye, it seems out of keeping with the fantastic subject. A sophisticated printing technique which allowed a new level of realism breaks the spell and for many commentators meant the end of the *lubok* tradition in the sense of a folk art of the people, for the people.

Славный силный и храбрый Витязь, Еруслан Лазаревичъ, ъдетъ на Чудо великомъ Змъи отрехъ главахъ; а Прекрасная Царевна Анастасія Вохрамеевна встречаетъ его

2.32 The Mighty, Valiant Hero Eruslan Lazarevich, 1876

Печат. позв. Моск. 1858 г: Ноля: 5 дня Цензоръ Н: Гиляр: Плетнева: Издан: А: Абрамова. Печ: въ Литогр: П: Лукьянова. 1858 г:

СКАЗКА ОТОМЪ КАКЪ МАСТЕРОВОЙ ЧЕРТА НАДУЛЪ.

Разъ мастеровой развеселился,
Сильно на водку напустился, пьетъ
Попиваетъ, работу забываетъ,
Такъ напивается безъ памяти,
Въ грязи валяется деньги проживаетъ
Сапоги съ ногъ скидаетъ,
Въ кабакѣ оставляетъ,
Себя вездѣ ославляетъ.
Чертъ около его увивается
Пріятно улыбается,
Во всемъ ему угождаетъ
Лакейскую должность исправляетъ
Въ кабакъ двери отворяетъ
Изъ грязи его вынимаетъ,
Мастеровой имъ повелеваетъ
Частенько позатылку катаетъ
А чертъ только жмется,
Да на мастероваго смѣется
Денегъ ему даетъ.

Мастеровой на нихъ пьетъ,
По утрамъ опохмѣляется,
А вечеромъ въ грязи валяется,
Съ мѣсяцъ такъ наслаждался,
А черту неподдавался,
Чертъ сильно разсердился,
На мастероваго озлился,
На похмѣлье недаетъ,
Къ дѣду Сатанѣ зоветъ,
Говоритъ, деньги у меня извелись
Ступай дѣду поклонись,
Душу ему отнеси, Да денегъ возми,
Напить съ ними попивай, На славу гуляй,
Такъ, такъ, сказалъ мастеровой,
И покачалъ Головой,
Думаетъ, нѣтъ не облетешь,
Души моей не Возмешь,
Мастероваго не провидешь,
Самъ скорый въ его когти попадешь

Мастеровой въ огнь и море бывалъ
И отвсюду здравъ вылезалъ,
Нѣтъ ты вотъ что, чертикъ, аль домовой
Сказалъ ему мастеровой,
Самъ на перво къ дѣду сходи,
И у него мнѣ тысячъ 5 попроси,
Что-бъ я на нихъ съ круга спился,
И самъ въ адъ къ нему явился,,
Чертъ хвостомъ веляетъ,
И такъ отвѣчаетъ,
И жалуй я услужу, у дѣда денегъ попрошу
Но только ты неоткажись,
И послѣ самъ къ дѣду явись,
Ему за деньги поклонись, Душой своею
Расплатись. Ужъ знаю я благодарю,
И нынѣ съ водки-же сгорю, чертъ съ нимъ
Тотъ часъ же разпростился,
И къ дѣду Сатанѣ явился,
О всемъ ему тутъ разказалъ,

И тысячъ пять у дѣда взялъ,
Къ мастеровому прикатилъ,
Отъ дѣда денежки вручилъ,
Мастеровой благодарилъ, Въ карманъ
Денежки положилъ, Живо съ чертомъ
Разпростился, Да и домой бѣжать пустился
А чертъ его сталъ догонять. Хотѣлъ свои
Деньги отнять, Мастеровой-же развернулся.
Посвойски ловко размахнулся,
И черта такъ хватилъ сплеча,
Что онъ свалился не крича,
И къ утру въ чувство лишь пришелъ,
До дѣда еле онъ дошелъ,
Мастеровой-жъ домой явился,
И самъ Хозяйствовать пустился,
Отъ Бѣды Большой онъ Магазинъ,
Живетъ теперь Какъ Господинъ,
А чертъ его воспоминаетъ,
И отъ побоевъ все хвараетъ.

2.56 *The Tale of How the Workman Fooled the Devil, 1858*

85

Love, Courtship and Marriage

The earliest *lubki* which took love or courtship as their subject, dating from the early 18th century, tended to divide into two types: those which treated the subject as a source of humour and those which concentrated on more elegant and fashionable figures many of whom were shown in theatrical settings. The comic *lubki* concentrated on the humour implicit in courtship and on the figure of the matchmaker. There was a less attractive side, however, a strong element of misogyny in the representation of married women, who were frequently portrayed as unfaithful or vain and were punished by their husbands.

In the 19th century publishers of *lubki* looked increasingly to popular songs for their subjects and to contemporary writers such as Pushkin and Koltsov and these were printed below the image. Many such prints were frankly sentimental and showed a more idealised approach to love and courtship centering on the virtuous peasant girl. This inclusion of a long text suggests the idea that *lubki* were produced for and sold to illiterate rural peasants is far from the case.

2.35 **'Give Me Back My Buckets'** First half 18th century (1770s)
Woodcut.

35.9 x 30.5; *inv. Ols.* 61219.

The print shows a courtship scene. It illustrates a comic dialogue between the two fashionably dressed characters.

2.36 **The Pancake Vendor** Mid 18th century (1760s)**
Woodcut, hand-coloured.

35.6 x 29.2; *inv. Pog.* 1-6.

The scene shows a cavalier flirting with a woman who is making pancakes. The ornate interior includes a highly decorated stove with glazed tiles. The print follows the theatrical convention of showing an interior with the fourth wall missing.

2.37 **'Just One Kiss, Blackeyes'** Mid 18th century*
Copper engraving.

34.7 x 28.4; *inv. Ols.* 6-1151.

This love scene is one of the earliest examples of the theatrical *lubok*. The lovers face us as though we are the audience; they are framed by a proscenium arch and the floor recedes to create the illusion of a stage-like space. The more sophisticated medium of copper engraving, as opposed to woodcut, has allowed the artist to include more detail in the costumes, which are fashionable and ornate.

2.38 **'In a Small Village Lived Vanka . . .'** 1874
Moscow, Andrei Abramov workshop
Lithographic transfer, hand-coloured.

28.1 x 32.1; *inv.* 132.

The print illustrates a Russian folksong that tells how a young man called Vanka loved a girl called Tanka. She loved him too and bought him a pipe as a present, on which he began to play a song for her. Vanka then brought a horse and harnessed it to a cart.

2.39 **'In the Evening a Beautiful Girl . . .'** 1881
Golyshevka (Mstëra), Vladmir, Ivan Golyshev workshop
Lithograph.

21 x 35; *inv.* 51475.

An Illustration to a popular song printed below the image. It tells of a peasant girl who, as she drives her geese to the pond in the evening, sings that she is not tempted by the love of a rich man but prefers to dream of a man from her village whom she would marry for love. The song, composed by N. Ibragimov, appeared in song-books of the 1850s.

2.41

2.40 **In the Meadows, In the Meadows . . .'** 1894
Moscow, Ivan Sytin cooperative workshop
Chromo-lithography.

26.3 x 38.5; *inv.* 51318.

The text is a popular song from the 1850s. The girl begs her father to allow her to marry a young man, not an old one. This is a common theme in earlier *lubki* where the subject was often treated in a coarse manner. Behind her is the horse which she has raised 'In the meadows' and which she gives to her father in order to win him over.

2.41 **A Bachelor's Deliberation on Marriage** Early 19th century
Copper engraving, hand-coloured.

28.6 x 23.4; *inv. Pog.* 3-250.

Like 2.38 this print is presented as a theatrical scene with a proscenium arch, curtains, a receding stage space and characters who address us as though we are an audience. The subject, the hesistant bachelor who cannot make up his mind about whether or whom to marry, is common in folk literature and is not confined to Russia. In the text the suitor is advised to consult 'good people'. The image shows his attempt to choose from four portraits.

2.42 Conversation Between the Foolish Suitor and the Stupid Matchmaker Second quarter 19th century
Copper engraving, hand-coloured.
37.6 x 29.5; inv. Pog. 4-260.

Matchmaking was one of the most popular subjects for comic *lubki*. The text, by Aleksandr Sumarokov, is in the form of a comic dialogue. The suitor, dressed in absurd clothes, has failed to cook the matchmaker the meal she wants since the chickens have pecked up all the grain, instead he offers her 'smoked ice'. Therefore when the foolish suitor asks her to find him a suitable wife she promises to bring him a nanny goat. The figures inhabit a stage-like space.

2.43 New Year 1858
Moscow, Pëtr Sharapov workshop
Copper engraving.
30.8 x 38.5; inv. 51213.

This print illustrates the tradition of 'fortune telling using hens' when, during the ten days after Christmas, peasant girls who wished to know whether they were destined to marry in the forthcoming year, and the identity of their future husbands, would gather together. Tradition had it that if a girl looked in a mirror at midnight she might see the face of her bridegroom. Likewise a hen, let loose in a room in which grain, water and a mirror had been placed on the floor, might indicate the character of a future husband. If the hen drank the water the husband would turn out to be a drunkard, if it looked in the mirror he would be vain and if it pecked up the grain he would be a rich man. The text, however, warned against the desire to see the future bridegroom before the right time.

2.44 'In the Field, In the Field...' 1894
Moscow, Ivan Sytin cooperative workshop
Chromo-lithograph.
24.5 x 39; inv. 51327.

The print shows a festive gathering on the public festival of Semik (held on the Thursday before Trinity). On this day girls would weave wreaths and hang them on the birch trees. If a wreath became untwisted before the holiday it would mean that its maker would get married that year. A girl *left*, is making a wreath. R*ight*, a musician plays while the women dance and sing a traditional song emphasizing that the man wearing the wedding crown should be young. A young groom is indeed being crowned.

2.47

2.45 Russian Wedding 1876
Moscow, Andrei Abramov workshop
Lithographic transfer, hand-coloured.
21 x 36.5; inv. 2094.

The text is a traditional wedding song in which the bride sings to the groom's parents and her own parents.

2.46 Songs by A. V. Koltsov Early 20th century
Moscow, Ivan Sytin cooperative workshop
Chromo-lithograph.
38.5 x 55; inv. 50249.

Aleksei Koltsov (1809-42) was known for his verses singing the praises of ordinary people, and these idealised descriptions of peasant life were very popular with the publishers of *lubki*. Below a portrait of the writer are six illustrations to verses by Koltsov which were made into songs.

2.47 'The Cossacks Set Off to War at Midnight' 1895
Moscow, Ivan Sytin cooperative workshop
Chromo-lithograph.
24 x 36.5; inv. 51950.

The text is a cossack song, in Ukrainian, with its origin in the 18th century. Leaving for war the soldier asks his mother to look after his bride Marusenka as if she were her own daughter. This print is a version of a subject first published in 1856 as government propaganda at the time of the Crimean War. The soldier taking leave of his wife or beloved was a popular theme at all times, providing an attractive mixture of sentiment and duty.

2.48 The Foolish Wife and the Cat 1820s or 30s
Copper engraving, hand-coloured.
30.9 x 36.9; inv. Pog. 4-281.

The unfaithful or foolish wife is a common theme in folk prints. This example illustrates the story of a wife who lied to her husband. She put some meat in a tin dish in the oven for her husband's meal and returned to find that the tin had melted and the food was lost. In fear the woman blamed the cat. Discovering the lie, the husband caught the cat and tied it to his wife's back. The text notes how he 'begins beating the cat, and the cat starts clawing the wife's back'.

2.48

Ну и треск-же, ну и гром-же
Былъ отъ нѣмцевъ подлѣ Ломжи!

2.92 Kazimir Malevich, *What a Boom, What a Blast*, 1914

2.49   A Lesson for Husbands, Poor Peasant Countrymen and Extravagant Wives 1874
Moscow, Andrei Abramov workshop
Lithographic transfer, hand-coloured.
32.1 x 39.6; inv. 1605.
This is an example of the use of a multiple narrative. Top left, a wife is persuading her husband to sell his cow and horse to buy her new clothes. In the subsequent scenes the wife is seen enjoying herself in her new clothes, even entertaining a goat with her music. In the winter the peasant decides to teach his wife a lesson and harnesses her to the sledge in place of the the horse which has been sold. Bottom right, two husbands, a merchant and an official, point out to their wives, the moral which is stressed as being of relevance to all classes.

2.50   'A Peasant Was Ploughing the Field . . .' 1876
Moscow, Andrei Abramov workshop
Lithographic transfer, hand-coloured.
29.6 x 35.1; inv 76.
The peasant is ploughing as the sun sets. He is angry that his wife who, unlike the dutiful wives of the other peasants, has not brought his lunch to the fields and he has decided to beat her when he returns home.

Humour

The *lubok* tradition is rich in comic figures. Erëma, Paramoshka and Savoska, buffoons and clowns with their origins in the repertoire of travelling performers, were heirs to *Commedia dell'Arte* traditions, as well as to the jesters and fools kept at court. Much of the humour in these scenes, particularly before the 19th century, is coarse with a strong scatalogical element.

In the 19th century the tone changes. The figure of the unworldly peasant visiting the city provides an amusing type and *lubok* artists concentrate more on the observation of everyday life rather than on the old stock of characters, although the older figures continued to feature at fairs and popular entertainments.

2.51   Baba-laga Dances with an Old Man First half 18th century (1770s)
Woodcut.
28.8 x 38; inv. Ols. 6-1225.
Baba means a married peasant woman, usually with disparaging connotations. The character Baba-laga appears in many guises, in folk tales as well as *lubok*. In some she is the evil crone, a figure of fear for the local children, while in the more fanciful tales she is a sorceress armed with magic potions who can either help or hinder the progress of the hero. Here she is seen in a more comic light, dancing with an old man who plays a form of the bagpipes.

2.52   Foma, Paramoshka and Erëma Mid 18th century (1760s)
Woodcut, hand-coloured.
29.2 x 34; inv. Pog. 1-5.
The brothers Foma and Erëma are comic heroes of numerous tales. Their escapades always end in hilarious disaster. The print illustrates three adventures: left and right the brothers go fishing, only to sink as their boats both have holes; centre they are seen brawling with Paramoshka and two dogs in the foreground allude to their failed hunt. The two buffoons were notoriously stubborn; the text records that after sinking 'they will not come up from the bottom'.

2.53   Foma the Musician and Erëma. Prokhor and Boris Second half 18th century*
Copper engraving, hand-coloured.
28.2 x 35.5; inv. Pog. 4-278.
The figures, left, are the luckless brothers Foma and Erëma. The text describes their comic appearance; they have hooked noses, pot bellies and whiskers like whips. Foma is mangy and Erëma crooked. The two characters also performed in fairground shows where they spouted nonsense verse and did tricks.

2.54   Savoska and Paramoshka Second quarter 19th century
Copper engraving, hand-coloured.
28 x 34.5 inv. Pog. 4-277.
The two comic characters Savoska and Paramoshka frequently appeared in folk stories and *lubki*. Savoska is unlucky, while Paramoshka, lively and resourceful, always lands on his feet. In this print Savoska, right, has lost money playing cards and the figure behind Paramoshka points this out to him. Savoska is searching for more money and scratches his head.

2.55   Taras the Bald 1820s or 30s
Copper engraving, hand-coloured.
33 x 30; inv. Pog. 3254.
Taras the Bald is a stock figure in Russian popular humour. Here three women taunt the old man suggesting ways he might regain his hair, including the application of rose water to his head. The print is a copy, with a few changes, of a woodcut of 1760. The subject comes from a story in the *Facetiae* (1438-52) of Gian-Francesco Poggio called 'About Young Girls Who Play Tricks on a Bald Man', translated into Russian in the second half of the 18th century.

2.56   The Tale of How the Workman Fooled the Devil 1858**
Moscow, P. Lukianov workshop, published by Anton Abramov
Lithographic transfer, hand-coloured.
27.5 x 35; inv. 50909.

2.56a   The Tale of How the Workman Fooled the Devil 1858 Moscow, P. Lukianov workshop, published by Anton Abramov
Lithographic transfer.
27.5 x 35; inv. 50907.

2.56b   The Tale of How the Workman Fooled the Devil 1874
Moscow, Anton Abramov workshop,
Lithographic transfer, hand-coloured.
27.5 x 35; inv. 1079.
Three versions of the same subject show the importance of hand-colouring in the effect of a *lubok* print. By this date, however, the four colours are applied in a slapdash manner with little control so that colour cuts across the lines. The later impression is coloured with the newly introduced aniline colours which are much harsher than the traditional palette. The story is told in consecutive episodes. The devil, having decided to capture the soul of a workman, connives at his getting drunk. The workman, however, is too clever and after tricking the devil out of five thousand roubles makes his escape to open a shop with the money.

2.57   'What a Noise Outside They're Making . . .' 1876
Moscow, Andrei Abramov workshop
Lithographic transfer, hand-coloured.
32.9 x 30.6; inv. 68.
The text is a comic song telling how the village women share out a sarafan (dress) by tearing it into pieces. They are watched by two men amused by this evidence of female folly.

2.58 Two Peasants Visiting a Tavern 1857
Moscow, A. Prokofev workshop
Lithographic transfer,
30 x 38.5; *inv.* 50594.

The adventures of peasants visiting the town were popular in the second half of the 19th century as the emancipation of the serfs (1861) made mobility possible. Here the newly arrived peasants are seen taking a drink in a tavern and watching a game of billiards through the doorway. The elder man, Pantiushka, explains to Sidorka how to play, but cautions against the dangers of gambling.

2.59 Pantiushka and Sidorka See the Sights of Moscow 1879
Golyshevka (Mstëra), Vladimir, Ivan Golyshev workshop
Lithograph, hand-coloured.
31.2 x 41.5; *inv.* 50597.

The same peasants who appeared in 2.58 now look round Moscow for the first time. Pantiushka points out the main sites and accompanies the tour with amusing explanations. They are identified in the print by captions: in the centre the 'Ivan the Great Bell Tower', in the left-hand column 'The Tsar Bell', 'The Spasskii Gates', and the Bolshoi 'Theatre' and in the right-hand column 'The Tsar Cannon', the monument to 'Minin and Pozharskii' and the 'Sukharev Tower'. All of the sites are in, or near, the Kremlin. As well as being entertaining such prints had an educational role, familiarising a rural audience with sites intimately linked with Russian history.

2.60 'Look There Filatka!' 1858
Moscow, Andrei Vasilev workshop
Copper engraving.
30 x 37; *inv.* 50508.

Two peasants, Miron and Filatka, are viewing the sights of Moscow. They are trying to identify the figures on a monument in Red Square. Miron argues that they must be the protagonists of the *lubok* tale of Eruslan Lazarevich (2.32), the knight Roslei and the Tsar of the Burning Shield. Filatka, who has attended to his lessons instead of looking at popular prints, recognises that it is the monument to Minin and Pozharskii, heroes of the Time of Troubles when Moscow was threatened by Polish troops. The monument has since been relocated closer to St Basil's Cathedral.

Secular Morality

There is strong moral element to the *lubok* tradition which found expression both as positive images for emulation and in images condemning a particular vice. The problems of drinking and gambling, in particular, attracted much attention. Work was also an important issue, often presented in the contrast between the fruits of labour and the curse of idleness.

2.61 'Know Thyself, Give Instructions in Your Own House' First half 18th century (1760s)
Woodcut, hand-coloured.
36.6 x 29; *inv.* Pog. 1-3.

A group of men dine with a servant and a musician in attendance. The text is a homily on how to behave when out visiting. It warns that guests ought to obey their host and eat and drink what they are offered, concluding that if the guest behaves well he will be respected: if not he will be thrown out onto the street.

2.62 'I Am Hop High-Head' Late 18th or early 19th century
Copper engraving, hand-coloured.
38.2 x 57.5; *inv.* Pog. 3-236.

In the central panel a lady and a gentleman pick hops; around them are scenes illustrating the dangerous consequences that can follow from such an innocent starting point. Drinking causes clouding of the reason, makes the teeth 'rusty', dreams terrifying and the nights restless. Drink is shown also to be a great social leveller as it affects all classes; the prince drinks away his wealth and loses his power, the deacon becomes the laughing stock of his parish, the merchant squanders his wealth and the drunken wife will be driven from her home. The text concludes that 'drink clouds the mind and turns a man into nothing', that evil and violent drunkards are 'the most wretched of all human beings'.

2.62

2.63 The Conversation of Big Nose and Bitter Frost 1874
Moscow, Andrei Abramov workshop
Lithographic transfer, hand-coloured.
33.1 x 37.6; inv. 1210.
The figure of Frost from the popular *Tale of the Red Nose* is shown admonishing the foolish 'Big Nose'. The moral is clear; neither tobacco nor drinking can help the boastful fool withstand a bitter frost.

2.64 Ariel Journey: or How They Fly Up the Chimney and the Creditors Are Amazed 1858
Moscow, Pëtr Sharapov workshop, published by Pëtr Sharapov
Copper engraving.
40.3 x 34.5; inv. 39489.
The fantastic imagery in this print is a pictorialisation of the Russian phrase 'to fly out of the chimney' meaning 'to go bankrupt'. A ruined merchant and contractor are seen escaping through the chimney of a house. The text and the objects they carry explain the reasons for their financial collapse: women, drink and gambling (the first man carries a bottle and the man in the rear holds some playing cards). A German creditor who has just arrived at the house to collect his debts shouts at them to return but a passer-by explains that this is useless.

2.65

2.65 Romance: 'Towards Evening One Bad Autumn...' 1857
Moscow, Andrei Vasilev workshop
Copper engraving.
28 x 34.6; inv. 51516.
Although many *lubki* were derived from the folk tradition others were based on, and in turn helped popularise, the writings of major writers such as Aleksandr Pushkin on whose poem, 'Romance', this print was based. Pushkin's poem was written in 1814 and was quickly adapted as a folk song and popularised through song-books. The subject was taken up by the *lubok* publishers in 1832. It tells the story of an unhappy girl who abandons her illegitimate child outside a stranger's house one autumn night. The popularity of the story is underlined by the fact that 30 versions were issued in 74 editions.

2.66 The Demon of Gambling 1853
Moscow, Evdokiia Lavrenteva workshop, artist Ivan Golyshev
Copper engraving.
41 x 31; inv. 39865.
The print condems the evils of gambling and card-playing. Card games are shown allegorically in the form of a dragon swallowing a castle. *Above*, a man points out the dragon to his son. The drawing on which the engraving was based was by the 15-year-old Ivan Golyshev who later founded the lithographic workshop in Mstëra. It is rare for us to know the identity of the artist on whose work an engraving is based.

2.67 The Slanderer and the Serpent 1873*
Moscow, Andrei Morozov workshop
Lithographic transfer, hand-coloured.
30.1 x 39.6; inv. 1049.
The text is based on a tale by Ivan Krylov written in 1818. In Hell a slanderer and a serpent dispute as to who has caused the most harm with their tongues. Beelzebub, who emerges from the flames in hell's mouth, resolves the argument in favour of the slanderer.

2.68 'The Husband Weaves Bast Shoes With Skill, the Wife Spins
-9 Fibres With a Will' First half 18th century (1770s)
Woodcut, on two sheets of paper.
30 x 26.6; 29.4 x 25; inv. Ols 11-2303, 2304.
The two peasants who symbolise honest toil and industry spend the winter months pursuing the traditional cottage handicrafts of spinning and shoe making. Bast, the layer of wood found under the bark of the lime tree, was the material from which the distinctive peasant footware was made.

2.64

2.70 The Peasant and Death 1865*
Moscow, Efim Iakovlev workshop
Lithographic transfer.
29.8 x 35.5; inv. 50272.

A woodcut, *The Old Man and Death*, based on a fable by Aesop, was published in the 18th century. In 1808 Ivan Krylov published his own version of the tale and this is the text that *lubok* publishers used after 1857. The tale tells of the old man who, after a hard-working life, calls on Death to release him from his misery. When Death appears, however, the old man is so appalled that he pretends that all he wanted was a help in carrying his firewood.

2.71 Muzhichek (The Peasant) 1849
Moscow, Grigorii Chuksin workshop, published by Arkhip Beliankin
Copper engraving.
49.8 x 39.8; inv. 50247.

The moral of the lazy and the industrious peasants is told as an instructive and effective contrast. *Left*, the lazy peasant either sleeps on the stove, rests on a bench or stares through the window. Outside his horses run free and his fields remain unharvested. In comparison the industrious peasant sees his crop off to market, having harvested it, *background*. Inside the peasant celebrates the sale of his crop. The subject and text is taken from the verses 'Why Are You Sleeping Peasant' by Aleksei Koltsov (1808-42) (2.46).

2.72 'Don't Awake the Pretty Maiden...' 1868*
Moscow, Efim Iakovlev workshop
Lithographic transfer.
30 x 38; inv. 51270.

The song tells how a herdsman is invited by a girl to join a dance. He does not notice that his herd has escaped and that his fellow villagers are having to return his animals. The text is attributed to Vasilii Kugashev, a poet and dramatist of the early 19th century.

2.71

The Marvels of the Age

With the introduction of copper engraving in the middle of the 18th century the *lubok* increasingly took on the function of spreading information, since the medium allowed the inclusion of a long text. In addition to the almost encyclopedic range of subjects already covered by *lubki*, contemporary events drawn from newspapers and from word of mouth accounts were now illustrated. These ranged from natural marvels, often rendered with a spectacular disregard for the literal truth, to later subjects such as the railway which demonstrated the advances of science and technology. The workshops of Ilia Akhmetiev were particulary important in this development and were instrumental in moving the *lubok* towards mass production. The prints showing contemporary events were presumably aimed at a literate audience, since they often include a long text.

2.73 The Eruption of Vesuvius in 1776 Second half 18th century
Copper engraving, hand-coloured.
26.6 x 33; inv. Pog. 3-217.

This print illustrates a report in the newspaper *Moscow Gazette* (*Moskovskie vedomosti*) on the eruption of Vesuvius in April 1766. Engravings were one way in which people in remote places learned about events in the outside world. In this case the artist, like his audience, had never seen either Naples or a volcanic mountain in action.

2.74 'Satyr' Shown in Spain in 1760 Second half 18th century**
Copper engraving, hand-coloured;
36.2 x 28.2; inv. Pog. 9-385.

This print illustrates a report in the *Moscow Gazette*. In many of the reports reality and fantasy are wildly mixed as in this case where a story published in July 1760 announced that a 'satyr' had been brought to Barcelona for display. It had a 'human head, forehead, eyes and eyebrows, the ears of a tiger, red cheeks, cat's whiskers, a goat's beard, a lion's mouth with a hoop of bone showing instead of teeth, and its arms were like human ones, except that they were covered up to the wrists with hair of different colours, as was its whole body'. The 'monster', apparently a wild man found in the woods, was however, only five foot three inches tall and ate bread and milk: in the print it dwarfs the figures and the landscape.

2.75 Cosmography Second half 18th century
Copper engraving, hand-coloured, printed on four pieces of paper.
72 x 58; inv. Pog. 9387.

The subject was a popular one from the early 18th century. The four points of the compass are described in texts in the corners. In the centre rivers, seas, lakes, islands and countries are marked, each with short descriptions taken from manuscript chronicles of the 17th century. The passage for England notes its rich, mercantile population, its skilled sailors and its good supply of tin.

2.76 The Mighty Elephant Beast from the Land of Persia Brought to Moscow in the Year (17)96 August 13. Late 18th or early 19th century
Copper engraving, hand-coloured.
28.5 x 35; inv. Pog. 9-384.

The exhibition of an elephant was bound to excite popular interest and thus stimulate the production of *lubki*. An elephant was first shown in Russia in the reign of Peter the Great in 1688, then during the reign of the empress Anna and again in 1796. This example, one of many versions, seems to date from the end of the 18th century. Even though the artist may well have seen the exotic beast it is not represented with a large degree of accuracy; the position and form of the ear, for instance, is badly observed.

2.76

2.77 News of a Whale Caught in the White Sea in June 1760**
Second quarter 19th century
Copper engraving, hand-coloured.
31.5 x 39.5; inv. Pog. 9-388.

The text, based on a report in *Moscow Gazette* for July 1760, tells of the appearance and capture of a whale near Archangel. The report details the size of the beast (26 people could stand on its head). The way it was captured differs from the fantastic nature of the illustration, which renders the beast as an overgrown fish with fierce head. Though the subject was popular and repeated many times, the form of the whale was later modified.

2.78 Portent in the Sky Over the Town of Shlonsk in 1736 Second quarter 19th century
Copper engraving, hand-coloured.
38.1 x 30.6; inv. Pog. 4-264.

Many natural phenomena — comets in the sky, as here, or eclipses of the sun — were intrepreted in supernatural terms in the chronicles and provided a rich vein of material for folk images.

2.79 Predatory Wolves Attacking Travellers 1867
Moscow, Ivan Gavrilov workshop, published by Pëtr Sharapov
Lithographic transfer.
30 x 34; inv. 51242.

The text, in verse, tell how two travellers in a troika (a traditional vehicle consisting of a sledge pulled by three horses) made their escape from wolves. The subject was repeated many times.

2.80 The Railway 1852
Moscow, Efim Iakovlev workshop
Copper engraving.
38 x 61; inv. 185.

The Moscow to St Petersburg railway opened in 1851 and was a popular subject for *lubki*. This engraving illustrates the departure from Moscow of the second train in September 1851 carrying a battalion of the Preobrazhenskii Guards with a military band.

2.81 The Railway 1874*
Golyshevka (Mstëra), Vladimir, Ivan Golyshev workshop
Lithograph.
33.1 x 42.6; inv. 1616.

Ivan Golyshev introduced a number of new elements in this representation of the railway. The text is spoken by a fairground seller of hot drinks, *foreground*, who praises the railway in a joking way. Images of a paddleboat steamer and a hot air balloon are also included to underline the theme of recent advances made in transport.

2.79

Fairs and Social Gatherings

Since it was at public gatherings and fairs that *lubki* were sold it is not perhaps surprising that they should feature prominently as subjects in the prints themselves. In other examples people are shown relaxing in less formal situations.

2.82 **The Bath-house** First half 18th century (1770s)
Woodcut.
30.5 x 37.5. *inv. Ols.* 6-1226.
The bath-house was an important part of the social life of both town and village. The text emphasises its restorative powers, though the image itself is voyeuristic. The women, *right*, ladle out water from a large tub, others gently beat themselves with birch twigs or massage each other. In the towns public bath-houses offered treatment for muscular and joint ailments.

2.83 **'Down Along Old Mother Volga . . .'** 1870
Moscow, Pëtr Glushkov workshop
Lithographic transfer, hand-coloured.
30 x 32.7; *inv.* 51075.
The jovial party row down the river to be welcomed at an inn. The text is a well known folk song from the late 18th century.

2.84 **Up the Volga from Nizhnii Gorod** 1896
Moscow, Ivan Sytin cooperative workshop
Chromo-lithograph.
29.3 x 39.5; *inv.* 51744.
Nizhnii (Nov)gorod is now known as Gorky. The text is a song from a play by Aleksandr Shakhovskii (1777-1846), *The Woman with Two Husbands*, sung by a brigand leader. A young man sings of the girl he loves and asks his companions to be thrown into the Volga if she rejects him.

2.85 **'Come On, Mishenka Ivanich'** 1863, reworked in 1874**
Moscow, Andrei Abramov workshop
Lithographic transfer, hand-coloured.
33.6 x 39.1; *inv.* 1641
From the early middle ages until 1866, when the Society for the Protection of Animals persuaded the government to ban the use of animals for entertainment, performing bears were toured around the towns and villages of Russia. This was a popular subject for *lubki*. The example shows a travelling group of three: the trainer, a drummer, and a youth dressed as a goat in order to tease the bear. The leader would accompany the show with rhymed, humorous jingles in which he would call upon the bear to perform amusing scenes from everyday life.

2.86 **In Marina Roshcha** 1858
Moscow, Efim Iakovlev workshop
Lithographic transfer.
31.1 x 38.5; *inv.* 50533.
Marina Roshcha, on the outskirts of Moscow, was a pleasure ground and a favourite spot for public holidays and recreation. There were taverns, public spectacles, peepshows and fair booths among the avenues of trees. The print shows a performance with a bear and a man dressed as a nanny goat; its text tells how the bear and the goat make friends, learn music and dancing together, and go to work for their master. Mummers dressed up in the costumes of a bear and a goat also performed at Shrovetide in an entertainment known as 'leading the she goat'. The Church castigated such performances as pagan survivals.

2.87 **Steam Bicycle at Shrovetide, near Novinsk** 1858
Moscow, A Prokofev workshop
Lithographic transfer.
31.5 x 28.5; *inv.* 39356.
During the festival of Shrovetide (the three days before Ash Wednesday) popular festivals were held to celebrate the end of winter. From the 1840s the Moscow festival was held near the Novinsk boulevard. The text is the sort of humorous patter by which showmen would try to raise interest in their attractions, such as a 'steam bicycle'. The picture actually shows a model railway engine.

2.88 **Moscow Mead Vendor and Picture Pedlar** 1858*
Moscow, A. Prokofev workshop
Lithographic transfer.
40 x 31.5; *inv.* 28135.
Street vendors were a popular subject for publishers. In this example a mead seller (see also 6.78) with a pot and a string of pastries is selling a hot drink of honey and spices to a print seller. The travelling pedlars carried their stock of prints bound to a pole in the way illustrated here. The print which is visible is a portrait of Julia Postrana, 'The Brazilian bearded lady' who toured Russia as a curiosity. The main centres for selling *lubki* in Moscow were around the Kremlin, in the markets and wherever a crowd was likely to gather; in the 19th century they were increasingly sold in shops too. Elsewhere in Russia travelling pedlars would tour the provinces, visiting fairs and markets.

2.89 **Peepshow** 1858*
Moscow. A. Prokofev workshop
Lithographic transfer.
40 x 30.5; *inv.* 39367.
The peepshow was the way in which many people saw *lubki* and was a common sight at fairs and markets. Inside the box the prints were either suspended on cords in succession or glued together on a strip. The peepshow manager rolled them from one drum to another turning a handle, accompanying the moving display with a comic rhyming commentary. The customers viewed the show through the holes at the front of the wagon after paying a fee. The flag on the wagon promises a 'worldwide cosmorama' and the text explains the attraction on view: the events of the Crimean War, a commentary on contemporary morals and the arrival of the bearded woman, Julia Postrana, seen in 2.88.

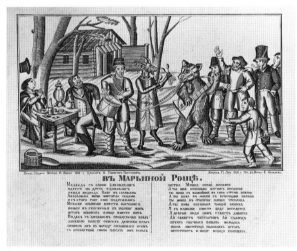

2.86

КРИНОЛИНЪ ИЛИ СРЕДСТВО ЗАМѢНИТЬ ИМЪ ПРИ СЛУЧАѢ ВОЗДУШНЫЙ ШАРЪ.

Знакомый, снявъ шляпу: А! почтеннѣйшій Прохоръ Никонорычь! мое вамъ всенижающіе! какими ето судьбами! вотъ оказія! бы-
вало въ паркѣ васъ калачомъ незаманишь, а ноничѣ ишъ какимъ франтомъ сюда явились. а что изволити здѣсь подѣлывати. никакъ
пригодай залюбовались, на солнечный закатъ глядите! дачто же ето вы не оглянетесь на меня, словно какъ бы ето въ вамъ и не от-
носится, Прохоръ Никоноровичъ, не спуская глазъ съ неба: Ахъ батюшки вы мой свѣты, вѣда какая! пропала теперь моя МАРѲУШЕНКА.
ишь какъ ее, сердечную, бурей-то подхватило, словно какъ бы перышко какое, такъ и мчитъ ее къ небу. Знакомый: да что же ето
такое случилось свами, почтеннѣйшій Прохоръ Никанорычь, раскажитека скорѣа. фу ты, право какой бестолковой! дa ты
погляди гдѣ моя Марѳа савишна. изволила доля кринолинъ свой надѣть; говорилъ ій. смотри Мароуша не надевай говорю
неравнс гроза молъ подымется, али вихарь какой, такъ послѣ говорю молъ съ тобой и не справишься; такъ нѣтъ види-
шь ты такой сябой говоритъ старыи хрѣнъ дискать все по старинѣ говоритъ наровишь, А я-по новизнѣ хочу, по нынѣшно-
му то есть вотъ те и по новизнѣ, вотъ те и по нынѣшнему... Ахъ ты Господи твоя воля, что теперь станешь дѣлать,
еще спасибо добрый человѣкъ попался, хотѣлъ было ее заноги попридержать, такъ куда тебѣ! и его съ нею туда же.
А что Сидоръ Панфилычь, куда ето они примѣрно залетятъ теперь. Знакомый: известно дѣло куда: Ужъ какъ они тамъ ни бейся, а далѣ Марьиной рощи не залетятъ: ишъ бурято попритихать стала, да и дѣло то идетъ къ ночи...А видь
поди ты, кажись 2-нъ баластъ ишъ, что ей за ноги уцѣпился, и хорошо бы для тяжести и проч.

Дозволено Цензурой. Моск. 16 Апрѣля 1866 г. Изданіе Петра Н.Шарапова. Печ. въ Лито. И. Говрилова Мясницк. Час. 3 Квар. Д. Гофъмна

2.18

Today's Lubok

At the outbreak of the First World War the government sponsored a publishing house *Segodniashnii Lubok* (Today's Lubok) to produce patriotic *lubki* as part of the war effort. Artists such as Vladmir Mayakovsky and Kazimir Malevich who were later to make a significant contribution in the production of Bolshevik posters, were engaged in the work. The government was particularly keen to raise morale as the war took a downturn.

2.90 **'Look, Oh Look, Near the Vistula/The Germans Are Blown Out: They Feel Sour (acidic)'** 1914*
Moscow, Today's Lubok Press, artist Kazimir Malevich
Chromo-lithograph.
51.4 x 33.5; *inv* 24464.
The battle of Warsaw, then part of Russian Poland, in September 1914 saw an important victory for the Russian forces. After initial successes the Russians had been pushed back. The Grand Duke Nicholas decided to try and hold Warsaw and after repulsing the German attack his forces were able to sweep south across the River Vistula to the south and harry the German forces. The print shows the Kaiser bloated and made uncomfortable by Russian resistance. The victory proved only short-lived.

2.91 **'A German Red-Haired and Rough/Was Smashed Over Warsaw . . .'** 1914
Moscow, Today's Lubok Press, artist Vladimir Mayakovsky
Chromo-lithograph.
33.5 x 53; *inv.* 066847.
The scene, *left*, which shows a cossack on a horse bringing down a German dirigible with a lance, is reminiscent of *lubok* images of heroes triumphing over supernatural foes. *Right*, a peasant woman is making a pair of trousers for her husband out of material plundered from the crashed dirigible.

2.92 **'What a Boom, What a Blast . . .' The Germans Made at Loma'** 1914**
Moscow. Today's Lubok Press, artist Kazimir Malevich
Chromo-lithograph.
33.3 x 51.4; *inv.* 24465.
The Russian peasant is shown flailing the German troops, reaping them as he would the harvest. Loma or Lomza is north-east of Warsaw in the area of lakes and swamps which, in spite of the celebratory tone of the print, was to see a major reverse for the Russians. The title is particularly poignant for it was lack of artillery which accounted for the Russian defeat here.

2.93 **'A Butcher Came Along to Lodz/We Said Welcome'** 1914
Moscow, Today's Lubok Press, artist Kazimir Malevich
Chromo- lithograph.
34 x 51.4; *inv.* 24465.
After the German failure to take Warsaw Hindenburg launched a more sustained attack on the Russian forces near Lodz south-west of Warsaw in November and December. The Russian forces were initially able to push back the attackers who suffered considerable losses. From this high point the Russian army's fortunes declined, as shortages of arms and ammunition began to make themselves felt. The jovial Russian peasant is shown welcoming the German army and in the second image striding off triumphant.

2.94 **'Hey, Sultan, Sitting in the Porte/Don't Spoil Your Mug with Such a Fight'** 1914
Moscow, Today's Lubok Press, artist Vladimir Mayakovsky
Chromo-lithograph.
33 x 52; *inv.* 24495.
Although concern with the increasingly dominant position of Germany in the north-west was an important issue Russia was equally threatened by the Austro-Hungarian Empire in the Balkans. On 1 November the Russians declared war on Turkey, who had blocked the Straits of the Bosphorus and the Dardanelles and thus the main supply route into Russia. In this image the defiant cossack is warning the Turks, caricatured as indolent and fat, not to block the Straits or advance further.

2.14

Bolshevik Posters

1917-25

Pre-revolutionary Russian was largely illiterate. Its rich literary tradition and artistic world were inaccessible to most of the huge 150 million population. After the October Revolution of 1917 the Bolshevik government, wanting to communicate the values of the new order, made major use of the immediate, expressive medium of posters. Campaigns celebrated the changes that had occurred, emphasising women's rights and the benefits of literacy, and called for the exchange of goods between town and country. The Civil War of 1918-20 increased the need to rally support, to resist the return of the old rulers and win the loyalty of all the different peoples of the federation. The work of the poster artists is remarkable for its power and intensity, and for the sophisticated vocabularly of images developed in this short period.

Persuading the People: Posters of the First Soviet Years

by Nikolai Shkolnyi, keeper of posters, Saltykov-Shchedrin State Public Library, Leningrad

'Russia is perishing', 'Russia is no more', 'May the memory of Russia live forever' — this is what I hear all around me. But Russia stands before me: that Russia which our great writers saw in fearful and prophetic dreams; that Petersburg Dostoevsky saw; that Russia Gogol called a rushing troika.

Russia is storm. Democracy is coming 'whirlwind-like' says Carlyle. Russia is fated to suffer torments, humiliations, and divisions; but she will emerge from these humiliations renewed and — in a new way — great.

Aleksandr Blok, *Intelligentsia and Revolution*, 1918

The October Socialist Revolution had a profound effect on all kinds of artists, who tried to find a way of expressing the changes taking place in Russia. Poster art had unique possibilities here, because of its immediacy. In it the most important political and artistic issues of the period found intense life.

Soviet art inherited a graphic tradition of a high artistic level. Russia at the end of the 19th century saw a flourishing of what is known there as 'Modern Style', which also influenced the artists of other countries: for example Art Nouveau in Western Europe, Secessionism in Austria-Hungary and Germany. In Russia, as in the West, the formation of poster art took place in the context of this style.

An influential precursor of Russian posters was the shop signboard: a visual image without text that was an important popular form. Signboard images are an example of the way the towns absorbed a variety of rural material and reworked it to their own liking, adapting it to the requirements of urban people, but at the same time shaping urban tastes and needs. Other precursors of posters were printed advertisements to publicise entertainment and books, for example the lithographic work of Aleksandr Agin to promote his album of illustrations to Gogol's *Dead Souls* in 1846.

The development of Russian poster art was stimulated by the *International Exhibition of Art Posters* in St Petersburg in 1897, which marked the first appearance in Russia of a new type of graphics. Some 700 works were shown, from 13 countries: about 100 came from Britain, including works by Dudley Hardy, John Hassal, Frederick Hyland, and the Beggarstaff Brothers, but only 28 Russian designers took part. Fifteen years later, however, by the time of the 1912 St Petersburg exhibition *Art in Books and Posters*, works were shown by 49 Russian artists, among them Mikhail Vrubel, Valentin Serov, Konstantin Somov, Alexandre Benois, and Alexandr Apsit.

The two-year revolutionary period in Russia following Bloody Sunday in 1905 brought wide publication of graphic work, in which political ideas then found their most direct expression. The persistence of the tsarist order prevented the dissemination of posters as a vehicle for politics: small-sized satirical graphics proved more suitable (see **ill**). Sharply pointed drawings by such artists as Mstislav Dobuzhinskii, Ivan Bilibin and Boris Kustodiev appeared

Field, Oh Field! Who Has Strewn Thee With Dead Bodies!, from *Gvozd* (Nail), No 2, 1906

in papers like *Zhupel* (The Bugbear) and *Adskaia pochta* (Letters from Hell); postcards were sold featuring images of political criticism. These were the first evidence of the possibilities for political comment when art could operate in a milieu of (albeit temporary and precarious) democracy. In posters, further development of content was only made during the First World War, when patriotic works by Konstantin Korovin, Viktor Vasnetsov and Abram Arkhipov were issued in large editions; particularly successful in its popular appeal was Leonid Pasternak's poster *Help the War's Victims* (1914), much reproduced at the time and reissued with a new title in 1918.

But there were also parallel, more radical design developments. The changed social and political sitiuation after 1905-7 — especially during the war, when the government was eager to rally broadbased support — raised the issue of art for a mass audience. The graphic art of 1905-7 had been fiercely critical of authority, but it had referred to sophisticated 19th-century West European traditions of magazine illustration, whose use of Symbolist and other complex imagery might not be accessible or make a direct appeal to a wide range of people. In the intervening period there were changes in the form and content of art, particularly around 1910, when the *avant-garde* developments of Goncharova, Larionov and Malevich began. Whether or not the content of this new art was understandable, its design was brightly coloured and immediate, with forms that were less bookish. Further changes in visual presentation came about when artists looked for inspiration at the kind of images known to be enjoyed by ordinary people, especially the *lubok*, the popular Russian print (see pp 61-96).

Lubki attracted artists because of their appeal to many classes of people. Those working in the Modern Style tried to impose their own principles on *lubki*, to 'ennoble' them. Using *lubok* principles of form, Bilibin and G. Narbut created works of revivalist aestheticism in imitation of the *lubok* of 1812. But a group of younger artists, Kazimir Malevich, Vladimir Mayakovsky, David Burliuk, Vasilii Chekrygin and Aristarkh Lentulov, rejected direct copying of *lubok* style, choosing rather to use its distinctive features in their own way. During the first months of the war the Moscow publisher Today's Lubok produced editions of around 20 such contemporary *lubki* on war themes (see **2.90-94**), some as postcards.

Contemporary critics, while noting the decorative qualities of these works, reproached the artists with 'posterishness' (*plakatnost*), finding them 'garish' and 'loud'.[1] Having mastered *avant-garde* innovations, the artists were able to bring a different life to features

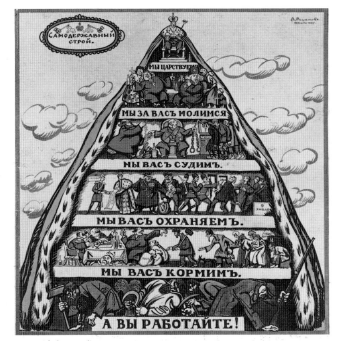

A. Radakov, *The Autocratic System*, 1917

typical of the popular form, developing and emphasising the simplicity and intensity, the bright '*lubok*-like' colours, the two-part compostition with its mischievous rhymed text. Many works could indeed be seen as lithographic posters: an attempt to invent a mass art based on *lubok* principles. Mayakovsky was to use this experience when he made ROSTA Windows in 1919.

In spring 1916 an exhibition of British wartime posters and postcards was held at the Petrograd Academy of Arts. Remarkable in the 200 works shown were the well-developed techniques of mass communication, especially the brief and telling captions, addressing the spectator with immediacy and wit: qualities not unnoticed by Russian designers.

Radical developments in artistic life followed the revolution and collapse of tsarism of February 1917. Art became an important element in mass street processions and dramatised enactments, manifested vividly in the solemn ornamentation of the city for the Petrograd funeral of victims of the revolution in March and in the decorations for May Day. In March the Provisional Government used a newspaper campaign to drum up support for its 'Freedom Loan' to help fight the war, a campaign extended in May to a poster design competition. The winners in Petrograd were P. Buchkin and Kustodiev; the latter's poster (see **4.1**), with a single, epic figure of a bearded soldier holding a rifle, was a precursor of the heroic posters of the Civil War period.

Also active now was *Parus* (The Sail), a publishing house established in Petrograd in 1915 by Maxim Gorky. Between March and August 1917 it issued popular prints by Aleksei Radakov, Mayakovsky and Vladimir Lebedev. The design and subject of Radakov's *lubok*, *The Autocratic System*. **(ill)**, were taken from N. Lokhov's poster *The Social Pyramid*, produced in Geneva in 1901, and considered the first Russian illegal poster. Published by the Union of Russian Social Democrats, Lokhov's work had been issued in 1905 as a postcard by the *Vperëd* (Forward) press. *Parus* prints are among the best examples of contemporary graphics for mass showing, as the artists matched their skills to interpreting the changes taking place.

Thus, although the concept of a political poster was an unfamiliar one in Russia at the beginning of the century, its rapid emergence in 1918-21 did not come from nothing.

*   *   *   *   *

In late winter 1917-18 Russia was already coping with economic ruin and on the brink of Civil War as the new Soviet government took its first steps in the sphere of cultural policy. In February 1918 the decree 'On the introduction of West European calendar in the Russian Republic' established new revolutionary festivals — May Day, the anniversary of the October Revolution, days for remembering dead revolutionaries — and offered possibilities for development of the form of art which had first appeared in February 1917, the involvement in shaping mass processions and celebrations. In April followed a plan relating to revolutionary monuments.

The Bolshevik Party was in overall control of this work via its department for agit-prop (mass persuasion). In November 1918 this set up a publishing agency, Tsentropechat, which functioned under the All-Russia Central Executive (VTsIK) of the Congress of Soviets, Russia's legislative body, and had branches in the regional soviets; in 1920 Tsentropechat became part of the State Publishing House (*Gosudarstvennoe izdatel'stvo*). The issuing of posters was given equal political importance to that of newspapers and pamphlets. Publishing departments were also formed in the military organisations serving the Civil War fronts, under the overall authority of the Revolutionary-Military Council of the Republic.

It was August 1918 before VTsIK issued the first Soviet posters, including *The Price of Blood*, a reprint under a new title of Pasternak's poster of 1914, and the new works *One Year of Proletarian Dic-*

tatorship **(3.1)** by Aleksandr Apsit, and *To the Grief of All Bourgeois* (3.66). Apsit's allegorical composition, organised on the principle of a book's title page, is characteristic of early Soviet posters in its 'illustration'-like appearance and in its style, which is close to that of easel-painting. But even at this early point there is a desire to create a poster language of symbols and social generalisation. In *To the Grief of All Bourgeois*, the unknown artist is already using a more economical and direct expression.

The new revolutionary art manifested itself in diverse areas that provided a stimulating milieu for poster work. The design of books and journals was radically changed, but also generators of ideas were the actual new art forms: the festive decoration of streets and squares, the visual transformation of trains, steamers and urban transport to attract a mass audience for the new thinking throughout the vast country.

A feature of the art of this period is the way work in different areas was carried out by the same artists, their experience of one form enriching another. We know that Vladimir Kozlinskii, later organiser of the Petrograd ROSTA office, made a modernist banner for the side of the Winter Palace (4.7) for the May Day 1918 celebrations. By the November 1918 anniversary of the revolution such aritists also working in posters as Kustodiev, Kozlinskii, Vladimir Lebedev, Vasilii Svarog and Ivan Simakov all took part in transforming the tsarist cityscape (see pp 135-52). Posters like *The Internationale* **(3.67)** and *Boldly, Comrades, Into Step!* (3.7), of 1919, are at once sheets produced to serve the new popular festivals

3.67 K. Boguslavakaia, *The Internationale*, 1919

3.10 V. Kozlinskii, RSFSR, 1919-20

and designs whose character is influenced by the experience of these events: banners wave, groups of people are on the move, expressing solidarity. The posters are buoyant and dynamic, combining the popular narrative approach of the *lubok* with the forms and colours current in the work of advanced Russian artists. Anatolii Lunacharskii, People's Commissar for Enlightenment, wrote in his notebook about the Petrograd decorations for May Day 1918: 'Actually, all that remains of Cubism and Futurism is the clarity and power of the general form, together with the bright colours which are so necessary for paintings displayed in the open air and intended for a giant audience with thousands of heads. . . . Here, certainly, the strivings of youth have merged with the strivings of the crowd.'[2]

The conditions prevailing during the Civil War (from May 1918) did not make it easy to keep records. The names of many poster artists are unknown even now. Recently, however, documents and sources have come to light and publications are helping to restore the names of artists and establish the dates and circumstances when work was produced. In the case of works represented here, it is possible to attribute the poster *The Internationale* to Kseniia Boguslavskaia Puni, through stylistic analysis of her sketches for a festive panel for the first anniversary of the October Revolution and her lithographs in the collection *October 1917-1918: Heroes and Victims of the Revolution*. Similarly, comparison of the posters *Long Live the Vanguard of the Revolution: the Red Navy* **(3.9)** *and* RSFSR **(3.10)** with sketches for street panels **(4.42-3)**, both by Kozlinskii and with very similar titles to the posters, and with his lithographs in the *October* 1917-1918 collection, makes it possible to identify the posters as Kozlinskii's work. The attribution is further supported by the style and content of seven linocuts by the artist for a projected album of 1919 which are also in the Public Library's collection.[3]

By 1920 three main themes had been established in Soviet posters: the war, the economy, and social and educational policy, reflecting the issues of the times. In 1919-21 more works were produced in the first category than in either of the others. At the beginning of this period, when the Civil War situation was particularly tense, Dmitrii Moor and Viktor Deni came to work for the publishing section of the Revolutionary-Military Council.

Moor has written that he wanted 'the language of the artist to resound as resonantly as the speech of a political orator'. His posters, especially *Have YOU Enrolled as a Volunteer?* **(3.8)** and HELP **(3.55)**, have become classics.

The first uses a composition employed by the British artist Alfred Leete in his 1914-15 poster *Your Country Needs YOU* and followed also the design for the US Army by James Montgomery Flagg. At the 1916 Petrograd exhibition of war posters a work had been shown depicting John Bull making a similar gesture: *Who's Absent? Is It YOU?* Moor did not visit the show, but he knew about the poster from Viacheslav Polonskii. In the First World War the political exhortations of the participating countries had much in common, and the closeness of aims produced a common iconography. Similar posters were designed in Italy by Achille Luciano Mauzan (1917), in Hungary by Konya Sandor (1919) and in Germany by an unknown artist (1915-16). The Russian artist rejected the 'illustration' style and detailed treatment characteristic of other versions. Employing the familiar composition, he created a poster whose clear, sculptural rhythm and epic form, restrained colour and intense concentration of meaning became a model for Soviet agitational art.

Moor considered HELP to be the peak of his creative work.

ПOMOГИ

3.55 D. Moor, HELP, 1921

The poster, he wrote, was a 'visual expression, an original symbol, which concentrated in itself the entire scene of the terrible famine raging on the Volga in those years'.[4] The artist believed in the high mission of art, and felt acutely his responsibility for the fate of the people. He created a work of great publicistic and emotional power, which made it not only a historical document but also an example of exalted humanism. In 1922 Moor's work was accorded recognition in a special government order, speaking of his 'immense services to the Red Army with his vivid brush and sharp pencil', the 'weapons at his disposal'.

In contrast to Moor, Deni was primarily a master of political satire, a creator of social portrait-masks which exposed the enemies of the revolution in such posters as *Manifesto! All Power to the Landlords and Capitalists!* (**3.20**).

The originality, punch, and artistic qualities of the Soviet posters made them widely popular. Their merits were recognised even by opponents of the Soviet order. Thus, a representative of the White movement, A. Drozdov, noted that the work produced by the corresponding department of General Denikin's Volunteer (White) Army 'seemed pathetic in comparison with the Bolsheviks' splendid posters, and this although such artists as Ivan Bilibin and Evgenii Lanseray were working in our art section'.[5]

The Soviet works were distinguished by high seriousness and grandeur, and their ability to communicate the meaning of the socialist revolution. These qualities are evident in such contemporary posters as Moor's *To the Peoples of the Caucasus* (**3.23**) and *Comrade Workers and Peasants! All Go to Courses for Red Commanders* (**3.11**), by an unknown Vitebsk artist; but they could be displayed also in works using an earlier style, more characteristic of periodicals and books, for example *The Red Ploughman* (**3.4**), again by an unknown artist. Visual motifs derived from the popular *lubok* tradition, as in Moor's *Cossack, You've Beaten the Tsars and Boyars*, offered more direct, colloquial possibilities.

The intensity and fluidity of the Civil War situation in the Ukraine meant that this area was well served. *To Horse, Worker and Peasant!* (**3.17**), a Ukrainian-language poster published in Kiev in connection with the forming there of units for the First Cavalry Army, shows the decorative sense and dynamic approach of a professional graphic artist. Many fine posters were produced in the Ukrainian city Kharkov by Aleksei Marenkov, who came there from Orël in 1919. His poster *Sons of Workers and Peasants: Red Warriors!* (**3.18**) uses an image close to the heroic popular epic.

Even greater immediacy than posters had provided so far was achieved in October 1919 when hand-made works first appeared in Moscow shop windows. These were produced by a section of Russia's chief information organ, ROSTA (Russian Telegraph Agency), set up in November 1918; in 1921 they were issued under the auspices of Glavpolitprosvet (Main Political-Education Committee), part of the RSFSR Commissariat of Enlightenment.

ROSTA posters — six to twelve displayed together on a single theme to fill whole windows — provided up-to-date information, explained and promoted the decisions of the Soviet government, exposed and ridiculed its enemies. Their purpose determined the need for clear-cut decisions about composition and colour, for apt and trenchant texts. This instant satire was produced in Moscow by the use of stencils, so that the posters were often in

3.11 Anon, *Comrade Workers and Peasants! All Go to Courses for Red Commanders*, 1921

3.18 A. Marenkov, *Sons of Workers and Peasants; Red Warriors!* 1920

place even before the newspapers came out.

The Moscow windows owed most to the work of Mayakovsky, Mikhail Cheremnykh and Ivan Maliutin. Cheremnykh invented the concept, and was responsible for the first posters. But the definitive style and structure of the windows was crystallised when Mayakovsky came to ROSTA, basing his designs on his experience at the Today's Lubok and *Parus* publishing houses and on his work in the theatre. Mayakovsky's play *Mystery-Bouffe* had been staged by Vsevelod Meyerhold in Petrograd to mark the first anniversary of the revolution, with scenery and costumes by Malevich. Mayakovsky was greatly influenced by Malevich, and in 1919 he made his own sketches for the play. When he came to participate actively in the ROSTA poster section his sketches for *Mystery-Bouffe* were among his sources for the creation of the totally original political graphics presented by ROSTA windows. Typical of his work are the series *Help the Starving* and *Our Foreign Trade*.

In 1927 Mayakovsky wrote: 'The ROSTA windows were a fan-

tastic thing — a service rendered by a handful of artists to 150 million people.' The windows attracted universal attention, met with a lively popular response, and soon began to be made in other towns. A poster by Iurii M. Bondi published by the ROSTA office in Kostroma, *A Call for Help* (**3.13**), a Cubistic image produced by coloured linocut, is an example of one of the variety of artistic methods used now. Another example is *The Red Army Is Fighting Heroically at the Front* (ill): printed in black and red, it has five small drawings showing how different groups can help the army, with a large Suprematist image underneath, designed to frame a slogan which is missing from this sheet. The latter design has attracted interest, having been attributed to Malevich,[6] to add to only four printed posters surviving known to have come from the Unovis (Affirmer of the New Art) workshop in Vitebsk headed by Malevich 1920-22 (one is the famous El Lissitzky poster *Beat the Whites with the Red Wedge*, which survives in a single copy in the Lenin Library, Moscow). However, some students of Malevich's work consider that *The Red Army Is*

3.13 Iu. Bondi, *A Call For Help*, 1920

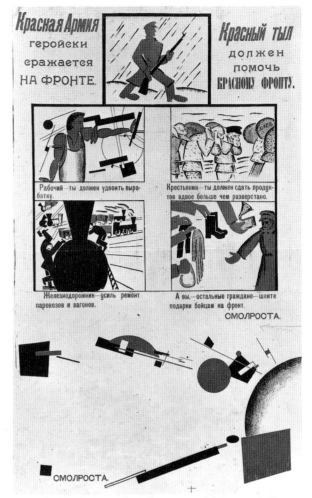

V. Strzheminskii (?), *The Red Army Is Fighting Heroically*, 1920

Fighting . . . was the work of Vladislav Strzheminskii, an active member of Smolensk Unovis and close to Malevich.[7]

Petrograd ROSTA was set up early in 1920, with the participation of artists who included Kozlinskii, Lebedev and Lev Brodaty; in the three years of its existence it produced over 1,000 posters, only one third of which have survived. The Petrograd ROSTA posters in the Public Library collection show examples of the two methods of producing the sheets used in this branch. Some, for example Lebedev's two posters *Just Show Us a Little Finger* **(3.41)** and *The Nation's Main Need is to Restore the Economy* **(ill)**, were made by hand, using size paint or gouache; the text was written separately and then pasted onto the picture, which is why some Petrograd designs have come down to us without titles or texts. The second method, used in Kozlinskii's *If You Work There Will Be Flour* (3.38) *or Lebedev's Work With Your Rifle Beside You* **(3.36)**, involv-

ed linocut printing. Like *lubok* pictures they were finished by hand with bright aniline colours, and text and picture were cut at the same time, on a single block. Linocuts were printed in the graphic workshops of the Academy of Arts, which was headed by Kozlinskii.

Petrograd ROSTA windows soon showed a distinctive style. Because they were not restricted by exclusive use of stencils, as was Moscow ROSTA, the Petrograd sheets were characterised by structural clarity and by greater attention to colour and broad coloured planes. Reworking the traditions of early 20-century graphic satire and *lubok* pictures, in a way that acknowledged *avant-garde* concepts, particularly Malevich's Suprematism, the artists sought fresh solutions to express the ideas in each poster.

Lebedev's work is especially strong, showing techniques varying from spontaneous immediacy to the use of ideas well work-

3.1 A. Apsit, *One Year of the Proletarian Dictatorship*, 1918

РОСТА РЕЧ ТРОЦЕАГО

I. ГЛАВНЫЙ ДЛЯ СТРАНЫ ИНТЕРЕС —
ВОССТАНОВИТЬ НОРМАЛЬНЫЙ ХОЗЯЙСТВЕННЫЙ
ПРОЦЕСС,
ДЛЯ ТОГО, ЧТО БЫ, ДАТЬ ХОД МАШИНАМ И ПЕЧАМ
НУЖНО ВЕЛИЧАЙШЕЕ ВНИМАНИЕ К ХОЗЯЙСТВЕННЫМ
МЕЛОЧАМ

V. Lebedev, *The Nation's Main Need Is*, 1921

ed over to arrive at a concentrated symbol. In his best posters the artist achieves genuine epic quality, for example in *Red Army Man and Sailor*, of 1920, and *Work With Your Rifle Beside You*, the following year. Kozlinskii pursued a condensed poster language, as in *If You Work There Will Be Flour*, as did Brodaty in *Festive Attire: Then and Now*, although both retain artistic individuality.

At the end of 1921 ROSTA windows were established in 70 locations in Petrograd: in streets and squares, in clubs, local centres for political propaganda (*agitpunkty*), and the quarters of army units, being made to meet the requirements of these individual locations.

The Petrograd 'window' artists did not confine themselves to poster-making: they also designed for mass celebrations, painted slogans on the agitational steamboat *Red Petrograd* and fulfilled orders for ROSTA's 'Living Newspaper' (*Zhivaia gazeta*) dramatic

group. The varied work enriched the language of the poster with different methods and expressive means of mass communication. Especially theatricality permeates many forms of mass-agitational art. The 'story' of many ROSTA windows could be seen as a dramatised enactment. The artists created new ways of influencing people, in which art techniques were fused organically with the popular culture: songs, jokes, sayings, for example in Lebedev's posters *Concerning the Ill-fated Rumour-monger* (**3.19**) and *Whose Side Will Win?* (3.33), both of 1920.

*   *   *   *   *

The development of poster art, the tasks it set itself, were determined by the course of events in Russia. Once the Civil War was over at the end of 1920, posters retained their importance, reflecting the major issues and the optimistic postwar spirit.

New, festive posters are exemplified by Moor's *1st of May: All Russian Subbotnik* (**3.31**), Nikolai Kogout's *1st of May*, and May Day posters by Simakov (**3.26, 28, 73**) and Svarog. The war theme gave place to questions of public health, and of reviving industry and agriculture, while communication of the idea of a cultural revolution also assumed great political importance. Education and the problems of illiteracy provided the subjects for posters by Radakov (**3.62-3**), Elizaveta Kruglikova (**3.60**) and Kustodiev (**3.61**). Works on the theme of labour and the advancement of the economy were made by Kogout (**3.30**) and Aleksandr Samokhvalov (**3.37**).

In the mid 1920s an increasing role in mass communication was played by the propaganda *lubok*. Viacheslav Polonskii, the most authoritative theoretician of poster art in this period, wrote: 'Having performed great organisational work, the revolutionary poster faded, as it were, from the scene. . . . The *lubok* picture has ever greater possibilities for development in peacetime.'[8] Two works by Vladimir Ikonnikov in 1922-3 (**3.56-7**) were realised in the spirit of the *lubok*, as was *Before, I Was a Machine-greaser*, by an unknown artist, in 1925.

The art of the Soviet political poster in the first post-revolutionary years provides an example of the communication of ideas to a broad mass of spectators. Revolutionary romanticism and dynamism, the established language of allegory, were combined in this new art with deep-laid strata of popular culture, with images and compositional models that were already familiar.

The graphic achievement of the first Soviet years developed in the second half of the 1920s and the beginning of the 1930s in

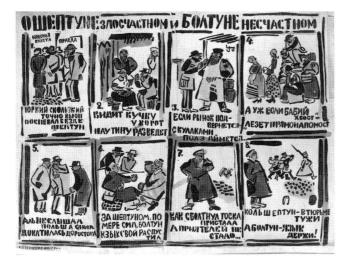

3.19 V. Lebedev, *Concerning the Ill-fated Rumour-monger*, 1920

newspaper and book graphics and in the Constructivist advertisement. During the Second World War the tradition of ROSTA Windows was revived as TASS Windows at the various fronts and in the activity of the Leningrad artists who came together to form the Batttling Pencil group (*Boevoi karandash*). The stylistic impulses that took shape in the 20s continue to develop today. In this sense the exhibition enables us to witness in these early Soviet poster designs the first beginnings of many developments in Russian contemporary art.

* * * * *

The Prints Department of the Saltykov-Shchedrin State Public Library possesses one of the largest collections of Russian and foreign printed graphics in the Soviet Union. Among more than one million items held, pride of place belongs to the poster collection, whose most valuable section covers the years 1917-21. The works began to be assembled in the 1920s and between the 1930s and 50s holdings were enriched with rare items from the collections of E. Gollerbakh, P. Stolpianskii, A. Iatesvich and N. Arkhipov. At the end of the 1930s a large number of posters published in 1920-22 by the Moscow and Petrograd offices of ROSTA were presented to the library by Vladimir Lebedev.

Today the Prints Department contains, with only few gaps, work of almost all the well-known Russian poster artists. Of particular historical and scholarly interest are works produced in the provinces: no other museum possesses such a variety of these and in most cases they were not preserved in their place of origin.

Many examples from local ROSTA offices, from Odessa, Rostov and the Urals, are original drawings, executed in gouache, watercolour and indian ink.

Cataloguing and recording the Soviet poster is a continuing task. The library holds regular exhibitions and its posters have been much exhibited in the USSR and abroad. Its Petrograd ROSTA windows have had large-scale exhibitions in Leningrad in 1967 and 1987; seven were shown at the major *Moscow-Paris* exhibition of 1981. Materials from our collection are made widely available to historians, art-historians, film-workers and all readers of the Public Library who are interested in the history of Russian art.

NOTES

1. V. Denisov, *Voina i lubok*, 1916, p 31.
2. A. V. Lunacharskii, 'May Day 1918', in V. Tolstoy, I. Bibikova and C. Cooke (eds),*Street Art of the Revolution: Festivals and Celebrations in Russia 1918-33*, Thames & Hudson, 1990, document 6.
3. V. Kozlinskii, *Sovremennyi Peterburg: Faksimil'noe vosproisvedenie 9 linograviur, sozdannykh v 1919 godu*, with an introduction by E. F. Kovtun, Leningrad, 1987.
4. D. Moor, 'Khudozhestvennyi obraz', in Iu. Khalaminskii, *D. Moor*, Moscow, 1961, p198.
5. V. Polonskii, *Russkii revoliutsionnyi plakat*, Moscow, 1925, p63.
6. Troels Andersen, *Malevich: Catalogue raisonné of the Berlin exhibition 1927 . . .* , Amsterdam, 1970, p10.
7. N. Khardzhiev, K. Malevich. M. Matiushin: *K istorii russkogo avangarda*, Stockholm, 1976, p91, and L. Shadowa, *Suche und Experiment: Russische und sowjetische Kunst 1910 bis 1930*, Dresden, 1978, p80.
8. V. Polonskii, *op cit*, p114.

3.57 V. Ikonnikov, *The Ring on Your Finger Shines No Brighter than Shines Our 1917*, 1923

3.8 D. Moor, *Have YOU Enrolled as a Volunteer?*, 1920

3.23 D. Moor, *To the Peoples of the Caucasus*, 1920

CATALOGUE

Catalogue notes are by Sarah Hyde, assistant keeper of prints at the Whitworth Art Gallery, and Nikolai Shkolnyi, keeper of posters at the Saltykov-Shchedrin State Public Library. In each entry the title and text details of the poster is followed by the place of publication and the name of the publishing organisation; the size given is that of the whole sheet. Where space allows, under each poster's title lines, any other lines on the sheet have also been translated. All works belong to the Public Library and the inventory numbers are theirs.

THE BOLSHEVIK REVOLUTION 1917

Events leading to the Bolshevik, or October Revolution, began early in 1917, when food shortages sparked off strikes and massive demonstrations in the Russian capital Petrograd. Pressure for change which had been building up for decades now gathered force, reinforced by war weariness. On 27 February a liberal 'Provisional' Government declared itself, stemming from the limited-suffrage State Duma. The Petrograd Soviet of soldiers and workers deputies, based on sectional councils that had evolved in 1905, was also re-established, providing an alternative basis for authority. Exiled members of various political parties returned to Petrograd at once, and on 3 March Tsar Nicholas II was persuaded to abdicate. Support for the Bolshevik party grew in the following months, fuelled by widespread opposition to the war with Germany and lack of confidence in the Provisional Government. Bolshevik majorities were returned to the soviets in increasing numbers. On 25 October 1917 the Provisional Government was overthrown, and the Bolshevik-dominated All-Russian Congress of Soviets took over.

The new government, or Council of People's Commissars, chaired by Vladimir Lenin, immediately issued a decree on peace with Germany; after protracted negotiations and a further advance of German troops into Russia, peace terms were agreed in March 1918 at Brest-Litovsk. In the same month, the Bolsheviks changed their title to the Russian Communist Party, and in July 1918 the Constitution of the Russian Socialist Federal Soviet Republic (RSFSR) was formally adopted; its declared aims were 'the complete elimination of the division of society into classes, the ruthless suppression of the exploiters . . . and the victory of socialism in all countries'.

3.1 ALEKSANDR PETROVICH APSIT (real name APSITIS) (1880-1944)
One Year of Proletarian Dictatorship: October 1917-October 1918** 1918
Moscow, All-Russia Central Executive Committee (of the All-Russia Congress of Soviets)
Lithograph; 101 x 66.4; *inv.* 165896.
Published to celebrate the first anniversary of the October Revolution, this poster presents an idealised picture of the improvements won by the revolution, as well as expressing hopes for the future. Guarding the stone gateway are two representatives of the proletariat whose 'dictatorship' has been declared the first stage in the gradual progress towards the ideal of a just 'communist' society. *Left*, is an urban worker with his metalworker's hammer and apron; *right*, is a peasant carrying a scythe and wearing bast shoes (made from the bark of birch trees). On the ground at their feet is the regalia of the overthrown tsarist regime, and chains representing the oppression from which both groups have now been freed. Both men, however, carry weapons — a reminder that the Civil War had already started.

Behind is a vision of new life, hope and abundance; the sun rises over a scene of industrial and agricultural prosperity, in the centre a mother holds high a young baby — perhaps one year old too.

3.2 BORIS VASILEVICH ZVORYKIN (b.1872)
The Struggle of the Red Knight with the Dark Force 1919
Moscow, State Publishing House
Lithograph; 106.2 x 71.8; *inv.* 170130.
Zvorykin's poster contains an odd mixture of contemporary and historical references; overall, the image is an allegorical representation of the struggle between labour and the old order, or perhaps more precisely, between revolutionaries and counter-revolutionaries; published during the Civil War, the colours of the two most prominent horses must have been seen to refer to the Red and White armies.

Zvorykin's hero is an urban worker who still wears his leather working apron, and who fights with his metal-worker's hammer; his shield is decorated with the hammer and sickle emblematic of the union of urban workers and rural peasantry seen as the foundation of the new order. The clothing and armour of his opponents contain traditional elements associated with old Russia. The outcome of the struggle is clear, even though the worker is outnumbered by the representatives of the 'dark force'. This poster was produced in connection with the second anniversary of the October Revolution.

3.3 Artist unknown
Marseillaise* 1919
Petrograd, Department of Non-School Education
Lithograph; 50.9 x 61.8; *inv.* E 54242.
The music of Rouget de Lisle's French Revolutionary anthem was adapted in Russia during the late 19th century, with a new text exhorting the Russian people 'From the Dnepr to the White Sea, the Volga and the distant Caucasus' to rise up against their oppressors.

3.4 Artist unknown
The Red Ploughman** 1920
'Over wild uncultivated ground, over the debris of an evil gentry and industrialists, we will plough our field and gather in a good harvest of happiness for all the labouring people!'
Moscow, State Publishing House
Lithograph; 52.8 x 70.9; *inv.* 170845.
In front of a symbolic landscape of clearing storm clouds and a rising sun, the peasant is ploughing up land littered with the trappings of the old regime, including the tsar's orb, crown and sceptre, and bags of money. The text suggests that the power and riches which the land and these objects represent will be redistributed to 'all the labouring people'.

3.5 Artist unknown
Under the Tsar and the Landlord . . . /Under the Communist Order . . . 1921
Saratov, State Publishing House
Lithograph; 71 x 53.3; *inv.* 165802.
The two pairs of scenes contrast life before the 1917 revolution with improvements evident four years later: now that, as the text states, 'the time of ignorance is over'. Particular stress is placed on the changes to women's lives. Before the revolution they were almost slaves, raising children and working in the fields, yet treated as idiots by men. Now they have access to education and to child-care, enhancing their lives socially as well as giving them a political voice. The borders of the upper pair of scenes are made from tsarist crowns linked by chains, whereas the lower scenes are decorated with a hammer and sickle flanking a star. The hammer and sickle, representing urban and rural labouring people, was adopted in July 1918, under the first Soviet constitution, as the state symbol; the five-pointed star was added in 1924.

3.6 Artist unknown; initials C. A.
Before, I was a Machine-greaser, I Oiled Wheels/But Now, in the Soviet, I Decide Important Issues 1925
Moscow, Mospoligraph

Lithograph; 35.1 x 53; *inv.* E 140375.

'Soviet' is the Russian word for the sectional, elected councils which were created by workers in cities throughout the country during 1905, gradually evolving from the functions of strike leadership to more general administration. The new government based its authority on these soviets; the poster reflects the great importance attached to soviet meetings where popular opinions could be voiced.

THE CIVIL WAR 1918-1920

Within months of the October Revolution, forces of the political right had begun to mobilise under generals Lavr Kornilov, and later A. I. Denikin in southern Russia, while Admiral A. V. Kolchak assembled another counter-revolutionary force in Siberia. By the end of May 1918 civil war had broken out in earnest between the 'Whites', as the anti-government armies were known, and the Bolshevik 'Red' forces. The war lasted until November 1920.

In the summer of 1918, the first political posters focusing support for the government appeared on the streets of Petrograd. Posters now became one of the most vital of a whole range of propaganda tactics underpinning the war effort, as the Bolsheviks attempted to muster support for the regime and strengthen resistance to counter-revolution.

1 In the Russian Heartland

3.7 Artist unknown
Boldly, Comrades, Into Step! 1919
Petrograd, Petrograd Military District

Lithograph; 49.9 x 66.5; *inv.* E 54244.

The rhyming verses of this revolutionary song, known in English as the *Red Army March*, exhort workers and peasants to join together in the final effort to overthrow the White forces and 'raise high over all the earth the red banner of labour!'. The imagery is typical of the way established symbols were developed to serve the new order. The central female figure with her 'classical' drapery is a familiar allegorical representation of Liberty; the sun behind her, traditionally used to represent knowledge and new life, here symbolises both the power and the benefits of the new Soviet state. Either side of her is a worker, *left*, and a peasant; these figures came to represent the new regime, whose success depended on its ability to unite and serve the interests of both groups.

3.8 DMITRII STAKHIEVICH MOOR (real name ORLOV) (1883-1946)
Have YOU Enrolled as a Volunteer?** 1920
Moscow, Revolutionary-Military Council of the Republic

Lithograph; 106.4 x 71.2; *inv.* Epl 25539.

This poster was produced in the last months of the Civil War to encourage recruitment. The Red Army had been founded in February 1918 and by the end of 1919 was three million strong. Although it was begun as a volunteer force, this was supplemented by mobilisation of different age groups, including younger veterans of the First World War, from September 1918.

D. S. Moor wrote that the poster was produced in a single night in June 1920, printed in some 47,000 copies for nation-wide distribution. The image itself was not new; the most famous of several other versions of the demanding, pointing finger was Alfred Leete's Lord Kitchener, who recruited men into the British army with the slogan *Your Country Needs* YOU. Moor's image in turn inspired other posters, both during the Bolshevik years and later; in the 1980s a similar figure was asking for help towards Mikhail Gorbachev's Perestroika.

3.7

3.9 VLADIMIR IVANOVICH KOZLINSKII (1891-1967)
Long Live the Vanguard of the Revolution/The Red Navy 1919-20
Petrograd, Revolutionary-Military Council of the Baltic

Linocut; 64.9 x 47.7; *inv.* Epl 1312.

The 'Worker-Peasant Red Navy' was established in 1918. This poster, formerly attributed to V. V. Lebedev, is here re-attributed to Kozlinskii by Nikolai Shkolnyi. Kozlinskii was the central figure in the production of the Petrograd ROSTA windows (see **3.39-41**. For Kozlinskii's street decorations, see **4.41-3**).

3.9

3.4 Anon, *The Red Ploughman*, 1920

2. „НАМ ПОКАЖИТЕ ЛИШЬ ПАЛЬЧИК
„А МЫ САМИ СХВАТИМ ВСЮ РУКУ,
„А ТАМ, АВОСЬ УДАСТСЯ – ЗА НОЖКИ
„И...ОБ ПЕНЬ ПОСРЕДИ ДОРОЖКИ?"

3.41 V. Lebedev, *Just Show Us A Little Finger*, 1921

3.10 VLADIMIR IVANOVICH KOZLINSKII (1891-1967)
RSFSR* 1919-20
Petrograd, Revolutionary-Military Council of the Baltic
Linocut; 65.6 x 48.2; inv. Epl 1320.

A soldier from the Red Army, *left*, and a sailor from the Red Navy, *right*, are shown jointly supporting the Cyrillic letters 'RSFSR', the initials of the Russian Socialist Federal Soviet Republic; this was the new name given to Russia proper and Siberia in 1918 (see map).

Whereas the majority of Bolshevik posters were printed lithographically, Kozlinskii had been using linocut since 1917 for prints such as *The Agitator*. Presumably it was Kozlinskii's influence which encouraged the Petrograd ROSTA group to use linocut rather than cardboard stencils, as was the practice in Moscow (see 3.34; for Petrograd ROSTA windows see 3.12).

3.11 Artist unknown
Comrade/Workers and Peasants!/All Go to Courses for/Red Commanders* 1921
Vitebsk, State Publishing House
Lithograph; 59.4 x 39.9; inv. E 166866.

For most of the Civil War the senior command of the Red Army was dominated by former tsarist officers. However, in 1919 special courses were set up to train more junior officers of proletarian origin; a total of 36,000 'Red Commanders' had graduated by the end of 1920. Although the Civil War was over in 1921, the Red Army's strength was maintained and consolidated for at least a further year. Vitebsk, where this poster was published, is on Russia's western borders and had been in the front line throughout the Civil War.

3.12 VLADIMIR VASILEVICH LEBEDEV (1891-1967)
Peasant!-If You Don't Want to Feed the Landlord/Feed the Front Defending Your Land and/Your Freedom 1920
Petrograd, Petrograd ROSTA Windows
Linocut with watercolour 77.7 x 47.2; inv. E 01082.

A continuing problem for the Soviet government was how to persuade the peasant farmers to produce enough food for the country's non-rural population. During the Civil War the state was acutely aware of its responsibilities for feeding both soldiers and urban workers; the harassed peasants, however, had little incentive to produce food surpluses, since they were already overstretched after years of war, a dearth of agricultural tools to buy, and serious inflation.

The persuasive tactic employed by this poster was to remind them that if the White army were to be victorious there would be a return to the hated landlord system, abolished by the Bolsheviks in 1917, when all private property in the form of landowners' estates had been appropriated. The upper part of the poster shows a fat landlord in a horse-drawn carriage, representing the class whose return is threatened. *Below*, is the positive alternative: a peasant taking food to be loaded onto a train for the Red Army in the war zones.

This poster was published by the Petrograd section of ROSTA, and, like most of this office's productions, it consists of black areas printed from lino, with further colours added by hand in watercolour (for Petrograd ROSTA windows see **3.19**, 27, 33, **36**, **38-41**. For Lebedev's street decorations see 4.37-40).

3.13 IURII MIKHAILOVICH BONDI (1889-1926)
A Call for Help* 1920
Kostroma, Kostroma ROSTA Windows
Linocut; 56.5 x 42.2; inv. I 40277.

Kostroma was one of about 30 regional centres from which branches of ROSTA produced informational posters along the lines of those made in Moscow. Local styles and techniques varied; although the technique used here - linocut - is the same as that use by Petrograd ROSTA, the style is very different. Often artists working in local centres have not been identified. The subject is unclear. It seems to be a plea for industrial workers to help the Red Army by acting as medical auxiliaries; the hammer carried by the auxiliary is a common emblem of urban workers, although it looks odd in this context. The five-pointed star, *upper left*, had been approved as a symbol for the newly-formed Red Army in 1918, and was officially incorporated into the arms of the Soviet state (the crossed hammer and sickle) in 1924.

3.14 DMITRII STAKHIEVICH MOOR (1883-1946)
The Soviet Turnip 1920
Moscow, Revolutionary-Military Council of the Republic
Lithograph; 70.6 x 53.6; inv. Epl 83.

Presented stage by stage in the traditional style of folk tales told in Russian popular prints or *lubki*, this piece of Civil War propaganda tells of a top-hatted capitalist who tries to steal a huge turnip. He is helped in his efforts to pull it out of the ground by other caricatured opponents of the Bolshevik regime: a moustachioed counter-revolutionary, disguised as an old woman; one of the moderate socialists whose parties co-operated with the propertied classes in 1917, dressed as a little boy; and a 'saboteur' working against the Soviet government, shown as a 'faithful female hound'. The turnip is eventually revealed as the helmet of a Red Army man, who literally blows them all away.

3.14

ПОПРЕЖНЕМУ ЗВУЧИТ НАШ РЕВОЛЮЦИОННЫЙ НАБАТ: -РАБОЧИЕ, КРЕСТЬЯНЕ, ТРУДЯЩИЕСЯ К НОВЫМ БИТВАМ И НОВЫМ ПОБЕДАМ !

3.16

3.15 Artist unknown

This is How Iudenich Thought He'd Celebrate the Anniversary of October/This is How WE Will Celebrate It 1919
Petrograd, Petrograd Military District
Linocut; 43.5 x 69.9; inv. E 161399.

The events of autumn 1919 were decisive for the Civil War; for a few months the fate of the Soviet regime hung in the balance. Admiral Kolchak held most of Siberia, and General Denikin had advanced to just over 200 miles from Moscow. On 21 October General Iudenich, who commanded an army advancing towards Petrograd, reached the outskirts of the city, which seemed bound to fall. The scene *left*, shows the outcome which the Bolsheviks had feared, with Iudenich triumphant over the workers of Petrograd. The situation was saved by the arrival in the former capital (officials moved to Moscow in February 1918 because of the German military menace) of Leon Trotsky, War Commissar, and of reserve forces from other fronts; by the time of the second anniversary of the October Revolution, the Whites were in retreat and Iudenich had resigned.

2 Campaigns in the South and West

3.16 Artist unknown

As Before our Revolutionary Tocsin is Sounding:/Workers, Peasants and Toilers/To New Battles and New/Victories! 1919
'Against the White cavalry we will advance the Red! Hurry to join the Red cavalry!'
Saratov, Saratov Province Tsentropechat
Lithograph; 53.6 x 70.6; inv. E 076126.

In the early part of the Civil War the Bolsheviks had regarded the idea of a cavalry as counter-revolutionary, strongly associated as it was with the repression of the tsarist period. However, in September 1919, after the Whites had used their cavalry units to win a string of victories, Leon Trotsky, the Bolshevik War Commissar, launched the slogan 'To horse, proletarians!', and two months later the *Konarmiia*, or Red Cavalry, was formed. It was one of the main factors which helped to turn the tide of the Civil War in the Reds' favour.

Most of the men recruited into the Red Cavalry were cossacks from the Don or Kuban areas; this print was published in Saratov, on the Volga, which lies to the north of the traditional cossack lands.

3.17 Artist unknown

To Horse, Worker and Peasant!/The Red Cavalry is the Guarantee of Freedom!** 1920
Kiev, Kiev District Military Command
Lithograph; 74.9 x 58.2; inv. Epl 892.

The Ukraine changed hands many times during the Civil War. Soviet forces had been sent into the area in December 1917, but the 1918 treaty of Brest-Litovsk had compelled withdrawal, and the Ukraine was occupied by German and Austrian forces. In the following months Kiev was fought over not only by the Red and White armies, but also Green partisans, the Polish army, and Ukrainian nationalists. Cultural issues were important here: this Ukrainian-language poster was part of a Soviet attempt, during the winter of 1919-20, to demonstrate that attention was being paid to local feelings.

3.18 ALEKSEI VASILEVICH MARENKOV (1888-1942)

Sons of Workers and Peasants: Red Warriors! The Black Front of Southern Counter-Revolution is in Tatters ... FORWARD! TO THE FINISH! VICTORY!* 1920
Kharkov, Revolutionary-Military Council of the South-West Front
Lithograph; 62.5 x 47.9; inv. 218023.

Kharkov, in the Ukraine and one of Russia's most important industrial centres, had been taken by General Denikin's White army in June 1919, but the Soviets had regained control of the city a few months later. Now the Red forces are being urged to press on to final victory.

With the Red Army's emblem (the five-pointed star) behind him, the soldier is about to deal a death blow to a monster representing counter-revolutionary forces. The soldier's helmet was part of a new uniform for the Red Army; its shape was influenced by the desire to sweep away the European style of the old imperial forces' uniforms, and to reintroduce elements of traditional, genuinely Russian, clothing. The belt, shoulder-piece and sword are reminiscent of heroes of Finnish and Nordic epics, as well as traditional Russian folk heroes such as Ivan Tsarevich (see **2.32**).

3.19 VLADIMIR VASILEVICH LEBEDEV (1891-1967)

Concerning the Ill-fated Rumour-monger and the Unhappy Chatterbox* 1920
Petrograd, Petrograd ROSTA Windows
Linocut with watercolour applied through stencils; 69.2 x 92; inv. E 01089.

The rhyming couplets below each of the eight frames within this poster describe the activities of a gossip who starts a rumour that the Polish army is advancing towards Rostov. The Poles had invaded the Ukraine in April 1920, and on 6 May captured Kiev. However, during June and July, the Red Army halted their progress, driving the Polish forces back to Warsaw. The Polish army never looked likely to reach Rostov, which is some 500 miles to the south-east of Kiev.

3.20 VIKTOR NIKOLAEVICH DENI (real name DENISOV) (1893-1946)

Manifesto! All Power to the Landlords and Capitalists!/To the Workers and Peasants — the Whip!* 1920
Moscow, State Publishing House
Lithograph; 68.5 x 51.2; inv. 4148.

The figure at the centre of this trio is General (Baron) P. N. Vrangel, commander of the White army fighting in south-western Russia; his hat is of the type worn by the cossacks. Vrangel holds up a manifesto declaring that a White victory will return landlords and capitalists to power, who will crush the proletariat. *Left*, is a 'kulak', a rich peasant, and *right*, a sycophantic 'bourgeois' capitalist in a top hat. Behind them is draped the pre-revolutionary Russian flag and an ermine-lined cloak, surmounted by a tsar's crown.

3.36 V. Lebedev, *Work With Your Rifle Beside You*, 1921

3.31 D. Moor, *1st of May: All-Russian Subbotnik*, 1920

3.20

3.22

3.21 DMITRII STAKHIEVICH MOOR (1883-1946)
Cossack, You've Beaten the Tsars and the Boyars/[now] Sweep the Boyar Vrangel into the Black Sea 1920
Moscow, Revolutionary-Military Council of the Republic
Lithograph: 70.4 x 50.6; *inv.* E 140100.

Descended from escaped serfs who had migrated to the southern and eastern parts of Russia, the cossacks were renowned as horsemen, and had traditionally given military service to the tsars; cossack troops had been used to put down the 1905 revolution. During the Civil War the cossack areas were fairly evenly divided in their support for the opposing Red and White armies. Since the use of horses was vital given the lack of roads in much of the countryside, the Bolsheviks were anxious to recruit cossacks into the Red Cavalry; the cavalry proved to be crucial to the victories of the Soviet government side.

Here, cossacks are being asked to join in the final campaign of the Civil War. Earlier in 1920 the Red Cavalry had pushed Denikin's White army southwards to the Black Sea, forcing him to withdraw to the Crimea, where he turned over his command to General Vrangel. Vrangel, with indirect support from the Allied forces in Europe, led the remnants of Denikin's army back into southern Russia, and a number of posters such as this drew attention to the unexpected danger which now threatened from this quarter. Vrangel's army was finally defeated at the end of the year.

D. S. Moor was himself the son of a cossack; he was born in Novocherkassk, a town in southern Russia which was the capital and cultural centre of the Don cossacks.

3.22 NIKOLAI NIKOLAEVICH KOGOUT (1891-1951)
Workers of All Countries Unite! 1920?
Moscow, Revolutionary-Military Council of the Republic
Lithograph: 71.3 x 53.3; *inv.* E 180196.

During 1920 a number of posters were produced appealing for loyalty to the Soviet government from the nationalities of the Russian south-west and Caucasia; this one, with text in Russian and Ottoman Turkish, is probably addressed to the Azeri people of the Caucasus.

The upper scene shows a non-Russian being encouraged by a group of people labelled, from left to right, 'Vrangel', 'Bourgeois', 'Joffre' and 'Entente', to turn his weapon against the flag-waving Red Army man. The red flag carries the slogan 'Workers of all countries unite!' Vrangel was in command of the White armies who, with the support of the Entente (Britain, France and the United States), were threatening the industrial and agricultural heartland of the Ukraine; the poster tells the local population 'If you want complete freedom and peace, . . . Don't listen to them'.

3.23 DMITRII STAKHIEVICH MOOR (1883-1946)
To the Peoples of the Caucasus** 1920
Moscow, Revolutionary-Military Council of the Republic
Lithograph; 69.1 x 105.1 *inv;* 0101106.

Against the background of the Caucasus mountains a Red Cavalry man is posed before representatives of the indigenous populations. The text announces, in Russian, Armenian, Georgian, Ottoman Turkish and Tatar, 'People of the Caucasus! The tsarist generals, the landlords and capitalists have, by the gun and the sword, suppressed your freedom and sold your country to the bankers of many lands. The Red Army of Soviet Russia has conquered your enemies: it has brought you liberation from servitude and the rich. Long live Soviet Caucasia!'

3.24 Artist unknown; initials A. Sh.
The Red Army Will Help the Oppressed of the East to Achieve Their Own October 1920
Tashkent, Puturka
Lithograph; 47 x 35.8; *inv.* E 180674.

The city of Tashkent had declared itself in support of the Soviet government in 1917 only a few days after Petrograd; in April the following year it became the centre of the Turkestan Soviet Republic. This area was at the heart of the fighting in Central Asia during the Civil War; it was cut off from Soviet Russia until September 1919, when the White Siberian army was defeated. This poster, in Russian and Uzbek, addresses the only non-Soviet centres remaining: the feudal Moslem states of Bukhara and Khiva, which finally fell to the Red Army and Moslem reformers in February 1920.

MAY DAY

The Bolshevik regime was committed to government based on soviets, or locally-elected councils, which necessitated the informed, active participation of all its citizens. The new regime thus took very seriously the need for widespread propaganda to inform and direct the activities of the country's huge (about 150 million in the early 1920s), geographically scattered and racially diverse population. Literacy levels were very low, especially in rural areas, so it was important that visual rather than written forms of communication be developed. To this end a wide range of activities were organised to celebrate anniversaries or other occasions associated with socialism. Processions and festive decorations transformed Petrograd, Moscow and other large cities and towns, fostering and channelling enthusiasm for the government cause (see pp135-52). One of the earliest of such occasions was 1 May 1917, when the workers' holiday which had been marked illegally in Russia since 1889 was celebrated publicly. May Day became a focus for annual festivities both nationally and internationally, and the subject of commemorative posters.

3.25 NIKOLAI NIKOLAEVICH KOGOUT (1891-1951)
First of May 1920
Moscow
Lithograph; 69.6 x 52.4; *inv.* Epl 133.

This poster demonstrates the important role which May Day and other such festivities were seen to play in establishing a sense of common purpose between disparate sections of a local community — soldiers, factory workers and peasants are here shown marching together.

3.24

3.26

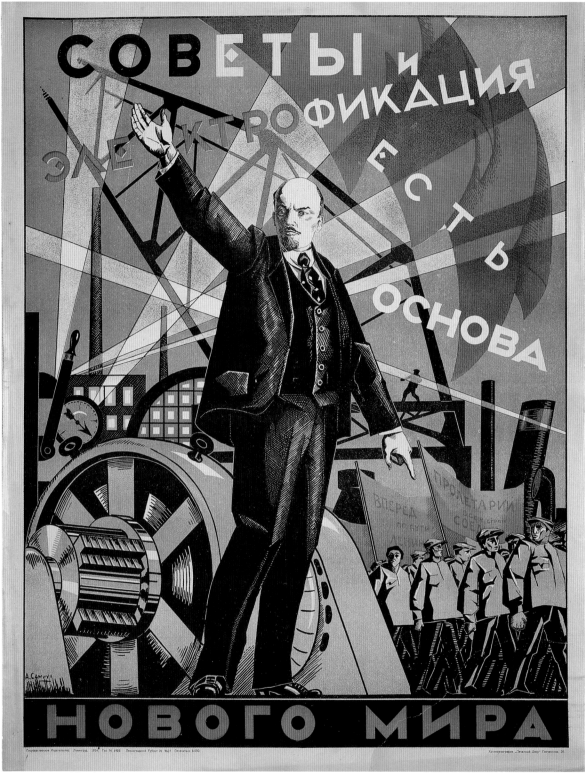

3.37 A. Samokhvalov, *The Soviets and Electrification Are the Foundation of the New World*, 1924

120

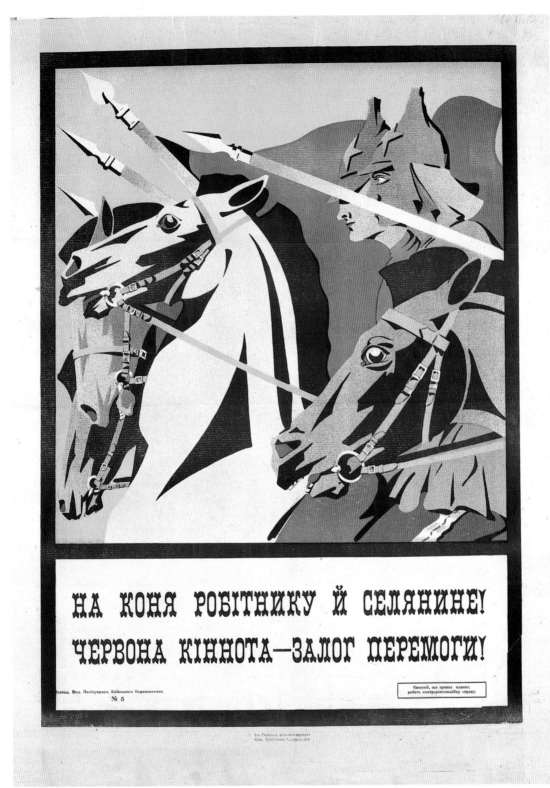

3.17 Anon, *To Horse, Worker and Peasant!* 1920

3.26 IVAN VASILEVICH SIMAKOV (1877-1925)
Long Live the Proletarian Festival/1st of May* 1921
Petrograd, State Publishing House
Lithograph; 106.5 x 73.7; inv. Epl 13323.

In the years immediately following the October Revolution, May Day posters presented the festival mainly as a celebration for industrial workers. During the 1920s however, as the need to foster economic relations between the town and the countryside became pressing, the festival became more of a joint worker-peasant celebration. Here, the importance of both genders is also stressed, as a female peasant and a male worker hold up the emblems of their labouring lives against the halo of the rising sun; they stand in the protection of two silver birch trees symbolising Russia in the same way the oak has come to stand for England.

3.27 LEV GRIGOREVICH BRODATY (1889-1954)
Festive Attire/Then and Now 1921
Petrograd, Petrograd ROSTA Windows
Linocut with watercolour applied through stencils; 41 x 60.5; inv. Epl 5199.

This poster was published in April 1921 in preparation for May Day celebrations in Petrograd. It contrasts the streets of the city before the revolution, when tsarist army officers policed the industrial areas, with an enthusiastic post-revolutionary procession.

3.28 IVAN VASILEVICH SIMAKOV (1877-1925)
Long Live 1st of May 1923
'international festival of labour!/May Day is the day of worker and peasant union'
Petrograd Branch, Russian Communist Party.
Lithograph; 66.6 x 98.1; inv. Epl 1298.

Jointly carrying the May Day banner are, *left*, a male peasant and, *right*, a male urban worker, emphasising the need for economic co-operation between town and countryside. The peasant is flanked by a Red Army man (traditionally drawn from the peasantry) and a female peasant, whilst the urban workers stands with a female worker and a sailor (sailors had taken part in radical urban activities during the revolution). The objects in the foreground, lit by the rising sun, further symbolise worker-peasant union: the tools represent the type of manufactured goods which the rural population wanted from the towns, garlanded with flowers from the countryside.

3.28

3.29 VASILII SEMENOVICH SVAROG (1883-1946)
1st of May 1925
'Play peasant accordion, we are celebrating workers' May!'
Leningrad, State Publishing House
Lithograph; 108 x 72.6; inv. 32212.

The May Day holiday gave urban workers the chance to escape to the countryside. Svarog also designed banners in Petrograd.

LABOUR AND PRODUCTIVITY

This group of posters is part of a campaign to revive industrial production after the devastations caused by six years of world war, revolution and civil war. The suffering was enormous; the country's population declined sharply, with deaths from disease, such as typhus epidemics, outnumbering deaths in battle; the number of industrial workers had more than halved. An acute shortage of labour, especially skilled, was therefore one of the many problems facing the Soviet government as, after the Civil War, it set about the task of reviving a country whose industrial output in 1920 stood at one seventh of its 1913 level.

3.30 NIKOLAI NIKOLAEVICH KOGOUT (1891-1951)
With Our Weapons We Finished Off the Enemy/By Our Labour We Will Get Food/Everybody to Work, Comrades! 1920
Moscow, Revolutionary-Military Council of the Republic
Lithograph; 69.7 x 53.6; inv. 165770.

With rifles at the ready in a pyramid behind, the male worker has removed his helmet and returned to the factory. Although most of the workers in the background are male, the foreground includes a woman worker; the war had made the whole of Russian society dependent on women's labour, in factories as well as in the fields.

3.30

3.31 DMITRII STAKHIEVICH MOOR (1883-1946)
1st of May/All-Russian/Subbotnik** 1920
Moscow, Revolutionary-Military Council of the Republic
Lithograph: 73.2 x 52.7; *inv. Epl* 25530.

Communist *subbotniki* (Saturdays) originated in May 1919, when the Soviet government appealed for help towards the Civil War effort, and thousands of workers in Moscow responded by working overtime without pay. The All-Russian *subbotnik* shown here, on May Day 1920, was the high point of the voluntary labour movement; it is estimated that in Moscow alone *subbotnik* work on this day totalled 4.5 million hours. In later years, party members' involvement became compulsory and participation more formalised.

The effectiveness of this poster stems to a large extent from its bold use of only two colours. This was in fact making a virtue out of necessity; during the Civil War only a limited range of inks was available and, since posters were frequently needed urgently and every extra colour used lengthened the printing process, there was often only time to use one or two colours.

3.32 Artist unknown
The Club is the School for Collective Labour early 1920s
Petrograd, Petrograd Military District
Lithograph: 50.4 x 66.5; *inv.* 142725.

During the 1920s the Soviet government was acutely aware not only of the need to revive industrial production, but also to introduce democracy and equality into a workforce in which older-established hierarchies had been strengthened by the drive to maximise production during the Civil War. This poster shows a large group of people working together to build a club. Since this construction involved voluntary work outside factory hours, such local initiatives would not have hindered industrial production, but they would have fostered a sense of joint commitment and shared responsibility among the workforce, helping to break down hierarchical barriers.

3.33 VLADIMIR VASILEVICH LEBEDEV (1891-1967)
Whose Side Will Win? 1920
'Not with kopecks,/not with roubles!/Don't boast as you go/into battle - in case you lose!'
Petrograd, Petrograd ROSTA Windows
Linocut with watercolour 51.5 x 60.5; *inv. Epl* 11949.

A worker and a capitalist are shown marching towards each other in a dramatic confrontation set against a background of smoking chimneys. The capitalist carries a banner marked 'concession', while the worker's reads 'world revolution'; the red ground is labelled 'Russia'. Following up an earlier plan interrupted by the Civil War, the Soviet government in November 1920 issued a decree granting concessions to foreign businessmen to allow them to exploit and develop Russian raw materials and mineral resources, with the aim of encouraging foreign trade. Reactions to this were divided, and the issue was much-debated in the press; in the following six months, however, no projects materialised.

3.34 VLADIMIR VLADIMIROVICH MAYAKOVSKY (1893-1930)
-35 Our Foreign Trade 1921
Moscow, Glavpolitprosvet (Committee for Political Education, People's Commissariat for Enlightenment)
Four drawings on two sheets, from window no 319, which originally comprised twelve drawings on six sheets
Gouache applied through stencils.

3.34 Sheet 1
1. Does Our Foreign Trade Amount to Anything, or is it Zero?
2. 'Here are the figures: March (1,602,469)'
103.2 x 45.1; *inv.* 96628.

3.35 Sheet VI
9. All Told (16,803,351)
12. 'Quite a lot of metal (3,616,492)'
103.3 x 45.2; *inv.* 96633.

These two sheets are from a group of six which would originally have been displayed together to fill an entire shop window; they were issued by Glavpolitprosvet, a committee for political education which took over this aspect of ROSTA's work during 1921. ROSTA's task was the distribution of any information which might be useful to the Soviet government; in this case recent figures for trade and industrial output are being circulated to hearten workers and to encourage further increases in production.

3.36 VLADIMIR VASILEVICH LEBEDEV (1891-1967)
Work With Your Rifle Beside You** 1921
Petrograd, Petrograd ROSTA Windows
Linocut: 76.5 x 56; *inv. Epl* 48776.

Lebedev had originally intended the caption on this poster to read 'A bayonet on the ground, a saw in the hand', but, during a visit to Petrograd, Mayakovsky intervened, suggesting its present form. The demobilisation of factories from war effort to peacetime output was under way in 1921.

3.37 ALEKSANDR NIKOLAEVICH SAMOKHVALOV (1894-1971)
The Soviets and Electrification Are the Foundation of the New World** 1924
Leningrad, State Publishing House
Lithograph: 86 x 66.6; *inv.* 32129.

After Lenin's death in 1924 his views were increasingly publicised to endorse government policy. In this instance, projects for intensive industrialisation are being particularly associated with Lenin; in 1920 he had written 'Communism is soviet power plus the electrification of the whole country'. (For paintings by Samokhvalov, see **1.45-6**).

THE NEW ECONOMIC POLICY 1921-6

The NEP was introduced in spring 1921 with the aim of rejuvenating the economy and establishing good relations with peasant farmers after the difficulties caused by grain requisitioning during the Civil War. This was replaced by a fixed 'tax in kind', leaving farmers free to market surplus produce. Freedom of trade was also allowed in the industrial sector, and small private businesses were legalised. By 1926, however, the policy was virtually abandoned; it had proved impossible to raise industrial output enough to encourage the marketing of grain on a sufficiently wide scale.

3.38 VLADIMIR IVANOVICH KOZLINSKII (1891-1967)
If You Work There Will Be Flour 1921
'If you sit with your arms folded [*doing nothing*]/There will not be flour [**muká**] /but torment [**múka**]'
Petrograd, Petrograd ROSTA windows
Linocut with watercolour: 65 x 42; *inv. Epl* 11950.

The poster's slogan puns on the word '*muka*' which in Russian means both 'flour' and 'torment'. It is aimed at workers in the cities, warning them that they must produce enough manufactured goods to encourage the peasantry to market their produce — grain for making flour and bread; experience had shown the rural population that it was pointless for them to earn paper money if there was nothing for them to buy with it. The situation in 1921 was, however, more complex than this poster would suggest, since industry was badly run down after six years of disruption, and the failure of two years' harvests tragically worsened the situation.

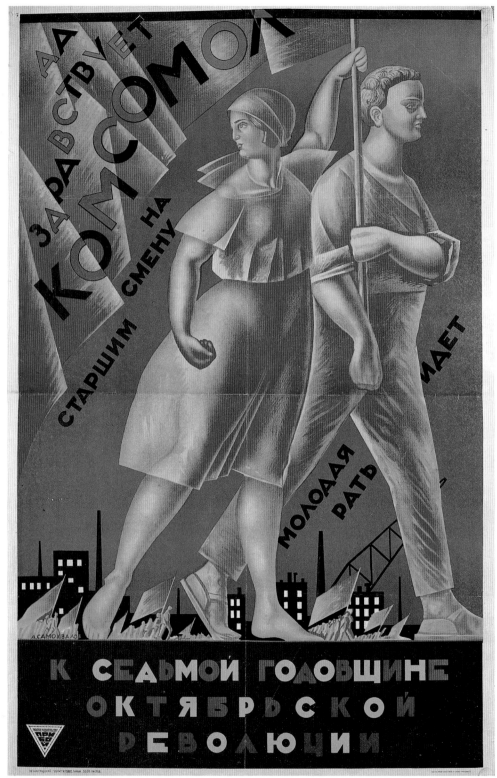

3.58 A. Samokhvalov, *Long Live the Komsomol*, 1924

3.62 A. Radakov, *The Illiterate Man Is Blind*, 1920

3.39 VLADIMIR VASILEVICH LEBEDEV (1891-1967)
Peasant,/You Received the Land, But/You Can't Eat Land 1921
'You must cultivate it./It will give its produce./You give/bread to the city./The city will give you all you need.'
Petrograd, Petrograd ROSTA Windows
Linocut with watercolour applied through stencils; 68.5 x 60; inv. Epl 11085.

Addressed to peasant farmers, as represented by the figure in the central frame, this poster is part of the continuing effort to encourage the rural population to produce and market grain surpluses in sufficient quantities to feed the urban workforce.

Although, as in Moscow, the Petrograd ROSTA windows were produced by the communal efforts of a group of artists, the characteristic style of certain individuals is sometimes discernible. Lebedev was, with Kozlinskii and Brodaty, one of the mainstays of the Petrograd ROSTA department. His work was experimental in style, causing controversy both at the time and later. Viacheslav Polonskii, the head of the official publishing house, Litizdat, wrote in 1925 that he felt Lebedev had taken his work to such a level of abstraction that it was incomprehensible to the masses to whom the posters were addressed.

Whereas the ROSTA windows made in Moscow had been produced using cardboard stencils, the Petrograd windows, such as this one, were created from a combination of linocut with colour applied either free-hand or through stencils. Lino was used to print a single colour, usually black, which would carry the main areas of the design; one or more colours could then be added on top. The initial design for the posters was usually entirely handpainted, often on a slightly larger scale. This was used as a guide for the production of lino and stencilled prints; up to 2,000 impressions could be produced in this way.

3.40 VLADIMIR VASILEVICH LEBEDEV (1891-1967)
Our Task Is Not the Amassing of a 'Pood' of Meat for You 1921
'The aim of our policy is/to make the enemies of the working class/serve it, blindly and involuntarily.'
Petrograd, Petrograd ROSTA Windows
Gouache; 107.8 x 71.3; inv. 01189.

After a period of fixed prices and strong centralised control, the changes introduced by NEP offered inducements to peasants to increase the supply of food, as well as promoting free trade and exchange. To many radicals, however, NEP appeared as a retreat from socialism. In defence of the policy the point was often made, as this poster claims, that skills learnt from the capitalists could be implemented for the benefit of the working class. A *pood* is 16.38 kilograms.

The poster exhibited here is one of a group of hand-painted designs for ROSTA windows owned by the Saltykov-Shchedrin Library. This sheet originally appeared in a window with **3.41** and others (see also 3.12).

3.41 VLADIMIR VASILEVICH LEBEDEV (1891-1967)
Just Show Us a Little Finger/and We'll Grab the Whole Arm 1921
'And later, maybe, we'll go for the legs/And . . . smash you against the nearest tree trunk?'
Petrograd, Petrograd ROSTA Windows
Gouache; 106.6 x 70.8; inv. 01184.

Many radicals feared NEP might prove to be the beginning of a wider betrayal of socialist values; they viewed with alarm the resurgence of the old and new bourgeoisie and considered that, given an inch, they would take a mile.

It has been estimated that, during the two years of its operation, the Petrograd ROSTA office issued over 1,000 separate 'windows', although only about 300 have survived to the present day. Lebedev himself is known to have created more than 600. The posters were produced and displayed in numbered sequences which were changed weekly — hence the numbers '2' and '6' on this and the previous exhibit. The texts were usually produced separately and then stuck below the pictures; in many instances they have not survived.

3.42 BORIS MIKHAILOVICH KUSTODIEV (1878-1927)
'Establishing Links/Between the Town and the Countryside/ Is a Fundamental Task of the Empowered Working Class' V. I. Lenin 1925'
'Leningrad Society for the Union [*smychka*] of Town and Country'
Moscow-Leningrad, State Publishing House
Lithograph; 106.4 x 70.8; inv. 166295.

An urban worker is here shown giving books, one marked prominently 'Lenin', to a man and a boy from a rural village, suggesting one way the peasants might benefit from a closer alliance with the townspeople. The failure of the '*smychka*', to foster the economic exchange of industrial and agricultural output was one of the main reasons for the enforced collectivisation of agriculture of the early 1930s, and the horrors that followed. (For paintings by Kustodiev, see **1.21-3**, for his street decorations, see **4.16-18**.)

DROUGHT AND FAMINE

In 1921, after two years during which severe drought ruined the harvest, a terrible famine struck areas of Central Russia and the Volga basin. An appeal for help was launched, both locally and internationally. In August agreements were signed with the American Relief Administration and with a Red Cross mission led by F. Nansen; both worked to help combat starvation and disease in the Volga region throughout the winter of 1921-2.

3.43 VLADIMIR VLADIMIROVICH MAYAKOVSKY (1893-1930)
-54 Help the Starving! 1921
Moscow, Glavpolitprosvet (Committee for Political Education, People's Commissariat for Enlightenment)
Window no 414, consisting of 12 drawings on 12 sheets
Gouache applied through stencils, 56 x 42 (average); inv. 111799-111810.

3.43 1 To this red/summoning cross/hurry, citizens,/from all parts.

3.44 2 So that who-ever, how-ever,/and by what-ever means may/rush to help/as fast as their legs can carry them.

3.45 3 Whoever has any spare/roubles/hurry up/and contribute them.

3.46 4 Whoever has bread,/a spare piece,/hurry up and bring it/as fast as your legs can carry you.

3.47 5 Arrange together/a money contribution/to give to the collectors/into the collecting box.

3.48 6 Put on concerts,/put on shows.

3.49 7 In a word/one way or another,/all the week,/one day after another.

3.50 8 Help the starving man/take care of him!

3.51 9 The main thing is to keep agitating/all these weeks:

3.52 10 It's essential, they say,/that the starving/eat every day.

3.53 11 And for this,/it's no good helping now and then/when you feel like it!

3.54 12 But regularly,/every day.

These stencilled sheets were intended for display together in one location; they would have filled an entire shop window, although increasingly ROSTA's posters were shown in other locations such as train and bus stations. Mayakovsky wrote most of the texts for posters produced by the Moscow ROSTA office; for this set he wrote in verse with a complex rhyming pattern, and designed the images as well.

For almost three years the production of ROSTA windows took up much of Mayakovsky's energies; later he wrote 'that was a fantastic thing. It meant a nation of 150 million being served by hand by a small group of painters. It meant news sent by telegram immediately translated into posters, decrees into couplets'. He clearly believed this work was important, not only for the immediate purposes it served (in this case famine relief), but also for the implications it had for the future of art and its relation to society: 'We don't need a dead temple of art where dead works languish, but a living factory of the human spirit'; art should be seen 'not in dead museum-temples, but everywhere — on the streets, in trams, in factories, in workshops and in workers' apartments'.

3.55 DMITRII STAKHIEVICH MOOR (1883-1946)
HELP* 1921
Moscow, Pomgol (Help to the Starving)
Lithograph; 105.7 x 70; inv. 165654.
Nearly 20 million people lived in the area around the Volga struck by famine; the scale of the relief effort was enormous. Moor thought this image of an elderly and emaciated peasant making an anguished appeal for help was his most successful poster. Behind the peasant is a single, dried-out, broken ear of corn through which, as Moor later recalled, he had tried to suggest 'the scorched and barren steppe lands, and the animals swollen with hunger, and the tears of the mothers, and the frightened eyes of the children'.

SOCIAL POLICY, EDUCATION, CULTURE

The programme adopted by the government in 1919 committed the new regime to 'a 'continually rising standard of culture, organisation and self-activity on the part of the masses'. Once the anti-Bolshevik forces had been defeated and treaties had been concluded with Britain, Poland, Turkey and several other border states, military matters were no longer a priority, and consequently the number of posters produced on such subjects declined. Now economic development and educational change became the major national priorities; indeed many posters linked the two by declaring that knowledge was the key to greater agricultural production and prosperity. Campaigns were conducted to improve public health, women's rights and, perhaps most urgent of all, literacy and reading.

3.56

3.65 Anon, *Literacy Is The Path to Communism*, 1920

3.56 VLADIMIR IVANOVICH IKONNIKOV

I'm Not Going to the Church to Marry/My Sweet and Tender Dear* 1922
'We're going to the commissar,/to register as a pair'
Moscow-Petrograd, State Publishing House
Lithograph; 54 x 34.7; inv. E 060176.

Before the October Revolution, the total inability of the Russian Orthodox church to adapt to the changing conditions produced by rapid urbanisation meant that in some cases men and women from the poorer urban areas simply could not get married. From the outset, however, the new Soviet regime made a determined effort to secure the support of working-class women; the government's first marriage law was issued as early as December 1917, replacing the religious ceremony with a civil transaction. This conferred no advantage on either party, provided for simple divorce proceedings, and made arrangements for the maintenance of children. Women no longer had to take their husband's name. Revolutionary feminists, however, were not entirely happy with the new law since it appeared to rehabilitate marriage rather than, as they would have wished, abolish it altogether. This poster shows a man and a woman turning their backs on a church, and walking towards a building marked 'Soviet' (council) where they are going to 'register as a pair.'

3.57 VLADIMIR IVANOVICH IKONNIKOV

The Ring on Your Finger Shines No Brighter/Than Shines Our 1917 Among the Anniversaries* 1923
Moscow, Mospoligraf
Lithograph; 35.4 x 52.7; inv. 71543.

This poster shows a Red Army soldier with his peasant sweetheart; in sentimental language, like that used on a Valentine, he is teaching her about earlier revolutions — the French Revolution 1789, the European Revolution 1848, the Paris Commune 1871, and the Russian Revolution 1905 — although he claims that the 1917 October Revolution was the most significant of all. Soldiers returning to their home villages after service in the Red Army played a vital role in spreading revolutionary propaganda to the peasants.

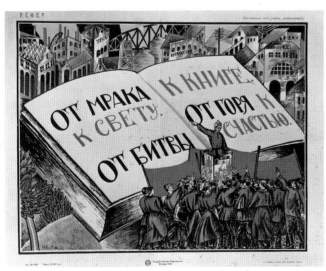

3.59

3.60

3.58 ALEKSANDR NIKOLAEVICH SAMOKHVALOV (1894-1971)

Long Live the Komsomol! (Young Communist League)** 1924
'Young forces are coming/to relieve their seniors./In honour of the seventh anniversary of the/October/Revolution'
Leningrad, Priboi
Lithograph; 92.9 x 59.8; inv. E 142216.

In 1924 the Komsomol was especially associated with Nikolai Bukharin. Today Bukharin is credited by many Soviet supporters of Perestroika with having envisaged, in the 1920s, a better way forward for the Soviet Union than the socially dangerous policies initiated by Stalin.

3.59 NIKOLAI NIKOLAEVICH KOGOUT (1891-1951)

From Darkness into Light/From Battle to Books/From Misery to Happiness 1921
Moscow, State Publishing House
Lithograph; 53.3 x 70.4; inv. 142608.

A Red Army man points out to an enthusiastic crowd that, now the Civil War has ended, they must turn their attention 'from battles to books'. Civil War posters, such as D. S. Moor's *Have YOU Enrolled as a Volunteer?* are shown pasted onto the rostrum from which he is speaking; the buildings behind him are marked 'Labour', 'Art', 'Science'.

3.60 ELIZAVETA SERGEEVNA KRUGLIKOVA (1865-1941)

Women! Learn Your Letters! 1923

'Oh, Mama! If you could read, you could help me!'
Petrograd, Petrooblit

Linocut: 70.4 x 59.7; *inv.* 142665.

Kruglikova, who designed a number of posters in this 'silhouette' style, was celebrated both before and after the October Revolution as a portrait painter and book illustrator as well as an experimental printmaker who introduced new methods of printing monotypes from glass plates. The department of prints and drawings in the Saltykov-Shchedrin Library owns one the largest collections of her work.

3.61 BORIS MIKHAILOVICH KUSTODIEV (1878-1927)

Lengiz 1925

'Leningrad Branch of the State Publishing House'
Leningrad State Publishing House

Lithograph: 105.5 x 71.8; *inv.* 758238.

This poster demonstrates the potential benefits of literacy to different sections of the community: the man in the centre holds a metal-worker's hammer in one hand and a book containing an illustration of a lathe in the other. *Left*, a peasant holding a scythe is reading a book called 'Tractor', while a soldier with a bayonet, *right*, reads 'Memories of the Red Army'. The following titles are included amongst the pile of books on the floor: 'Lenin', 'Technology', 'Marx', 'Engels'. Open at the bottom of the pile is an illustration of the Lenin Mausoleum in Red Square, Moscow. Lenin died in 1924 and Petrograd was re-named 'Leningrad' in his honour. The model for the standing worker was probably the writer and literary critic Kornei Chukovskii.

3.61

3.63

3.62 ALEKSEI ALEKSANDROVICH RADAKOV (1877-1942)

The Illiterate Man is Blind** 1920

'on all sides failure and misfortune lie in wait for him'
Petrograd, State Publishing House

Lithograph: 95.4 x 65.8; *inv.* Epl 481.

The perils which beset those whose illiteracy leaves them in ignorance are summed up in this image of a blindfold man. Literacy levels were very low amongst the Soviet population at this time, especially outside the major towns. Some improvement had been made since the end of the 19th century, but by the 1920s the overall level of literacy in areas under Soviet control was still only 44.1%, and within this overall figure there were vast variations between men and women, and urban and rural populations.

3.63 ALEKSEI ALEKSANDROVICH RADAKOV (1877-1942)
Illiterate People. ... Literate People. ... 1920
Petrograd, State Publishing House
Lithograph; 80.5 x 57.2; *inv. Epl 32207.*

In a simple 'before and after' format this poster demonstrates the advantages of literacy by contrasting the ill-fed couple *above*, whose land is unproductive, whose animals are starving, and who are unable to protect themselves from natural disasters such as lightning striking their house, with the prosperous and portly couple *below*, surrounded by fertile fields and well-fed animals, who have installed a lightning conductor to protect their property. The text explains that books can give reliable advice on everything from how to buy the best cattle and fertiliser, to how to cure a sick child.

However, presentation of the benefits of literacy in these terms did not go without criticism; Lev Sosnovskii, editor of the paper *Bednota* (Poor Peasants), complained of a similar poster by Radakov that instead of presenting literacy as something necessary for the struggle for a new life and a new society, he had shown it simply as something which would help people earn more money, appealing to their selfish instinct for individual gain.

3.64

3.64 Artist unknown
Day of Soviet Propaganda/KNOWLEDGE — TO ALL! 1919
Moscow, State Publishing House
Lithograph; 68.3 x 48.3; *inv. E 020670.*

In front of buildings labelled 'Academy', 'Library', 'University' and 'School', the giant worker-figure is handing out books with such titles as 'Art', 'Market-Gardening', 'Capital', 'What is Religion?' and 'The History of Slavery' to an eager crowd. As stressed by the poster's title, under the new regime schools were open to all, not just to the children of a privileged minority.

3.65 Artist unknown
Literacy Is the Path to Communism 1920
Moscow, State Publishing House
Lithograph; 71.6 x 53.6; *inv. 142654.*

By contrast to Radakov's poster (**3.63**) which stresses the economic benefits of literacy, the unknown designer of this poster has used traditional allegorical figures to suggest that literacy will lead to a better, communist, society. Flying over a landscape of factory chimneys, fortifications and houses, surrounded by flames which are dispersing dark storm clouds, the rider carries a torch, traditional symbol of knowledge, and holds an open book. He sits astride a winged red horse which symbolises freedom or deliverance, perhaps from the ignorance or fear suggested by the clouds. A total of 75,000 copies of this poster were printed, with further editions appearing in Hebrew, Polish and Tatar.

REVOLUTION AND THE WORLD

The founding congress of the Communist International, or Comintern, was held in Moscow in March 1919; its aim was to unify and direct communist parties around the globe, helping to maintain ideological solidarity across national boundaries. There had been two previous Socialist Internationals: the first was formed by Marx himself, and the second founded in Paris in 1889; this had disintegrated in 1914. The belief underlying all three was that, since capitalism is an international force, it can only be overthrown by the combined power of the proletariat of the major industrialised countries.

3.66 Artist unknown
To the Grief of All Bourgeois/We Will Beat Up a World-wide Bonfire!... 1918
Petrograd, Petrograd Soviet
Lithograph; 74.2 x 50.1; *inv. Epl 11939.*

The two lines heading this poster compare the spread of revolution throughout the industrialised nations to a spreading bonfire; they are taken from *The Twelve* (*Dvenadtsat*), a poem by Russia's leading poet and Symbolist, Aleksandr Blok (1880-1921), first published in the socialist paper *Znamia truda* (Banner of Labour) in 1918. Blok, along with Mayakovsky and Meyerhold, was one of the first artists to declare his support for the new Bolshevik regime; in *The Twelve* he describes the progress of a band of Red militiamen, led by a mysterious Christ-like figure, through revolutionary Petrograd during a fierce blizzard in 1917. The giant worker-figure seen here was frequently used in Russian painting and graphics during the early decades of the 20th century to suggest the power of the proletariat. (See also **4.41**).

West Surrey College of Art and Design
Falkner Road Farnham Surrey GU9 7DS
Telephone 0252 722441 Fax 0252 733869

МЫ НА ГОРЕ ВСЕМ БУРЖУЯМ
МИРОВОЙ ПОЖАР РАЗДУЕМ!...

3.66

3.68

**3.67 KSENIIA LEONIDOVNA BOGUSLAVSKAIA (Puni)
(1892-1972)**
The Internationale* 1919
Petrograd, Petrograd Military District
Lithograph; 57.4 x 67; *inv.* 166240.

The music for *The Internationale* was written in the 1880s; the Russian text given in this poster was added in 1902 by A.Ia. Kots. It calls on the 'hungry and enslaved' of the whole world to 'raze the world of violence' 'to its foundations' and build 'our own new world' in its place. From 1917 until 1944 *The Internationale* was the Soviet national anthem.

3.68 Artist unknown
Master of All the World/Will Be/LABOUR! 1920
Iaroslavl
Lithograph; 72.9 x 49.6; *inv.* 166918.

The subject of this poster is the role of trade unions in the world-wide communist movement; against a schematic globe, a worker and a peasant together support a banner, the middle section of which reads 'The Red unions of Russia are a resinous torch kindling the world-wide communist revolution'. The final section, at the foot of the poster, reads 'Trade Unions are the school of communism'; this was endorsed officially in 1920, formalising the position of unions as organs of the state, educating their members, but themselves under Communist Party tutelage. Their educational and social role is emphasised by the book, mask and music-stand included amongst the array of emblematic objects in the foreground.

3.69 SERGEI IVANOVICH IVANOV (1885-1942)
Long Live the Third Communist International! 1920
Petrograd, State Publishing House
Lithograph; 65.9 x 87; inv. 166252.
This poster was produced to commemorate the second congress of the Third, or Communist, International, held in Russia in March 1920. Its Russian title is repeated in English, French, Italian and German. (See also **1.22.**)

3.70 DMITRII STAKHIEVICH MOOR (1883-1946)
Long Live the Third International! 1920
Moscow, Revolutionary-Military Council of the Republic
Lithograph; 106 x 68.6; inv. 166263.
An urban worker in a red shirt bids welcome to the delegates to the second congress of the Third International in 1920 in five languages; behind him is the Moscow Kremlin.

3.71 DMITRI IVANOVICH MELNIKOV (1889-1966)
25 October 1917 — 7 November (25 October) 1920 1920
Moscow, State Publishing House
Lithograph; 91.7 x 59.6; inv. 165888.
In a series of paired 'before and after' scenes, this poster proclaims the improvements which have been made, during the three years following the October Revolution, to the lives of workers and peasants. Now, through the Soviet government, they can control their own lives, rather than being at the mercy of the industrial and agricultural masters as they were in the past. During 1920 many still expected the revolution to spread outside Russia; the second congress of the Komintern held in the summer of 1920, as Soviet forces were advancing into Poland, was larger than the first. The banner above the hammer and sickle at the base of this poster reads 'The three-year struggle and stubborn toil has secured Soviet power in Russia. Forward! To world-wide October! Long live Soviet power in the whole world!'

Russian dates had changed from the 'old style' Julian calendar to the 'new style' Gregorian system in February 1918, when 15 February became 1 March; hence the anniversary of the October Revolution, 25 October, fell on 7 November in 1920, according to the 'new style' Western dates.

3.72 Artist unknown; initials B. V.
In a United Front With the Workers of All Countries/Against the Advancing Tyrant — Capital early 1920s
Orël
Lithograph; 68 x 43; inv. 166241.
This poster was produced in 1922 to commemorate the fourth congress of the Communist International. The figure of a woman in 'classical' drapery blowing a trumpet, traditionally used in European art as an emblem of Fame, was frequently used in Bolshevik posters and street art to suggest the spread of liberty and freedom through communism (see **4.64**).

3.73 IVAN VASILEVICH SIMAKOV (1877-1925)
Long live the 1st of May! 1921-3
'the international proletarian festival!/May Day is the day for strengthening proletarian education!'
Moscow-Petrograd, Petersburg Branch, Russian Communist Party
Lithograph; 68 x 100; inv. Epl 32211.
The workers' festivals held in celebration of May Day had traditionally crossed national borders. Here the dancers are shown in national costume from all over the world, although the central figures are of Russian workers and peasants, male and female.

3.69

3.70

ЕДИНЫМ ФРОНТОМ С РАБОЧИМИ ВСЕХ СТРАН
ПРОТИВ НАСТУПАЮЩЕГО ТИРАНА-КАПИТАЛА!

3.72

3.73

3.74 Artist unknown
1917 - October - 1920 1920
Saratov, Saratov Branch of the State Publishing House
Lithograph: 106.3 x 70.1; *inv*. 165882.
Produced in 1920, as the Civil War was ending with victory for the Soviet forces, this poster celebrates the third anniversary of the October Revolution; it also fuels expectations, widespread at this date, that revolution will spread to other parts of Europe. A Russian worker stands proudly victorious over emblems of the fallen tsarist regime; his banner is emblazoned 'RSFSR', while the crowd carry banners with slogans in French, English and German. The verses below the image proclaim that 'Soviet Russia has become the focus/of the whole labouring world — with us/In all lands peasants and workers are raising/The Red Banner of Proletarian Revolution'.

Street Art of the Revolution

Petrograd, 1918

'Art is breaking out of walls onto the streets' was a slogan of the post-revolutionary period, celebrating the fact that art could now reach all the people instead of a narrow group of connoisseurs. The Bolsheviks believed that visual images were a direct way of spreading to all sections of the population ideas about the new life that was opening up. Some artists looked for revolutionary artistic forms to express the changes, while others argued that modernist art got in the way of communication. This debate began at the moment when almost two hundred artists pooled their efforts in Petrograd to celebrate the first anniversary of the revolution in mass festivities which in some ways marked the continuation of more traditional popular holidays.

Tradition Reworked for Revolution

by Catherine Cooke, joint editor of 'Street Art of the Revolution: Festivals and Celebrations in Russia 1918-33', Thames & Hudson, 1990

> The need has arisen to change the external appearance of our towns as rapidly as possible, in order to express our new experiences in an artistic form as well as to get rid of all that is offensive to the feelings of the people.
> Anatolii Lunacharskii, 10 October 1918

In a year which has seen extraordinary upheavals of revolutionary scale enacted before television cameras, it requires a conscious act of mental refocusing to grasp what the Russian revolution of 1917 actually felt like: to grasp its speed — or rather its slowness, and the problems of communication that it posed. Among the accounts of the revolution, Leon Trotsky has left us a uniquely vivid insider's view, with an attractively ironic eye for the details. He also shows how those revolutionaries too, making historical comparisons backwards — particularly to the French Revolution — recognised that their own times were characterised by a 'new tempo' made possible by new technologies.

The initial wresting of power is often the easy bit of a revolution, as this last year's events in Eastern Europe have also reminded us. The consolidation of power, both practically — into a functioning administration — and psychologically — to win recognition of its legitimacy among the whole of a factional population — is a far more complex and extended process. In Russia in 1917 the Bolsheviks were well aware of how much in this task depended on control of communications, on the successful utilisation of techniques and technologies to spread revolutionary ideas and keep the important issues before the eyes of the larger Russian population. The process of consolidation became bloody and destructive in Russia as tsarist forces rallied in the spring of 1918, fighting a two-year civil war in which they had the moral support at least of British and other Allied troops, who entered Russia at different times in the course of 1918.

The White general Denikin, whom the British were reinforcing in the South was described with characteristic asperity by Trotsky as 'not without character, but for the rest a perfectly ordinary army general who had read five or six books'.[1] Thus spoke the Bolsheviks' military organiser and strategist who takes major credit for the final defeat of the Whites, but who was also a supremely scholarly intellectual. The general thrust of his remark highlights the difference between the shambling old regime and the new.

The Bolsheviks were intellectuals who had been debating and writing for years about their programme, and formulating its ideological and philosophical bases. On many fronts, their internal differences of interpretation, and the divergence between Russian reality and what any theoretical model could have predicted, led to some serious oscillations of policy and the devising of operational principles 'on the run'. Although in cultural matters opposing viewpoints became within a short period matters for divisive debates (see pp 26-31), in 1918 disagreements were not yet substantial. The basic premise from which both Lenin and Anatolii Lunacharskii, the highly cultivated Commissar for Enlightenment (education and propaganda), agreed was that the art of the revolution would look critically at tsarist culture, but not hold back from making use of what was best and most suitable from the past, as a well assimilated vessel to fill with new content.[2]

From the beginning, however, the Bolsheviks were united on the crucial importance of culture in the communication of new ideas. They understood perfectly that ingrained attitudes were as solid an obstacle to political transformation as the structures of the old economic system. A central element in the 'planned appropriation of the heritage of the old world'[3] on which the pragmatic art policy was based was the reinvention of the traditional mass public festivals that were deeply rooted in the experience and expectations of every Russian. Lenin discussed with Lunacharskii the utopian socialist work of Tommaso Campanella, *City of the Sun*, in which the Renaissance thinker described how the walls of the ideal town would be decorated with frescoes to provide young people with a visual education in natural science and history and arouse civic feelings. Lenin advocated the adaptation of these ideas by the erection of 'expressive inscriptions', didactic slogans and new, revolutionary monuments. Lunarcharskii responded by harnessing the arts, as they had never been used by a government before, perhaps anywhere.

As early as 6 November 1917 the Central Committee of the Bolshevik Party had called a meeting of leading representatives of Petrograd's painters, writers and theatre designers at the

4.1 Saltykov-Shchedrin Public Library on May Day with modernist banner

Smolny Institute to discuss their collaboration with the new Soviet regime. Among those present were such progressive figures as Vladimir Mayakovsky, Vsevelod Meyerhold and Natan Altman. With equal speed Lunacharskii won the support of the more established artists, in particular the members of the World of Art group. Sections of his commissariat, Narkompros, were headed by such modernist artists as David Shterenberg, whom Lunarcharskii had known in Paris, and the Constructivist Vladimir Tatlin. Lunacharskii frequently expressed his appreciation for the energy the *avant-garde* artists brought to their organisational tasks; the *avant-gardists* spat on the more conservative of the World of Art brigade, like Alexandre Benois, for joining up with the very Bolshevism they had railed against the year before; but in the end, at this momentous time, they all worked together. A decree of April 1918 launched the programme for revolutionary statues and also set in motion great twice-yearly public festivals for May Day and the anniversary of the revolution. Narkompros committees were instructed to 'organise the decoration of the cities ... with emblems, inscriptions etc, reflecting the ideas and mood of revolutionary, working Russia'.

Lunacharskii's diary for May Day 1918 revealed him ecstatic at what the young artists had achieved in transforming Petrograd: 'Is it not intoxicating to think that the state, until recently our worst enemy, now belongs to us and has celebrated May Day as its greatest festival?' The poet Aleksandr Blok described the processions more cynically, seeing them converge on the memorial Field of Mars 'with neat little red posters' in an 'exemplary Nicholas II formation'. The cosmopolitan World of Art painter, Mstislav Dobuzhinskii, satirised the view of Leftists that they were 'ex-

ploding a bomb' — rebelling against the 'despotism of architectural lines which have imprisoned the artist's free eye for long enough!'; he found the effect 'futile' and criticised the young painters' inexperience in handling the monumental scale required for open-air work.[4] But it was a start, and six months later the first anniversary of the revolution gave the artists a chance to develop their technique.

This enormous festival involved a total of 85 separate design projects across the length and breadth of Petrograd, and double this number of designers. The results were as diverse as the contributors' artistic origins. Some were architects, like Iosif Langbard, Aleksandr Klein or Vladimir Shchuko, who had done festival decoration before the revolution. The painters ranged from abstractionists like Ivan Puni or such modernists as Altman and Vladimir Kozlinskii to well established realists of the World of Art group like Dobuzhinskii, Boris Kustodiev and Kuzma Petrov-Vodkin: most were now teaching in the Svomas, or Free Studios, that had been formed out of the old St Petersburg Academy of Arts.

Some schemes were barely more than essays in decorative colour and playfulness. Dobuzhinskii believed in principle that it was wrong to alter the architectural character of the city. Some of the decorative work was especially imaginative, like the addition of sails and prows to the pillars of the Neva bridge newly named after the 17th-century Volga rebel Stenka (Stepan) Razin, to transform them into brightly coloured Volga pirate galleys (**4.23**). Elsewhere there were simplified, realistic images whose tone was heroic, celebrating the fact of revolution and the workers' role in achieving it, and using catchy slogans to remind the city's population of its goals. More controversial were the modernist forms of an artist like Vladimir Lebedev (**4.37-40**), whose

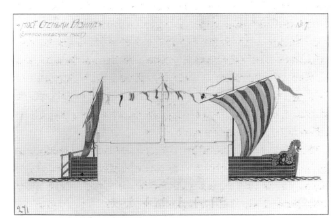

4.23 A. Dideriks and V. Alvang, Design for Stepan Razin Bridge

abstracted images, full of movement, were designed to be in themselves an expression of change. Despite the encroaching Civil War and the threat from abroad as foreign and anti-Bolshevik troops entered Russia, the bold satire and caricature of 'class enemies', which soon became characteristic of these bi-annual festivals, are still embryonic here.

In autumn 1918 the economy was still suffering the chronic shortages which began in 1914 with the war and the ensuing profiteering. The aim for this great revolutionary festival in October 1918 was a further injection of revolutionary enthusiasm into a nation where the pressures of civil war and the straitened economic situation were daily increasing the problems of existence to the point of threatening morale. There was no television through which to address the cold, illiterate and often hungry population. The Bolsheviks' political message was carried continuously through street newspapers and propaganda windows in cartoon form, and was taken to the provinces through massive poster campaigns and carts and trains emblazoned with colourful slogans. Like so much else to which the mass of people were now exposed these features of life were novel. But the great street festivals, — though new in content — had a reassuring familiarity.

Still intensely religious, the Russian towns and countryside had long-established traditions of festive processions involving the carrying of sacred images and banners, be it the Procession of the Cross in the provincial village (see p 23) or the celebration of church services in the great spaces of the city like Palace Square. On the annual holiday of Shrovetide (Maslenitsa), Moscow, St Petersburg and every Russian town had several days of parades and mass merry-making (see 6.9 etc). In the past, any military victory worthy of fireworks had been marked almost on the scale of the great coronation celebrations (see ill), when the capital would be entirely decorated to designs by leading artists. This pattern was adapted by the Bolshevik festivals to encompass a new content (4.50).[6]

The Bolshevik celebrations were revolutionary in character in that they were not overawed by the aristocratic grandeur of a tsarist city like Petrograd, where Altman's flames licked the base of the Alexander Column and modernist designs proclaimed an iconoclastic visual ethic. New heroes were celebrated and a revised mythology expressed the aspirations of ordinary people. The festivals derived a certain legitimacy in socialist theory from references to Paris in 1789, but they were directly related to the seasonal doses of holiday colour and jostling humanity which had historically enlivened the existence of all classes in Russia. Follow-

4.50 N. Tyrsa. Sketch for decoration of a bridge, with fireworks.

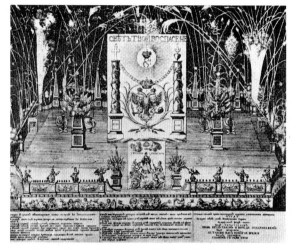

A. Zubov, *Firework Display in 1726 in St Petersburg*, 1720s

ing their policy of building upon those elements of the cultural heritage which remained valid or adaptable to the new ideology, the Bolsheviks established a new tradition — combining the familiar festival enjoyment with political education — that developed over the 1920s into a new genre of popular art.

NOTES

1. Leon Trotsky, *The History of the Russian Revolution*, vol 3, Sphere, 1967, p 243.
2. This debate is documented in Zenovia A. Sochor, *Revolution and Culture: the Bogdanov-Lenin Controversy*, Cornell, 1988, especially chapter 6.
3. *ibid*, pp 144-5.
4. C. Tolstoy, I. Bibikova & C. Cooke (eds), *Street Art of the Revolution: Festivals and Celebrations in Russia 1918-33*, Thames & Hudson, 1990, document 6, note to document 8, document 8.
5. See for example A.F. Nekrylova, *Russkie narodnye prazdniki, uveseleniia i zrelishcha, konets XVIII-nachalo XX veka (Russian Popular Festivals, Amusements and Spectacles, the late 18th to early 20th centuries)*, Iskusstvo, Moscow, 1988.

The New Beauty of a Victorious People

by Liudmila Tugova, keeper of prints, Museum of the Great October Socialist Revolution

The fundamental changes in all spheres of Russian life brought by the Great October Socialist Revolution found their first cultural expression in Lenin's project for 'monumental propaganda'; this plan to replace the statues glorifying the tsarist order with images of thinkers and other revolutionary heroes took shape in a decree of April 1918, which also established the principle of a mass agitational art that would draw the people as a whole into the activity of transforming the country and creating a new life.

The days celebrating the first anniversary of the revolution were marked by special solemnity and splendour. In Petrograd, a commission of the soviet (council) had drawn up a list of streets to be decorated and created a central bureau to oversee the work. Three days of festivities were planned, which would include the official unveiling of the first Soviet monuments and obelisks. Some idea of this ambitious festival can be had from photographs, contemporary reminiscences, and from the artists' drawings and plans preserved in museums and private collections, among them that of the State Museum of the Great October Socialist Revolution in Leningrad. From these records, varying approaches to the decoration of the city can be distinguished, reflecting the different

4.15 Mstislav Dobuzhinskii. Sketch for pediment of the Admiralty

convictions and generations of the artists. Some made wide use of traditional motifs and methods, while others sought new techniques to convey the meaning of the changes these events were designed to mark.

The main core of artists took account of the existing layout of the city and were respectful of the relationships of buildings, relying on purely decorative elements to give a festive air. In this respect the work of Mstislav Dobuzhinskii for the Admiralty and its Neva embankment is especially successful. Dobuzhinskii used generalised decorations such as five-pointed stars, evergreen garlands and flags, but also specifically nautical emblems — galleons, anchors and sea horses (see **4.13-15**) — to reflect the building's function. The triumphal pyramids on the Admiralty's Neva frontage are reminiscent of a similar celebratory tower of the time of Peter the Great (**6.22**). Many artists made effective use of painted panels positioned on urban facades between columns and windows, in the apertures of arches, without interfering with the architectural unity of the building (the designs made for May Day had been criticised for this).

Typical motifs such as laurel wreaths, sacrificial altars and triumphal chariots were borrowed from classical antiquity and the festivals of the French Revolution: they were visually appropriate for Petrograd's Classical architecture and reflected the current interest in the French precedent. The interpretation of these motifs ranged from very direct Classical references (4.61) to contemporary adaptations like Baranov-Rossiné's chariot-borne revolutionary soldier (**4.27**). In his sketch for the pediment of the Academy of Sciences, G.K. Savitskii created a powerful contemporary allegory, using symbols that appear frequently now (**4.59**). Against a central image of the sun, representing universal good and constant rebirth, is placed an open book, symbol of enlightenment, and other emblems of science and learning; to right and left beside the tools of their labouring life are the heroes of the new age, peasants and workers, who can now aspire to the emancipation brought by education. Other typical images are the procession (for example, **4.31**), embodying the movement of the mass of people towards a bright future, and the fraternal handshake of the worker and the peasant (4.34), symbolising their union, as did their crossed tools, the hammer and sickle. (After an official competition the latter, seen against a rising sun, had been adopted in the spring as the motif for the national emblem of the new Soviet state.)

In maritime Petrograd, the River Neva is in some sense the main thoroughfare, and a whole series of designs survive for the decoration of the city's bridges. Night illumination and firework displays beside the water were an important part of the celebrations: in the season of the revolutionary anniversary darkness descended early, but the murky waters of the Neva were brought to life by elaborate lighting schemes involving ships and the sparkling reflections of the garlands of lanterns on bridges and embankments (4.83).

The artists who saw their role as an innovatory one were in a minority among those taking part in the festive decorations, but an important minority; they argued that the creation of a new mass-agitational art would be the beginning of a properly proletarian culture. These artists rejected realism in favour of an art of geometrical forms and expressive movement. Among them, an artist like David Shterenberg nevertheless used symbols typical in the work of the first group. His panel for the bridge over the Winter Canal (4.47) shows a stylised 'sun of freedom', with rays penetrating clouds to warm an unfolding flower, emblem of the new life.

The modernist Natan Altman described his own approach in decorating Uritskii (Palace) Square, the heart of the aristocratic former capital: 'I set myself the task of changing the appearance of the square as created by history and transforming it into a place to which the revolutionary people had come to celebrate its victory. I decided not to decorate it. The creations of Rastrelli and Rossi required no decoration. I wanted to set against the beauty of imperial Russia the new beauty of the victorious people. I was seeking not harmony with the old, but a contrast with it.'[1] In his project (**4.8**) a speaker's tribune with tongues of flame flaring up from it was erected in the middle of the square. The leaves had already fallen from the trees in adjoining Alexander Gardens, so

Altman designed green shapes with which to deck the bare branches.

By no means every onlooker understood the artistic language of the *avant-garde* group: familiarity was an important consideration when many participants were illiterate and the artists' innovation represented an abrupt departure from traditional ideas of street decoration. A loftily celebratory style accessible to everyone characterised the work of Kuzma Petrov-Vodkin for Theatre Square (**4.19-20**) and Boris Kustodiev for Armoury Square. Around the latter were positioned masts and flag-poles linked by garlands of scarlet flags and greenery. Between the masts were six shields on which the artist had painted images of local trades: a baker, a shoemaker, a carpenter, a tailor, a reaper and a market-garden girl (4.17), with a large formal banner dedicated to 'Labour' as a centrepiece (**4.18**). Anatolii Lunacharskii, the commissar for propaganda and education, to whom the artists were ultimately responsible, wrote of the 'outstanding' work of both these artists: 'I remember Petrov-Vodkin's large panel with its wonderful range of yellow, orange and blue tones... and [recall]to this day seeing before me Kustodiev's precise, stern, beautifully composed panels, celebrating all forms of labour ... which resembled some sort of large coloured engravings.'[2]

Those who saw the October celebrations reported that the decorations in the city were popular, colourful and festive. The artists not only made a broad and flexible use of established art practices, they also incorporated new forms and methods in this work of spectacular visual propaganda.

NOTES

1. V. Tolstoy, I. Bibikova and C. Cooke (eds), *Street Art of the Revolution: Festivals and Celebrations in Russia 1918-33*, Thames & Hudson, 1990, document 20.
2. V. Tolstoy, I. Bibikova and N. Levchenko (eds), *Agitatsionno-massovoe iskusstvo: Oformlenie prazdnestv 1917-32*, Iskusstvo, Moscow, 1984, vol 1 p48.

4.59 G.K. Savitskii, Sketch for the Academy of Sciences

4.31 Iakov Guminer, *Glory to the Heroes*

Art Breaks the Walls

by **Liudmila Vostretsova, research assistant, State Russian Museum**

Newspaper articles rightly compared festive Petrograd in November 1918 with a street exhibition of contemporary art. The whole compass of artistic groupings, from academic to *avant-garde*, was represented in this major commission offered to the creative intelligentsia of all generations by the young Soviet state. In the first years of the revolution the art that erupted onto the streets of Petrograd, Moscow, and other Russian cities was unprecedented. It addressed itself directly to the people, invading everyday life and adopting monumental decorative forms; new art genres were born that openly and spontaneously reflected the triumph of a people who had made the revolution and believed in the future.

In its many aspects the agitational mass art of the first Soviet years is a key to the artistic culture of the succeeding decades. These first commissions established new images in art — the worker (**4.41**), for example, and the revolutionary sailor; they proclaimed iconoclastic modernist forms; many young artists like Samokhvalov, Pakhomov and Rusakov who were to be important figures in Soviet art were involved in the collectives working on different schemes; even established artists, like Kustodiev, produced works expressing the new spirit (see **4.18**).

Each artist was given free rein to express his imagination without prescription or restriction, as the work was divided into almost 90 individual projects. There does not appear to have been endorsement of any particular groups in allocation of the sites. Natan Altman, still under 30 and a modernist, was entrusted with Palace Square at the city's heart; the other central ensemble, the Admiralty, was in the hands of Mstislav Dobuzhinskii, who had been very critical of the modernists' efforts in May. Decoration of the routes along which the processions would travel — the Nevskii and Liteinyi prospekts, the Okhta and the Palace embankment — was given to Leftist, radical artists.

As well as the scarlet banners and triumphal arches more customary in urban festivals, vast panels were erected depicting new heroes and proclaiming the slogans of the revolution: 'Land to the Working People' (Lebedev), 'Factories to the Working People' (Altman). One of the most popular historical figures of the post-October era was Stepan Razin, leader of a 17th-century

4.18 Boris Kustodiev, Sketch for banner *Labour* (a mason)

peasants' revolt on the Volga. In 1916 Vasilii Kamenskii had published a novel based on Razin's life: now the old Sampson Bridge on the Bolshaia Nevka was renamed for Razin and decorated with Volga river-boat sails billowing in the wind; in a huge panel for Theatre Square, Kuzma Petrov-Vodkin presented an interesting characterisation of the rebel leader, who is seen — preoccupied and full of presentiment — among his feasting men (see **4.20**).

The architect Lev Rudnev, designer of the memorial to victims of the revolution in the Field of Mars, decorated it for the October celebrations with painted panels, including one depicting *Glory*, an angel with a trumpet. Symbols and allegorical figures from Classical art are particularly characteristic of the Petrograd

4.20 Kuzma Petrov-Vodkin, Sketch for panel *Stepan Razin*

decorations. Other examples are Nikolai Tyrsa's *Young Man Sowing Seed* (4.52), and Kozlinskii and Shterenberg's *Worker With a Hammer*, but there are many instances where laurel wreaths, Classical drapery, youths bursting their chains acquire a new resonance in the revolutionary era. We still do not know the identity of all the artists, even such works of particular distinction as the group of four sketches entitled *Glory* (**4.62-4**), designs imbued with triumphal energy and exultant joy.

Some six hundred sketches and designs have been preserved, about half of them in the State Russian Museum. What was in effect subsidiary material has been treated favourably by fate. Preparatory sketches and outlines of ideas are often consigned to the wastepaper basket after the concept itself has been realised. If in Petrograd in 1918 there had been the time and money to translate all the designs into decorative panels, complex constructions and banners, it is unlikely that the collections we have would be in our hands today. An article in the journal *Plamia* (January 1919) explained what happened: 'In the event barely a fifth of what had been planned was ready for the start of the celebrations, and we can only judge the remainder from the sketches collected for exhibition at the Palace of Labour'.[1] After the exhibition the designs were stored by the Fine Art Section of Narkompros and later became part of a museum archive attached to the Hermitage; in 1939 they were transferred to the State Russian Museum.

Petrov-Vodkin spoke later about the fate of his Stepan Razin panel, which in its finished version was about 15 metres wide: 'It was an important and interesting work which, according to a resolution of the Art Workers' Trade Union, was to have been preserved, but it somehow found its way into the backyard of some local soviet and was later used for foot-bindings, because the canvas was relatively good. I did it with a group of 13 of my students, and we worked on it day and night, as they say. You must remember that at this time nothing was available and we had to resort to such measures as hijacking horses and cabs and driving round the city confiscating whatever we could.... When I saw the parades passing in front of Stenka Razin, I felt for the first time that I was in my place, that my work was where it should be.'[2]

Although agitational mass art remained a feature of public life in the succeeding decade and beyond, the works for the first anniversary have unique significance. Leading painters would never again be attracted in such numbers to this work and the decoration of Petrograd was never again undertaken on such a broad scale. In future celebrations, the leading role passed from artists to directors, from monumental painted ensembles to theatrical spectacles. But in this first year of revolutionary enthusiasm, in the vision and adventure with which artists looked for a new artistic language, the possibilities of art took on different dimensions and the most important traditions of Soviet art were established.

NOTES

1. Tolstoy, Bibikova and Cooke (eds), *Street Art of the Revolution: Festivals and Celebrations in Russia* 1918-33, Thames & Hudson, 1990 document 23.
2. *ibid*, document 19.

4.64 Unknown artist, Sketch for panel *Glory*

CATALOGUE

The works listed come from the State Russian Museum (SRM), the State Museum of the Great October Socialist Revolution (MGOSR), and the Museum of the History of Leningrad (MHL); the numbers after the museums' initials are their own inventories. Unless otherwise noted, works relate to the celebrations for the first anniversary of the October Revolution, November 6-8, 1918.

May Day, 1918

4.1 The Saltykov-Shchedrin State Public Library*

A large banner by an unknown artist proclaims 'Long live the Petrograd Commune', the name given to the city and environs in 1918. The image on the banner is modernist: these first festive designs were criticised for lack of respect for the architecture. The poster is *Freedom Loan*, by Boris Kustodiev (see p 99). Photograph.

Field of Mars

4.2 May Day: A procession in the Field of Mars, focus of the May Day parades in Petrograd

Formerly a place for popular fêtes and military manoeuvres, the Field of Mars changed its character in 1917, when the dead of both revolutions were ceremonially buried there. The banner here has the first lines of the *Internationale*, which became the Soviet hymn in October 1917. Photograph.

4.3 L.V. RUDNEV (1885-1957)
First Anniversary of the October Revolution: Drawing for the banner on the obelisk, showing the flying figure of Glory

67 x 23.5; *wc and indian ink on paper*; SRM SR-B 901.

Rudnev was later chief architect of Moscow University, 1949-53. For angels with trumpets, see also **4.62-4**, 66, 3.72.

4.6

4.4 Memorial to the Victims of the Revolution, Field of Mars

Obelisk, arch and panels designed by L.V. Rudnev. Inscription: 'To the host of great ones who have departed this life, sons of Petrograd join themselves in the name of the flowering of life'. Photograph.

4.5 K.I. GORBATOV
Sketch for banners and archways on the Field of Mars

47 x 65; *pencil and pastel on paper*; MGOSR IV-908.

4.6 Parade of tramway workers in Senate Square

Slogans on first banner: 'Proletarians of All Countries Unite! All Power to the Labouring People! Workers of the Central Tramway Station'. Photograph.

Palace Square and the Winter Palace

4.7 May Day: General view of Palace Square

Shows a large painted panel by Vladimir Kozlinskii on the facade of the Winter Palace, *left*, and screens around the Alexander Column. Palace Square, scene of Bloody Sunday in 1905, was renamed for M.S. Uritskii, head of the Petrograd Cheka (secret police) after his assassination there in August 1918. It reverted to its old name many years ago. See also **1.22**, 6.37. For Kozlinskii, see 4.41.3, **3.9-10**. Photograph.

4.8 NATAN ALTMAN (1889-1970)
Design for Uritskii Square.** Separate section showing night-time illumination, looking to the Admiralty. Altman's repainting of his 1918 work, 1957

27 x 111; *wc on paper*; MHL IB-1371.

Design shows the Winter Palace, *left*, the Alexander Column, *centre*, and the Main Staff building. 4.9-11 make a complete tour of the square. For Altman, see 1.1.

4.9 NATAN ALTMAN
Design for the decoration of the Winter Palace. Separate section showing transformation of the Alexander Column. Altman's repainting of his 1918 work, 1957

27 x 97; *wc on paper*; MHL IB-1372.

Worker in the central panel holds a banner saying 'He Who Was Nothing Will Be Everything', above horizontal banners reading 'Art to the Workers'. Hanging banners either end of the building read: 'Palaces to the Working People' and 'Benefits of Culture to the Working People'.

4.10 NATAN ALTMAN
Design for the decoration of the Main Staff building of the Army. Separate section added later showing its arch. Altman's repainting of his 1918 work, 1957

27 x 97; *wc on paper*; MHL IB-1370.

Slogans on the two large panels: 'Land to the Working People'; 'Factories to the Working People'.

4.11 NATAN ALTMAN
Design for the decoration of Alexander Square
29 x 105.5; *wc, pencil and collage on paper;* MGOSR IV-886.
View west from Uritskii Square, to St Isaac's *left*, and the Admiralty. As the leaves had fallen, Altman had structures erected around the trees, covered with green fabric.

4.12 Alexander Column with decorations, seen from the south
Photograph.

Established Figurative Artists

4.13 MSTISLAV DOBUZHINSKII (1875-1957)
Sketch for decoration of the Admiralty, side elevation
26 x 69.5; *wc, pencil, tracing paper on card;* MGOSR IV-891.
The part of the building on the left-hand edge of this drawing appears on the right-hand edge of 4.11.

4.14 MSTISLAV DOBUZHINSKII
Sketch for decorative elements, a ship and banners, above pediment in 4.13
30.5 x 47.5; *wc, pencil, on paper;* SRM SR-B 1104.

4.15 MSTISLAV DOBUZHINSKII
Sketch for Admiralty pediment*
54.5 x 63; *wc, pencil, on paper on card;* MGOSR IV-925.

4.16 BORIS KUSTODIEV (1878-1927)
Sketch for decoration of Armoury Square
38.5 x 47.3; *wc, pencil, paper on card;* MGOSR IV-649.
See also **1.21-3**; 3.7, 3.43.

4.17 BORIS KUSTODIEV
Sketch for panel Market Garden Girl for 4.16
78 x 55; *wc, pencil, on card;* MGOSR IV-651.
Other panels were *Reaper, Tailor, Baker,* etc.

4.18 BORIS KUSTODIEV
Sketch for the banner Labour (a mason) for 4.16*
55 x 39.5; *wc, pencil, on paper;* MGOSR IV-650.

4.19 KUZMA PETROV-VODKIN (1878-1939)
Plan for decorating Theatre Square
34 x 68; *gouache, wc, pencil on paper;* MGOSR IV-922.
Theatre Square houses the Kirov (formerly Mariia).

4.20 KUZMA PETROV-VODKIN.
Design for the panel Stepan Razin for 4.19*
36.8 x 63.5; *wc on paper;* SRM RS-1437.
Stepan Razin (d. 1671) was the leader of rebel Cossacks and peasants on the Don and Volga rivers on Russia's south-east frontier: in 1669 he defeated the fleet of the Shah of Persia; then, in a major uprising against the tsar, he took Tsaritsyn (Volgograd) and Astrakhan on the Volga. He was captured and ceremonially executed in Moscow. Razin was a hero of the revolutionary period. Another panel in the square was *Vasilisa the Wise,* and Petrov-Vodkin made sketches for *The Firebird* and *Mikula Selianinovich* (State Tretiakov Gallery; Pskov Museum). For Petrov-Vodkin, see **1.33-8**.

4.21 ANDREI DIDERIKS (artists, 1884-1942) and VIKTOR ALVANG (architect, 1892-1959)
Scheme to decorate Stepan Razin (formerly Samson) Bridge: side view and plan
43.3 x 101.5; *gouache and indian ink on paper;* SRM SR-B 761.
For Stepan Razin, see 4.20. The idea was for wooden prows and sterns to be fixed to the pillars of the bridge, with brightly coloured sails, to resemble Razin's rebel fleet in full sail on the Volga.

4.22 ANDREI DIDERIKS and VIKTOR ALVANG
Detail of ship No 5 for 4.21
31.9 x 50.3; *gouache and indian ink on paper;* SRM SR-B 767.

4.23 ANDREI DIDERIKS and VIKTOR ALVANG
Detail of ship No 7 for 4.21*
33.4 x 51.9; *gouache and indian ink on paper;* SRM SR-B 766.

The Avant-Garde

4.24 May Day 1918: Former Mariia Palace with very large Cubo-Futurist panels
Up to February 1917, the palace was the seat of the Tsar's Council of Ministers; it was then used by the Provisional Government (it is now Leningrad's town hall). Photograph.

4.25 Anti-clerical panels by an unknown artist
-6 These decorated buildings near the Mariia Palace, November 1918. Photographs.

4.25

4.27 VLADIMIR BARANOV-ROSSINÉ (1888-1942)
Sketch for panel 365 Revolutionary Days, to decorate Uprising
Square**

63.5 x 77.5; wc, pencil, on paper on card; MGOSR IV-882.
See also 1.3

4.28 VLADIMIR BARANOV-ROSSINÉ
**Sketch for panel There is No Higher Calling Than That of a
Soldier of the Socialist Revolution**, to decorate Uprising Square
29.6 x 43.6; wc and indian ink on paper; SRM SR-B 1004.
Text continues: 'By the spring we need a Red Army of 3,000,000
under arms'. Design is on two pieces of paper. The Soviet Republic
faced serious military threats in the summer and autumn of 1918.
The Red Army was founded in February 1918 as a volunteer force,
but by September mobilisation was necessary. See also 4.38, 4.72;
3.8.

4.29 Uprising (formerly Znamenskaia) Square
-30 Shows some of the decorations in place to hide the monument
to the very unpopular tsar Alexander III (1881-94); the large
building is the Nikolai (now Moscow) railway station. One year
later (4.30) the statue was symbolically imprisoned in a circular
fortress. Photographs.

4.31 IAKOV GUMINER (1896-1942)
**Sketch for panel Glory to the Heroes Who By Their Lives Have
Given Birth to the World Revolution**, for interior of the Smolny
Institute*
33.8 x 67.8; wc and indian ink on paper; SRM SR-B 753.
The drawing is labelled 'Proletkult': see 4.33.

4.32 IAKOV GUMINER
**Sketch for panel Glory to the Heroes Who By Their Death Have
Given Birth to the World Revolution**, for interior of the Smolny
Institute
33.4 x 68.2; wc and indian ink on paper; SRM SR-B 752.

4.33 IAKOV GUMINER
**Sketch for panel Creativity of the Proletariat Is The Pledge
of the World Commune**, for decorating the Smolny
22.1 x 29.1; gouache and indian ink on paper; SRM SR-B 748.
The sheet behind the figure reads 'Proletkult', acronym for Proletarian Cultural Education Organisations, a network of workshops
set up all over Soviet Russia in 1917 to foster a true workers' art.
Working people were taught to read and encouraged to write plays,
novels and poems. Independent of the state at first, the scheme
was subsidised by the government, and lasted until 1923.

4.34 IAKOV GUMINER
**Sketch for panel Glory to the Social Revolution of Workers and
Peasants**, for the Smolny Institute
46.5 x 68.2; wc and indian ink on paper; SRM SR-B 751.
Central slogan: 'R.S.F.S.R.' (Russian Socialist Federated Soviet
Republic); beneath the meeting processions of workers and
peasants: 'Workers of All Countries Unite!'.

**4.35 SERGEI MAKLETSOV Sketch for decorating a building with
a large panel and flags**
33.8 x 51; wc and indian ink on paper; SRM SR-B 805.
The banner in the panel reads 'OKT. REV.' and hangs above a
bookshop and a hairdresser's.

4.36 SERGEI MAKLETSOV
Design for panel for 4.35
45 x 44.5; wc and indian ink on paper; SRM SR-B 1106.

4.37 VLADIMIR LEBEDEV (1891-1967)
**Scheme for decorating Narodnyi (People's, formerly Police)
Bridge**
22.7 x 25.7; pencil, gouache and indian ink on paper; SRM SR-B 812.
Slogans to left and right: 'Everybody to Arms'; in centre: 'Towards
Socialism'. The bridge crosses the Moika River on the Nevskii Pro-
spekt, a main parade route. For Lebedev, see also 3.12.

4.38 VLADIMIR LEBEDEV
Sketch for panel Long Live the Red Army for 4.37
23.2 x 38.6; gouache and indian ink on paper; SRM SR-B 829.
For the Red Army, see also 4.28.

4.39 VLADIMIR LEBEDEV
Sketches for panel Land to the Working People for 4.37
19.3 x 18, 19 x 18.9; gouache, gouache and indian ink, on paper; SRM SR-B 823-4.

4.40 VLADIMIR LEBEDEV
Sketch for panel Long Live the International for 4.37**
23.2 x 34.3; gouache and indian ink on paper; SRM SR-B 828.

4.41 VLADIMIR KOZLINSKII (1891-1967)
Sketch for panel The Worker, for Neva embankment near the
Okhta**
65.5 x 50.5; size paint on paper; SRM SR-B 863.
The giant worker strides easily into Palace Square, heart of
aristocratic and military Petrograd, against a distant background
of factory and works chimneys.

4.42 VLADIMIR KOZLINSKII
Sketch for panel RSFSR, the Okhta
37.5 x 21.5; gouache and indian ink on paper; SRM SR-B 858.
The letters stand for Russian Socialist Federated Soviet Republic,
name of Russia proper and Siberia from 1918. See 3.10.

4.43 VLADIMIR KOZLINSKII
Sketch for panel Long Live the Red Navy, for the Okhta
44.5 x 19.5; gouache and wc on paper; SRM SR-B 857. See 3.9.

4.44 IVAN PUNI (1894-1956)
Sketch for panel for the Okhta
33.8 x 22.5; wc and gouache on paper; SRM SR-B 909.
For Puni, see also 1.41.

4.45 IVAN PUNI
Sketch for panel Armed Workers in a Motorcar for Liteinyi Prospekt or the Okhta
38.3 x 34.4; wc and indian ink on paper; SRM SR-B 910.
Workers' militias, set up from the start of the revolutionary period,
were authorised by the Provisional Government to carry arms in
August 1917, when an army under the tsarist General Lavr Kornilov threatened Petrograd.

4.46 DAVID SHTERENBERG (1881-1948)
**Sketch for the decoration of Palace Embankment and the small
bridge over the Winter Canal**
36.5 x 65.5; pencil and indian ink on paper; SRM SR-B 1007.
For the bridge see 6.45.

4.40 Vladimir Lebedev, *Long Live the International*

4.27 Vladimir Baranov-Rossiné, 365 *Revolutionary Days*

4.47 DAVID SHTERENBERG
Sketch for panel The Sun of Freedom for 4.46.
37.5 x 44; pencil on paper on card; MGOSR IV-896.

4.48 DAVID SHTERENBERG
Sketch for panel Worker With a Rifle
40 x 31; wc and indian ink, on paper on card; MGOSR IV-866.
See 4.45 for the arming of workers.

4.49 NIKOLAI TYRSA (1887-1942)
Sketch for street decorations
21.6 x 27.9; wc on paper; SRM SR-B 963.

4.50 NIKOLAI TYRSA
Sketch for decoration of a bridge, with fireworks*
23.4 x 31.4; wc and indian ink on paper; SRM SR-B 1136.

4.51 NIKOLAI TYRSA
Sketch for panel Worker With a Hammer
27.9 x 13.2; wc and indian ink on paper; SRM SR-B 956.

4.52 NIKOLAI TYRSA
Sketch for panel Young Man Sowing Seed
27.9 x 12.4; wc and indian ink on paper; SRM SR-B 957.

4.53 MIRON AGULIANSKII
Sketch for panel The Furnace of a Metallurgical Plant
35.3 x 26.3; wc and indian ink on paper; SRM SR-B 694.

4.54 VLADIMIR MESHKOV (1884-1961)
Sketch for decoration of Trinity (now Revolution) Square
37 x 109.5; wc and pencil on card; MGOSR IV-881.

Neo-Classicism

4.55 SERGEI SERAFIMOV (1878-1939)
Sketch for the decoration of the former Senate and Synod buildings on Decembrists (Senate) Square
28.5 x 156; pencil and pastel on card; MGOSR IV-888.

4.56 ALEKSANDR KLEIN (b 1878)
Sketch for panel The Old World Is In Ruins, the New World Is Pushing Forward, for the former Senate building.
37.5 x 53; wc on paper; SRM SR-B 851.

4.57 VLADIMIR SHCHUKO (1878-1939)
Sketch for decorating the Tauride Palace
29 x 91; wc, pencil, heightening; MGOSR IV-887.
In 1917-18 the palace, built by Catherine II for Potëmkin, housed briefly and in succession the Provisional Government, the Petrograd Soviet and the Constituent Assembly.

4.58 IOSIF LANGBARD (1882-1951)
Sketch for decorating a tram stop
69.5 x 38.5; pencil, gouache, indian ink; MGOSR IV-875.

4.59 G.K. SAVITSKII
Sketch for the pediment of the Academy of Sciences*
27 x 79; pencil, indian ink, gouache; MGOSR IV-942.

4.60 SAVITSKII, V.N. KUCHUMOV, V.L. SIMONOV
Sketch for decorating the Academy of Sciences, with 4.59 in place
49.5 x 72; pencil, wc, indian ink, gouache on paper on card; MGOSR IV-890.

4.61 ALFRED EBERLING (1871-1950)
Sketch for panel From Ruin To Creation
26.5 x 73.5; tempera and oil on paper; SRM SR-B 687.

4.62 Artist unknown
-4 Sketches for panels Glory*
No 871: 49.5 x 23.7, SR-B 641; no 869: 50.8 x 24.1, SR-B 639; no 872: 50.6 x 23.6, SR-B 642; all wc and indian ink on paper, SRM.
For angels, see also 4.3.

4.65 Artist unknown
Sketch for panel Power To the Working People
24.5 x 63.6; charcoal, wc and indian ink on paper; SRM SR-B 1109.

4.66 TIKHON CHERNYSHEV (1881-1948)
Sketch for panel The Call, to decorate a metallurgical plant near the Okhta
16.1 x 31.4; wc and indian ink on card; SRM SR-B 1009.
See also 4.3

4.58

4.67

Flags and Streamers

4.67 IOSIF LANGBARD (1882-1951)
-8 Three-tier arch at the entrance to Smolny Institute
The slogan 'Proletarians of All Countries Unite' was picked out in lights; banners and arch were bright red. The number on the foot of the banner, *left*, is part of a sequence on all the works, locating them in the general scheme. One year later (4.68) the illuminated slogan is still in place, but the pictorial drapery is more ambitious. Photographs.

4.69 IOSIF LANGBARD
Sketch for decoration of Lafonskaia Square
44 x 143; *pencil and wc on paper*; MGOSR IV-889.

4.70 Team of artists under Langbard
Sketch for celebratory arch in Lafonskaia Square
33.5 x 89.5; *pencil, wc, gold paint on card*; MGOSR IV-933.

4.71 P.I. SMUKROVICH, V.V. EMME
Sketch for decorations of Leitenant Shmidt embankment in front of the Naval College
57 x 102.5; *indian ink, wc, gouache on paper on card*; MGOSR IV-940.

4.72 Artist unknown
Design for street banners
36.5 x 54; *gouache and indian ink on paper*; SRM SR-B 979.
Slogans: *left*, 'Workers will go to the village to rouse the whole multi-million body of the poor peasantry to fight for socialism'; *right*, 'The Red Army is rescuing the workers' and peasants' revolution. By the spring we must have an army of three million'. Oddities of alphabet and spelling may indicate a semi-literate artist. See also 4.28.

4.73 S.P. IVANOV
-4 Sketch for decoration of the City Duma
68 x 51.3; *pencil, wc, indian ink, gouache and heightening on paper on card*; MGOSR IV-917.
City Duma (4.74), showing most of Ivanov's designs in place. Photograph. The Duma, known as Lassalle's House, was the pre-revolutionary centre of municipal government. In October-November 1917, it was the rallying point for forces opposing the move to government by soviet (councils).

4.75 ERNEST SHTALBERG (1883-1955)
-6 Design for decoration of Equality (formerly Trinity) Bridge
39.5 x 77; *indian ink and wc on paper*; MGOSR IV-911.
Equality Bridge (4.76), showing Shtalberg's designs in place. Photograph. For angels, see 4.3.

4.77 SERGEI OVSIANNIKOV (b 1880)
Perspective drawing of his decorations for the Anichkov Bridge on Nevskii Prospekt
37 x 67; *pencil, wc, indian ink*; MGOSR IV-877.

4.78 SERGEI OVSIANNIKOV
Sketch for 4.77
32.5 x 96.5; *indian ink and gouache on paper*; MGOSR IV-883.
Slogan: 'Proletarians of All Countries Unite'; the portraits are of Marx and Radishchev, an aristocrat exiled by Catherine the Great in 1790 for publishing his 'seditious' *Journey From Petersburg to Moscow*, a critical social commentary.

4.79 K.K. BIKSHE
Design for decorations on Pestel Bridge
32 x 68; *wc and indian ink on paper on card*; MGOSR IV-904.

4.80 A.B. REGELSON
Sketch for decoration of Mikhailovskaia (now Arts) Square
44.5 x 66.5; *pencil, wc, indian ink, gouache on paper on card*; MGOSR IV-918.

4.81 V.L. SIMONOV
Sketch for the decorating the University
20.5 x 40; *pencil, wc, gouache on tissue on card*; MGOSR IV-863.

4.82 V.A. VOLOSHINOV
Sketch for the decoration of Stock Exchange (now Constructors) Bridge
68.5 x 48.5; *wc and indian ink on paper*; MGOSR IV-920.

4.83 V.A. VOLOSHINOV
Sketch for night illumination of 4.82
28 x 59; *gouache on paper*; MGOSR IV-892.

4.72

4.8 Natan Altman, Design for decorataion of Uritskii Square

4.41 Vladimir Kozlinskii, Sketch for panel *The Worker*

Workplace Banners

4.84 ALEKSANDR ARNSHTAM (b 1881)
Design for a banner for the Baltic Shipbuilding Works
32.3 x 23.8; wc on gray paper; SRM SR-B 701.
Text: 'The Red Army Will Save the Workers' and Peasants' Revolution'. See also 4.28; 6.74.

4.85 VASILII SVAROG (1883-1946)
Design for railway workers' banner
51.4 x 34.3; wc on paper; SRM SR-B 936.
Text: 'Long Live the International!'

4.86 VASILII SVAROG.
Design for a banner All to the Defence of the Revolution!
31.5 x 37.1; wc and indian ink on card; SRM SR-B 933.

4.87 Banner of the Rozenkrants works, 1917, altered in 1919
210 x 146; rep; MGOSR 1419.
Before the revolution Rosenkrants was a private metal-works; it was later known as 'Red Vyborger'. In the painted image a Red Army man shakes hands with a peasant, while a worker points to a rising sun with 'Communism' written in its rays. Slogan, *top*: 'Long Live the III International'; *bottom*, 'Proletarians of All Countries Unite!' Initially, the figure of the worker was on the left, the peasant on the right. The rising sun was a common image now (3.4, 4.61); for the Third International, see 3.69-70.

4.88 Banner of the rail workshop of the Putilov works, 1917
217 x 115; satin; MGOSR 1562.
The Putilov metal-works was the most modern and largest industrial enterprise in Petrograd, with 30,000 workers. It was sequestered by the government, because of its crucial war work, in 1916. Its workers were active in workers' control moves in 1917 and the works was nationalised in December. Text: 'Long Live the International', *front*; 'Railway Workshop of the Putilov Works 1917'. The bare-breasted figure of Liberty carrying a palm and a torch is in the Neo-classical tradition of the French Revolution, as are the garlands to her right and left.

4.89 Banner of the Moscow-Vindava (Latvia)-Rybinsk Railway, first
-90 division, 1917, 1918
317 x 217; silk; MGOSR I-688.
The train is painted in oil paint. Slogans: 'Long Live the Socialist Federal Soviet Republic!' (underneath this was formerly written 'Long Live the Democratic Republic!'); *bottom*, 'Employees (office-workers), Craftsmen (skilled workers) and Workers of M.V.R.Zh.D. (MVR Railway): 1917'. Photograph (4.90) shows 4.89 being paraded at an unknown time.

4.91 Banner of the Union of Workers in Water Transport
-2 (Petrograd Naval Section), 1921-4
258 x 147; velvet; MGOSR I-661.
Text: 'R.S.F.S.R.'; 'Petrograd Naval Section of the All-Russia Union of Workers in Water Transport'. Photograph (4.92) shows 4.91 raised at a parade of Navy men.

4.74

Agit-Trains

4.93 G.P. LIUBARSKII, G.A. SHAKH
Design for the livery of a propaganda train leaving for the Civil War front, 1919-20
26.5 x 74.5; indian ink and gouache on paper on card; MGOSR IV-903.

4.94 A.N. SIMAKOVA
Design for a poster showing the livery of an agit-train, 1919-20
28.5 x 69; wc and gold paint on paper; MGOSR IV-880.

4.95 V. VINOGRADOV
Poster showing the literacy-educational train of the All-Russia Central Executive Committee (Congress of Soviets), 1919-20
70 x 53; lithograph; MGOSR V-970.
Published by VTsIK (All-Russia Central Executive of the Congress of Soviets).

Posters of Perestroika

Satire and anti-authority jokes exchanged verbally are a well established outlet for frustration in the Soviet Union. With the advent in 1985 of permissible open-ness in social criticism, this ironic — often black — humour found visual expression in an explosion of independent designs by artists. After decades when posters served official purposes, presenting up-beat images that had become stereotyped and lost their ability to surprise and move people, designers looked to a range of sophisticated techniques of communication not previously available to them in order to flesh out the familiar, grumbling verbal humour. The works illustrated here come from one of the first competitive exhibitions, organised by Interplakat, an independent group of designers.

5.14 Aleksei Borisov, *What To Be?...*

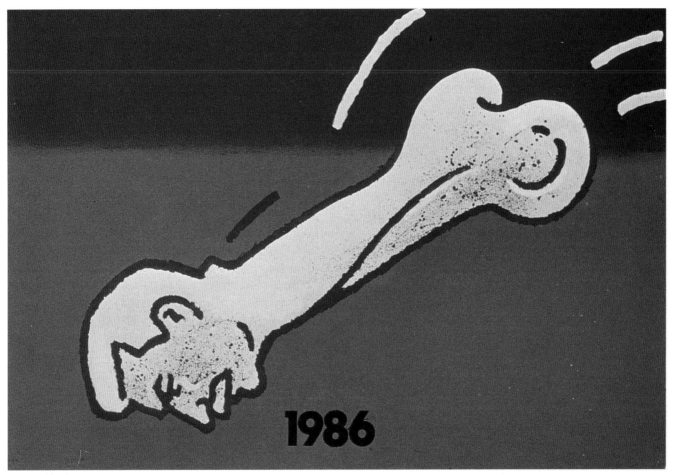

5.22 Mikhail Tsvetov, *1986*

Glasnost and the Graphic Conscience

by Vladimir Filippov, president of Interplakat, Leningrad

Perestroika and Glasnost (open-ness) made possible the public showing of a new kind of graphic art in the Soviet Union. The poster designs here were chosen for the competitive-entry exhibition 'Sovest' (Conscience), that has been seen in Leningrad and Moscow, as well as Sverdlovsk and Izhevsk in the Urals, and other cities. It was organised and selected by Interplakat, an association of poster artists from all over the USSR who have joined together to tackle new topics that are now permissible.

Interplakat is one of the first organisations of its kind in the Soviet Union, where since 1932 groups operating in this way have been initiated officially, centrally organised and more strictly divided according to professional categories. It began in 1988, when ten Leningrad graphic artists decided to hold the first competitive exhibition (**5.27** and 5.11 are two designs from this competition: the former was awarded the main prize). The show was mounted at the Leningrad Museum of Ethnography and met with great success, attracting queues of visitors; it raised 70,000 roubles (then about £70,000) in aid of the Leningrad rehabilitation centre for disabled victims the Afghan war.

The theme of that exhibition was also 'conscience', expressing a commitment to establish moral obligations and evaluate all actions from this perspective. Interplakat received official recognition from the Union of Artists before the second show, and had attracted so much attention that it was able to judge entries from artists from all over the Soviet Union. The organisation chose as its emblem a sphinx, which has association with Leningrad, and also suggests the riddle that the design of a poster presents for artists. Interplakat was registered officially in August 1989 and was able to arrange the tour of other Soviet cities.

In each location it has visited, this exhibition has raised funds for causes relating to major contemporary issues or of relevance to the city where the show was being mounted. The 1989 Leningrad exhibition raised 30,000 roubles, shared equally between the city's homes for orphaned and disabled children (some of whose parents are Aids victims or drug addicts) and a fund to restore Leningrad's historic 18th- and 19th-century buildings. Profits from its showing in the Arbat, Moscow, went to Nadezhda (Hope), the group of mothers of the approximately three hundred Soviet

5.27 Vladimir Zhukov, 1985

soldiers lost in Afghanistan whose fate remained unknown, to support the mothers in their efforts to find out whether their sons were prisoners in Pakistan.

Interplakat members emphasise the importance of the individual point of view, the need for each designer to appeal to human beings in the name of other human beings (see **5.14**). The artists receive no payment for their work for the exhibitions. So far, none of the designs have been officially endorsed for publication, although all those chosen for the first exhibition were donated free to the Leningrad branch of the Soviet Culture Fund; some have received limited circulation in postcard form.

Interplakat's next project is an international poster competition, the Nevskii Poster Triennial, to be held late in 1990. The association uses the programmes of Unesco to help draw up its plans.

Even a few years ago it would have been out of the question to put many of these poster designs on show in the Soviet Union. Their public display was made possible only by the changes in our society over the past four to five years, thanks to the democratic principles that became the emblem of Perestroika and of its main instigator, Mikhail Gorbachev. It is no wonder that the desire to examine moral standpoints attracted participation from as far afield as the Kurile Islands on the edge of the Pacific Ocean in the east of the USSR, and Odessa in the south west.

Posters Mark a Soviet Turning-point

by Stephen White, department of politics, University of Glasgow

Posters have always been a distinctively Soviet art form. Although commercial capitalism was much slower to develop than in Western Europe there were theatrical, advertising and other posters in the years before the revolution; and as the Bolsheviks struggled to retain power during the Civil War they made extensive use of the opportunities that posters provided to communicate with a still largely illiterate society; some of the posters of the Civil War years became classics (see pp 97-134). The 1920s saw very interesting work in film posters, photo-montage. During the Second World War, as invading forces once again seemed close to success, Soviet poster artists roused themselves to new endeavours; as well as older artists, a new generation like the Kukryniksy (a collective pseudonym for three Moscow artists) acquired widespread recognition not only in the USSR itself but also among her wartime allies.

Soviet poster art, these achievements notwithstanding, had rather lost its way in the 1960s and 1970s. There was a heavy emphasis upon successes, real or (quite often) imaginary. Independent-minded artists and designers found little outlet for their talents in poster work and turned elsewhere. The main publishing house, Plakat (Poster), was criticised even by the authorities themselves for its sluggish response to the issues of the day. And work of this kind, it appears, had little effect upon those for whom it was intended.

The slogans, in the first place, were too often abstract and banal: 'Weeds Are the Enemies of the Field', for example, or 'Harvesting is a Serious Matter'. They were put up beside fire and safety regulations, and rarely changed. And the slogans, sometimes, were simply incomprehensible. A *Pravda* journalist found a display in a jam factory in the early 1970s calling for 'a *tub* of tomato paste about the Plan'. But the first worker he asked had no idea what a *tub* was: only later did it emerge that it referred to a standard unit of 1,000 jars. At a local collective farm he met the even more obscure slogan 'Let Us Ideologically Guarantee the Collection of the Harvest!' Surveys at this time found that only 15 per cent of those who walked past a poster paid it any attention, and only 7 per cent of those who were polled could recall the content of any of the posters they had seen.

The changes that have taken place under the Gorbachev leadership since 1985 have affected all areas of Soviet life, from the 'democratisation' of the political system to the 'radical reform' of the economy and 'new thinking' in international relations. There have been equally dramatic changes in Soviet culture. The literature of earlier years from *Doctor Zhivago* to *Gulag Archipelago*, has become available to a mass readership. Cinema, in works like *Pokaianie* (Repentance), has begun to address the Stalinist past and

5.37 Anonymous artist, *Brezhnev Exultant*

5.47 Sergei Prikazchikov, *Russian Rodeo*

HOMO SAPIENS?

человек разумный?

ПОСЛЕДНЕЕ ВРЕМЯ В РЕЗУЛЬТАТЕ ДЕЯТЕЛЬНОСТИ ЧЕЛОВЕКА НА ПЛАНЕТЕ ЕЖЕДНЕВНО ИСЧЕЗАЕТ ОТ ОДНОГО ДО ДЕСЯТИ ВИДОВ ЖИВОТНЫХ, ЕЖЕНЕДЕЛЬНО – ПО ОДНОМУ ВИДУ РАСТЕНИЙ.

5.62 Vladimir Grishchenko, *Homo Sapiens?*

complex issues of morality and choice. Major exhibitions have taken place of previously disfavoured artists (see p19); Western, formerly 'decadent' artists like Francis Bacon and Salvador Dali have appeared in Soviet galleries and Soviet painters have begun to enjoy a ready sale abroad. Soviet poster artists, in line with these changes, have begun to enjoy greater freedom to explore social issues and have found other ways of producing and exhibiting their work than through the official bureaucracies, as this widely travelled and already celebrated exhibition makes clear.

The Soviet past and Soviet present have always been closely connected; and Soviet poster artists, like their colleagues in other fields, have been using the opportunities that are now available to examine the whole question of the historical origins of the crisis in which the country found itself in the late 1980s. The Brezhnev era of 'stagnation' was an early and fairly easy target (see, for instance, **5.37**). The former leader's weakness for medals and decorations was one of the features of the period that came in for the sharpest criticism: when he died, it appears, soldiers followed the coffin on foot carrying more than 200 awards, many of them authorised by Brezhnev himself as head of state. The Stalin question, however, has always been the central one for Soviet reformers, and for those who have pursued the cause of reform through the visual arts. The reality of collectivisation, for instance, emerges from these posters (see 5.29) as well as from the work of revisionist historians. The damage that Stalinism inflicted upon Soviet cultural life is another theme; Olga Ivanova's *Triptych* (5.33) notes the names of Akhmatova, Pasternak, Bulgakov, Mandelshtam and many others. Kovalenko's *Citizen and the Law* (5.31), with its prisioner tightly bound in barbed wire, commemorates those who were repressed, as does Lev Pomialovskii's drawing of vultures that can be read as Stalin's familiar moustache **(5.35)**: a telling image for the leader's harsh disregard for human life.

What about the future? How, in particular, can a system be constructed that will make it impossible for Stalinism to repeat itself? One answer, Aleksandrov's *Glory to the* CPSU (5.9) implies, is a leading party that has tried to learn 'lessons of modesty'. Another solution is suggested by Pogrebinskii's *Free the Party From Careerists!* (5.20). This, however, is only a start (and one that diverges only slightly from the position of the leadership itself). A larger part of the answer emerges from Kudashev and Romanov's poster dedicated to the First Congress of People's Deputies (5.12), which met in Moscow in May-June 1989, with its figure of Lenin, jotting down some notes, in the foreground. The Congress was an im-

portant part of the attempt to restore 'all power' to the Soviets, or elected organs of government. There were calls for the party to abandon its constitutionally guaranteed leading role (as it began to do in 1990); there were particularly strong attacks on the KGB, with one deputy describing it as an 'underground empire', guilty of crimes 'unprecedented in the history of humanity'. The whole spectacle was watched by an avid nation; labour productivity fell by 20 per cent during the two weeks the Congress was in session. Poster artists have also called the the KGB archives to be opened (5.52) and have warned of the dangers of a Stalinist restoration **(5.22)**.

The central concern for most citizens in the Gorbachev era has however been the critical state of the Soviet economy. Rates of growth fell steadily from the 1950s, when it looked as if the Soviet Union might achieve its historical goal of 'catching up with and overtaking' the West, to the late 1970s, when according to some calculations real economic growth may have come to a complete stop. Gorbachev, on his accession, identified the resumption of economic growth as the 'key to all our problems', and the results achieved in the first two or three years of his leadership appeared to hold out the prospect of a real turnaround in economic performance. But by the late 1980s the impetus of reform had largely petered out, with the industrial growth rate in 1989 the lowest since the Second World War and mounting problems of inflation, budgetary deficits, shortages and industrial dislocation. The official explanation for these difficulties, reflected in some poster designs, was bureaucracy: in other words the 'bloated administrative apparatus', as Gorbachev described them, 18 million strong and hostile to radical reform. The emphasis in most of the

5.35 Lev Pomialovskii, *No Person — No Problem*

works on exhibition, however, is on the effect of economic difficulties on the wider society.

Rising prices were among the most serious of these consequences for ordinary citizens. Official data reported a rise of 7.5 per cent in 1989; unofficial sources put the figure rather higher than this. Vladimir Dulov's 'flowerseller' (5.23) shows one of the forms that higher prices could take: an able-bodied man, a member of a cooperative, selling flowers for more than twice their state retail price. It was 'shameful' to Iurii Leonov (5.40) that the Soviet rouble had become the equivalent of 'zero' in terms of access to commodities. Rising prices hit pensioners and the handicapped particularly hard: Anatolii Gusarov's *Provision For Old Age* (5.73) shows an all but invisible pensioner, shopping bag in hand; Lekomtsev and others in Odessa, inspired perhaps by newspaper reports to this effect, show pensioners reduced to foraging for discarded bottles in order to supplement their meagre entitlements (5.75). There were queues at the counters of the Soviet airline Aeroflot despite its nominal commitment to Perestroika (5.25), and even World War veterans had difficulty in obtaining what they needed (5.48).

Most of all, however, it has been the supply and quality of food that have mattered to ordinary people. Viacheslav Liubimov's *Tocsin* (5.43) tolls a mournful peal for the shortage of foodstuffs. Viktor Cherenov's *Red Book of Tasty and Healthy Food* (5.50), implies a comparison between foodstuffs and endangered species of animal, Sergei Prikazchikov's *Moscow-Ivanovo* (5.46), a Soviet sausage on wheels, points to the injustice by which the major cities are the first to be supplied, leaving the rest of the population little option but to travel there to obtain the foodstuffs they require. Prikazchikov likens the whole process to a Russian-style 'rodeo', with provincial shoppers dreaming of acquiring salami, sausage and even some fresh meat **(5.47)**. For Andrei Simonov (5.45) the comparison with earlier times is not a flattering one: sugar, soap, tea and many othe commodities have been rationed in the contemporary USSR, while in the New Economic Policy years of the early 1920s, if the horse-drawn van is any guide, these and other necessities were in plentiful supply.

The poster designs reflect many of the other concerns of Soviet society today. The theme of environmental pollution emerges with particular force: understandably so, as official sources have indicated that the air in more than 104 Soviet cities exceeds permitted pollution levels by more than ten times. Nikolai Litvinenko's *When the Trees Became Tall* (5.58), for instance, condemns the indiscriminate felling of timber that took place during the construction of the Baikal-Amur railway across Siberia during the 1970s. Filippov's ironic *Thank You, Land of Our Birth* (5.57) is concerned with the emission of poisonous gas by industry in the Orenburg region in 1988-9. Grishchenko's *Homo Sapiens?* **(5.62)** attacks the loss of flora and fauna that has taken place as a direct result of human activities. Viktor Bushkov's *What Have You Become Today, Man?* (5.63) puts this question in the mouth of a thoughtful-looking monkey. The position of children is raised in Dulov's *Remainder Principle* (5.70), showing a primitive toy rather that the 'best of everything' that they should enjoy. Kovaleva's *Show Concern!* (5.72) deals with the institutionalisation of children in state homes, and Ramil Khasanshin's *Papa?* (5.71) raises the question of illegitimacy.

In any selection of this kind there will be omissions — the position of women themselves, for instance, is scarcely addressed; nor is the ethnic unrest that has convulsed the Soviet Union over the past two or three years. Much of the work here, by the same token, can hardly be considered dissident. The well-known design showing Gorbachev conducting Soviet affairs to a score by Lenin (5.11), for example, falls entirely within the assumptions of the regime itself, in terms of which it is reverting to 'healthy' Leninist principles after decades of deviation from them. Zhukov's 1985 **(5.27)** makes a similar point. At the same time there are designs that directly raise the sensitive question of privilege, such as Nadezhda Aliferenko's *The People and the Party Are One?* (5.51). There is a suggestion in Liudmila Ogryzko's work (5.21) that the official version of Glasnost is a poor substitute for freedom of information; much the same point is made by Mikhail Tsvetov's blinkered *Glasnost?* (5.53). At least two of the designs (5.55-6) commemorate the deaths that took place in the Georgian capital Tbilisi in April 1989 when a peacful demonstration was broken up by troops and Glasnost (in the words of an investigating committee of Soviet deputies) was 'turned off like electricity'.

Like those who work in other mediums, Soviet poster artists in the years of Perestroika are clearly exploring the limitations as well as the opportunities of the complex and changing situation within which they work. Equally, as this exhibition makes clear, they have been doing so with a vigour and inventiveness that recalls the best in the tradition that they inherited.

5.6 S. Mosienko, *Three Cheers for Soviet Sex!*

5.10 S. Mosienko, *Even the Smoke of the Homeland is Sweet and Pleasant*

CATALOGUE

Notes provided by Vladimir Filippov. Numbers 5.11 and 5.27 were part of the first Interplakat exhibition in the summer of 1988. The following artists' work was selected for the 1989-90 exhibition in the Soviet Union, but for reasons of non-availability or lack of space is not included here: Galina Lopatina and Tatiana Nemkova, both from Moscow; Egor Prokishin, Ufa, Irek Valiakhmetov, Magadan, and Valerii Viter, Kiev. The designs have been divided into seven sections. Apart from the two works mentioned above, all were made in 1989; the date given is that of the artist's birth: the designs range between 60 x 90 cm and 70 x 100 cm in size.

Contemporary Soviet Life

The first stimulus for the wide changes in the Soviet Union under Mikhail Gorbachev was the need to improve the country's economic performance. An essential first step proved to be the democratisation of many aspects of everyday life. Attitudes to such fundamental issues as religion, nationality, history and even sex have been reviewed as part of the process.

5.1   **ANTOLII TANNEL, Rostov-on-Don, 1953**
'Arise Mighty Land . . .'
The words come from a patriotic song. The ragged bedding hiding an unseen sleeper is in the form of a map of the Soviet Union, marked with its rich mineral resources. The image refers back to Oblomov, the figure in 19th-century Russian literature who never managed to get out of bed, and represented the lazy Russian upper classes. The poster considers the problem has not gone away.

5.2   **LIUDMILA KOVALEVA, Moscow, 1952**
Rebirth of the Nation's Culture: Rebirth of National Consciousness
Behind the pieced-together icon can be seen the pre-revolutionary Russian flag, implying the need for understanding and knowledge of specifically Russian culture. (See also 5.3).

5.1

5.3   **GEORGII RASHKOV, Leningrad, 1937**
Slogans, Slogans, Slogans
The banners are some of the many propaganda campaigns of the Soviet era; for example: 'Land to the Peasants!', 'Equality!', 'Perestroika!'. Behind them can be seen the pre-revolutionary Russian flag, and beneath is a quotation from M. E. Saltykov-Shchedrin, 'I love Russia to the point of heartache'. What the new slogan will be is uncertain. This design, together with 5.2, suggests a Russian version of the national feeling more familiar in the other republics of the Union.

5.4   **GENNADII BITIUTSKII, Tashkent, 1937**
The Progress of Computerisation
A comment on social and economic progress: traditional, birch-bark peasant shoes are bound on with computer tape.

5.5   **R. AKMANOV, Leningrad, 1954**
Talent & Talant
The English word is written in dollars, its Russian equivalent merits only a single three-rouble note. There have been rows lately because Soviet sporting or cultural figures who earn large sums abroad are only able to keep a small proportion, the rest going to the organisation that employs them.

5.6   **SERGEI MOSIENKO, Novosibirsk, 1948**
Three Cheers for Soviet Sex!**
Sex has not been considered a subject for discussion or information in the Soviet Union. Here functionaries in bed exchange bureaucratese: 'I express full confidence . . .' 'I experience a deep satisfaction . . .'

5.7   **SERGEI ALEKSANDROV, Omsk, 1955**
'Welcome'
The phrase on the door of state offices is meaningless when no further help is offered.

5.8   **ALEKSANDR PRESNIAKOV, Donetsk, 1955**
Evacuation of the Vegetable Store . . .
From the fire regulations for a church used by the state as a warehouse. Affirmation of the value of religion is a frequent theme in the contemporary Soviet Union after seven decades of official materialism. This work echoes a painting by the very successful painter, Ilia Glazunov: In the Warehouse (1986), where a side of meat hangs beside a crumbling mural of Jesus entering Jerusalem, in a church used as a butcher's store.

5.9   **GENNADII ALEKSANDROV, Omsk, 1955**
'Glory to the CPSU'. Lessons in Modesty
The design asks that children be left to make up their own minds about the CPSU (Soviet Communist Party).

Perestroika Culture

An important element in the new political culture is Lenin's call in the early Soviet period for activisation of the grass roots, emphasising the importance of individual initiatives. In debates over the past year in the Soviet Union's first 'parliament', the Congress of Deputies, interest-group politics and issues of purely local relevance both had their place. There has been constant concern to ensure the permanence of Glasnost (openness) and to prevent the abuse of its principles.

5.10   SERGEI MOSIENKO, Novosibirsk, 1948
'Even the Smoke of the Homeland Is Sweet and Pleasant...'**
Russian saying, a quotation from the early 19th century classic *Woe from Wit* by A. S. Griboedov. Here the hastening leader carries a torch labelled 'Perestroika', enveloping those behind him in smoke. The artist asks whether his countrymen, know where they are going.

5.11   ALEKSANDR and SVETLANA FALDIN, Leningrad, 1953, 1955
Bravo!
A volume of Lenin's works is on the music-stand. The subject is the perceived return, under Gorbachev, to Leninist values.

5.12   RAVIL KUDASHEV, IURII ROMANOV, Leningrad
First Congress of Peoples' Deputies, 25 May — 9 June 1989
The freely elected congress is associated with a return to Leninist ideas. Superimposed on the image of the congress is a photograph of Lenin taken at a conference during the early Soviet period.

5.13   GENADII ALEKSANDROV, Novorossiisk, 1949
Pluralism
Each button has a right to its own place on the jacket.

5.14   ALEKSEI BORISOV, Kharkov, 1965
What to Be? . . .**
'In the Soviet political system: Communist? Non-party? Pioneer (children's Communist group)? Komosomol (Communist youth)? Choose the most important — according to your conscience — to be a HUMAN BEING.' Quotations from Maxim Gorky ('Human being! How marvellous the word sounds! How proud!'), Seneca, Cyrus, Pythagoras.

5.15   M. GORDON, Leningrad, 1913
SOVEST (Conscience)
The hammer and sickle of Soviet conscience breaks barbed wire, here probably symbolising the labour camps.

5.16   I. REZNIKOV, S. VASILEV, Tashkent, 1960, 1958
Uzbek Pravda, Moldavian Pravda . . .
The names of different Communist Party newspapers. The designer implies that there can be only truth (*pravda*).

5.17   ALEKSANDR SEGAL, Leningrad, 1954.
1.9.1939.
Date of the outbreak of the Second World War: the world turned upside down, a sentiment of the contemporary peace movement. An unspoken reference is to the Ribbentrop-Molotov Pact, signed three weeks before, which guaranteed Nazi-Soviet non-aggression and thus in theory kept the USSR out of the world war.

5.18   ALEKSANDR SEGAL, Leningrad, 1956
Pravdu, Pravdu Pravdu
Truth (in the accusative case). The designer implies: how long we have waited for it.

5.19   A. LEKOMTSEV, E. MOROZOVSKII, O. STAIKOV, Odessa 1958, 1938, 1957
'Communism is Soviet power (government by popular councils) **plus the electrification of the whole country** (industrial modernisation)': V. I. Lenin
This famous slogan was put forward by Lenin in 1920 (see also **3.37**). In 1990 the popular journal *Ogonĕk* (small light), offers illumination. Glasnost in Soviet journalism was pioneered by *Ogonĕk*.

5.20   MIKHAIL POGREBINSKII, Voroshilovgrad, 1942
Free the Party From Careerists!
A reference to the privileged position of Communist Party members, which makes membership desirable because of what it can offer the individual rather than vice versa.

5.21   LIUDMILA OGRYZKO, Moscow, 1968
GLASNOST With Strings
The implication is that the move to a certain kind of Glasnost is a way of keeping people quiet. If they refuse to let this 'dummy' satisfy them, they risk the strap of possible punishment (for too much open-ness). As in English the Russian word for 'sop' has its origin as a child's dummy.

5.22   MIKHAIL TSVETOV, Leningrad, 1949
1986**
The design sees the official indictments of Stalin in 1986 as a sop to preoccupy and concentrate attention (see also 5.21).

5.23   VLADIMIR DULOV, Leningrad, 1946
Flowerseller Aniuta '89
The title refers to the name of a popular pre-Second World War musical. Here a potentially more usefully productive able-bodied man tries to make a financial killing by selling carnations at the high cooperative price of two roubles a flower (double the regular price for greenhouse flowers, at a time when the average Soviet wage is 180 roubles a month).

5.24   LARISA PRESNIAKOVA, Donetsk, 1957
Keep Your Mouth Clean
Habitual Russian swear words spatter out of the tooth brush. The term 'foul-mouthed' translates directly into Russian.

5.25   IURII LOGACHEV, Piatigorsk, 1958
Let's Fly Aeroflot!
The design parodies the airline's advertisement: a customer frustrated by problems of tickets and services dosses down in the waiting room under the newspaper headline: 'Perestroika is everyone's task (everyone should review their own efficiency)'.

5.44 A Pluzhnikov Miss MIN-LEG-PROM

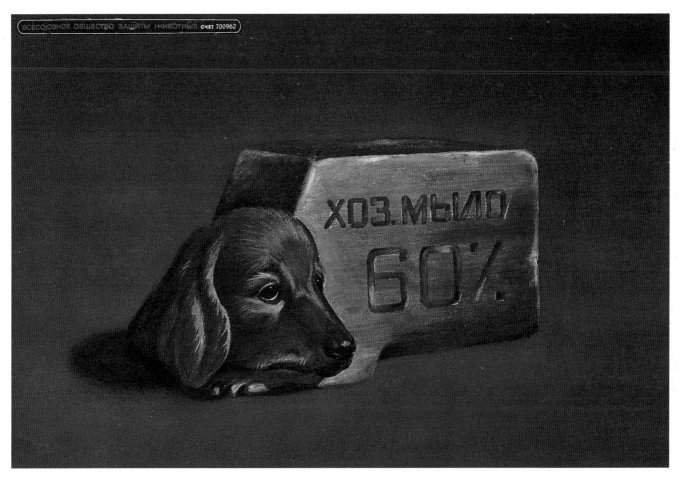

5.64 I. Markovskaia, *Society for the Protection of Animals*

Politics and the Past

At a turning-point in the 70-year history of Soviet Russia, the truthful and realistic evaluation of the period became a high priority. The regime's presentation of itself has been examined to detach techniques of exhortatory propaganda — especially in the years when the Soviet Union was struggling to establish itself — from deliberate falsifications designed to hide the crimes of Stalin or the lazy mismanagement of Brezhnev.

5.26   B. EFREMOV, S. VORSHCHOVKIN, Leningrad, 1960
S S S = ?
The first three Cryillic letters representing 'USSR' are drawn to show the profiles of Stalin, Khrushchev and Brezhnev, the 'R' appears as a question mark. What direction will the succeeding leader take?

5.27   VLADIMIR ZHUKOV, Leningrad, 1946
1985**
Perestroika began with the plenum of the Communist Party Central Committee in April 1985, with resolutions to speed up the USSR's socio-economic development. This has been seen as a return to Leninism after the long years of Stalinism and the 'stagnation' under Brezhnev (1968-83).

5.28   ALEKSANDR KONDUROV, Leningrad, 1845. The Fourth Dream of Vera Pavlovna
Vera Pavlovna is the heroine of the famous 19th-century novel *What Is To Be Done?*,by Nikolai Chernyshevskii: her 'fourth' dream envisaged a glittering socialist future. The artist's design shows the Marxist vision perverted by Stalin.

5.29   GALINA KORBUT, Leningrad, 1939
Blank (white) **Areas of History**
The white overlay on the hammer and sickle is peeled back to show the word 'collectivisation', referring to the forced reorganisation of agriculture 1929-34 when huge numbers of people perished.

5.30   VALERII RYBALCHENKO, Rostov-on-Don, 1952
1927-1953 = ?
The dates mark the years of Stalinism. The Russian word '*posadka*', which the grid of barbed wire implies, can refer to a planting scheme for seedlings or to putting people into prison or camps.

5.28

5.26

5.31   VASILII KOVALENKO, Leningrad, 1951
The Citizen and the Law
The design relates to the mass of political prisoners formerly held in prisons or camps because of their convictions: forcibly gagged and their minds imprisoned with barbed wire.

5.32   GEORGII SHEVTSOV, Kiev, 1940
Sovest (Conscience)
The word is written on a padded jacket open over convict's garb, the shadow of the cross suggesting the martydom of the labour camp population.

168

5.33 OLGA IVANOVA, Shakhty, 1962
Triptych
'It is the duty of our conscience to return (to cultural history) those who were not able to return themselves'. The design commemorates Russian cultural figures who suffered and died under Stalin, in connection with the memorial to 'the victims of illegal repression' planned to be erected in Moscow. Names in left-hand panel: V. Kuzmich, A. Akhmatova, L. Chukovskaia, D. Gachev, B. Pasternak, M. Boichuk, M. Bulgakov, N. Zabolotskii, Iu. Khait, O. Bertgolts, V. Meyerhold, V. Sedliar, M. Iarchak; right: I. Kulik, K. Malevich, M. Iogansen, N. Zoshchenko, M. Tsvetaeva, A. Vvedenskii, Ia. Korchak, O. Mandelshtam, O. Vishnia, Iu. Vukhnal, D. Kharms, K. Kotko, I. Virgan, V. Shalamov.

5.34 RAVIL KUDASHEV, IURII ROMANOV, Leningrad
'Heat up that bath-house for me till the smoke burns white. I've lost contact with the whole world of white.'
The first two lines of a song about the return of a man who has spent years in a labour camp; in the bath he will relax and tell his whole story. The song is by Vladimir Vysotskii, Soviet actor and trenchant balladeer (1938-80). The man's chest has a portrait of Stalin tattooed alongside a picture of his girl: many inhabitants of the camps believed that Stalin himself knew nothing of the mass arrests of the 1930s and the network of forced labour settlements.

5.35 LEV POMIALOVSKII, Moscow, 1944
A Person Can Be a Problem: No Person — No Problem*
The aphorism is attributed to Stalin, describing the ruthless way he eliminated such troublesome critics as Trotsky. The vultures are drawn to resemble the generalissimo's famous moustache.

5.36 NADEZHDA TZHASKA, Leningrad, 1950
Putting Back the Clock
The artist refers to the official publication in 1989, well after the authorities' indictment of Stalin's crimes, of a tear-off calendar which included the marking of the day of the former leader's birth. The calendar was published in an edition of a million copies and gave rise to widespread indignation.

5.37 ANONYMOUS ARTIST
Brezhnev Exultant*
The leader (1968-82) who guided Russia into a maze and cul-de-sac, was known for his campaigns extolling his own virtues.

5.38 VIACHESLAV RODIONOV, Orël, 1952
Emptiness
One nonentity decorates another, knowing he will receive a decoration in return. This is a reference to the Brezhnev era, when the awarding of meaningless medals took on broad dimensions.

5.39 VLADIMIR FILIPPOV, Leningrad, 1944
Eternal Glory to the Heroes
'13,310 soldiers lost fighting abroad'. The poster sees Brezhnev as the gravedigger for men lost in Afghanistan.

Management of the Economy

As the Soviet Union moves away from a centrally planned economy, Glasnost has given consumers the chance to assert their interests and voice grievances.

5.40 IURII LEONOV, Moscow, 1952
IT'S A PITY . . .
. . . that the rouble equals *zero* (final letter of the Russian word on the poster).

5.41 ANATOLII GUSAROV, Leningrad, 1941
Cosmonauts and Costs
'Soviet cosmodromes have now put over 2,000 space vehicles of various kinds into orbit'. The artist notes the cost of the achievement.

5.42 A. LEKOMTSEV, E. MORODOVSKII, O. STAIKOV, Odessa
So Many Celebrations : It's Time to Commemorate Working Days
The vodka bottles are marked with calendar tear-offs: 'Building-worker's day', 'Miner's day'. 'Teacher's day', 'Soviet trade day' — but the artist implies that these people's work productivity (partly affected by vodka consumption) is not much to be proud of.

5.43 VIACHESLAV LIUBIMOV, Petrodvorets, 1953
Tocsin
A mournful peal for the shortage of food.

5.44 ALEKSANDR PLUZHNIKOV, Essentuki, Ukraine, 1953
Miss MIN-LEG-PROM**
Miss Ministry of Light Industry is dressed in sackcloth and peasant sandals. This ministry is responsible for the output of clothing, such as tights in particular, which have been in short supply. Beauty contests are a current, new Soviet phenomenom.

5.45 ANDREI SIMONOV, Leningrad, 1961
This Is What We've Come To . . .
At a time when sugar, soap, washing powder have recently been rationed in the Soviet Union, the designer contrasts present-day Gorky Street in Moscow with a horse-drawn delivery van of the period of the New Economic Policy (NEP, early 1920s) advertising an abundance of sugar, soap, coffee, tea etc.

5.46 SERGEI PRIKAZCHIKOV, Ivanovo, 1953
MOSCOW — Ivanovo — Kostroma — Iaroslavl — Riazan — Tula — Penza
The artist creates an image for the unfair situation whereby supplies of sausage all go to Moscow from smaller cities, which then have none. People travel from them to Moscow to buy sausages on so-called *kolbasnye poezdki* (sausage journeys).

5.47 SERGEI PRIKAZCHIKOV, Ivanovo, 1953
Russian Rodeo**
The dream of a provincial Russian shopper: to be able to buy salami sausages, and sometimes even some fresh meat.

5.48 IGOR GORIAINOV, Renevka, Voronezh, 1952
'We Will Give Everything, Even Our Lives . . .'
The words are from a song in a film made in the 1970s, *Belorussia Station*, in which soldiers in the Second World War vow to die rather than give way. Today, war veterans do not have to wait in queues in the shops, but even being first does not mean they can get the goods they want.

5.49   OLGA SEMËNOVA, Leningrad, 1954
No Comment
The word on the plate is 'canteen food'.

5.50   VIKTOR CHERENOV, Rostov on Don, 1953
The Book of Tasty and Healthy Food
The insertion of the word 'red' makes the title read 'The Red Book . . ', where endangered species are listed in the Soviet Union.

Glasnost Under Pressure

Official policy on the reporting of serious accidents and political failures used to be to ignore them: to emphasise instead a bland, up-beat quality. Glasnost has allowed the spreading of information and the open apportioning of blame.

5.51   NADEZHDA ALIFERENKO, Leningrad, 1955
The People and the Party (bureaucracy) **Are One?**
The artist contrasts the poor clothing of one, with the smart gear of the other obtained through privelege.

5.52   VLADIMIR AKSËNOV, Novorossiisk, 1959
The KGB Archives Are Not Yet Open
The lines and black squares traced in a grid of the repeated masthead of the Communist-Party newspaper *Pravda* (Truth), suggest the outline of the Moscow building of the KGB (Committee for State Security).

5.53   Mikhail Tsvetov, Leningrad, 1949
GLASNOST?
Does it still mean limited information (vision directed by official considerations)?

5.54   Valentina Egorova, Leningrad, 1971
GLASNOST: The Sufficiency Principle
The artist considers that some officials still want historical and contemporary revelations to go through some prior selection.

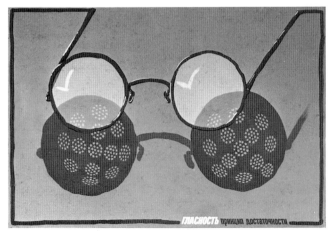
5.54

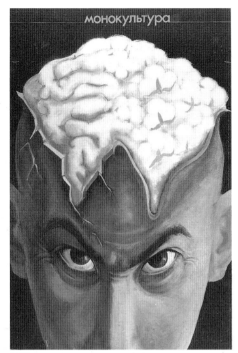
5.59

5.55   ALEKSANDR MARCHENKO, Leningrad, 1947
9.4.89.
The Georgian flag is transformed into a short-handed sapper's spade. The artist recalls that civilians died in Tbilisi on 9 April last year, when spades were used to break up a demonstration.

5.56   ANATOLII GUSAROV, Leningrad, 1941
' . . . we have the great honour of defending by force of arms and putting into operation the sacred concepts of the brotherhood of peoples', V. I. Lenin
A police baton, marked with the images of paratroopers, also refers to the events in Tbilisi in April 1989 (see 5.55).

5.57   VLADIMIR FILIPPOV, Leningrad, 1944
'Thank You, Land of Our Birth, For Our Happy Childhood'
The words of a song of the Stalin period comment ironically on the illustration, which refers to reports of emissions of poisonous gas by industry in Orenburg in January 1989 and April 1988.

5.58   NIKOLAI LITVINENKO, Voronezh
When the Trees Became Tall
The subject is the ecological disaster in Siberia when the forests were cut down for construction of the Baikal-Amur mainline railway, disturbing the watertable. The title refers to a popular film, *When the Trees Were Tall*.

5.59   NEMAT KHAKIMOV, Tashkent, 1951
Monoculture
The subject is the unhappy consequences for Uzbekistan, the Soviet republic in Central Asia, of the move into single-crop cultivation of cotton with the aim of maximising output. Production of food crops was abandoned and, in order to cope with the pests peculiar to cotton cultivation, there was massive use of chemicals which are particularly harmful to the health of children.

5.60

5.60 NIKOLAI CHERVOTKIN, Nikopol, 1955
'I Came Home, Mama'
The last Soviet soldier to die in Afghanistan was killed by a shell twenty minutes before his unit reached the Russian border, 15 February 1989. The design is based on a newspaper photograph, showing the return of the soldier's body.

5.61 VIKTOR SOITU, Leningrad, 1932
'I'm Alive'
As elsewhere, for soldiers who survived the Afghan war, the end of the war does not mean an end to fear and guilt, to pity for the victims or the suffering of those with permanent disabilities.

Ecology and Conservation

Questions of industrial pollution were important rallying points for permitted criticsm of authority before Glasnost. But Green issues and conservation concerns have been pursued more effectively in the new era, as specific data relating to these questions has become available.

5.62 VLADIMIR GRISHCHENKO, Khmelnitskii, 1955
Homo Sapiens?**
'In recent years as a result of human activities the planet has lost 1-10 species of animal daily and one species of plant every week.'

5.63 VIKTOR BUSHKOV, Bratsk
'What Have You Become Today, Man?'
The monkey's wise face questions human beings,

5.64 IRINA MARKOVSKAIA, Kiev, 1951
Society For the Protection of Animals**
. . . from knackers and dog snatchers, who sell the fur for hats and the rest of the creature to be boiled down for soap. The image refers to domestic soap, which is 60 per cent fat.

5.65 SULEIMAN KADYBERDIEV, Kostroma, 1951
Disinformation
The image inside the ears is Lake Baikal, in Siberia, the world's largest volume of fresh water: the subject is the lake's pollution by industrial waste. The poster gives a graphic illustration of the way the degree of pollution reported diminishes according to the source of the information: unofficial reports (*neformaly*) paint a gloomy picture, the town party committee (*gorkom*) says it's better, and the improvement continues according to evidence of the provincial committee (*obkom*) and the ministry, until the Central Committee of the Communist Party pronounces the lake clear of all pollution.

5.66 M. BELAN, Dushanbe
On Our Conscience!
Dam building has been destroying the national cultural heritage.

5.67 **NATALIA BALLO, Kharkov, 1966**
After All It's Not So Difficult NOT To Destroy
The standing stone which the plough has preserved is the kind of monument that is easily destroyed or lost: here, an ancient Scythian ritual figure.

5.68 **GEORGII KAMENSKIKH, Moscow, 1949**
Every Day We Lose Three National Monuments
The broken tablet marks an architectural monument of the 17th century, protected by the Soviet state. The designer notes: '30-40,000 monuments are in need of restoration'.

5.69 **R. AKMANOV, Leningrad, 1954**
Advance! Party of 'the Greens'!

Children and Old People

As it has become possible to admit the failures of Soviet society the media, especially television and journalism, have looked at the ways individuals can help voluntarily with social problems as well as by putting pressure on official organisations.

5.70 **VLADIMIR DULOV, Leningrad, 1949**
The Reminder Principle, or What's Best For the Children?
Families sometimes consider children's needs last of all: the design shows a toy made from a metal bottle-cap and matches.

5.71 **RAMIL KHASANSHIN, Tashkent, 1960**
Papa?
The man's shoe steps on a toy and the hearts of a string of female conquests. With womanising a priority, the question-mark suggests the problems of illegitimacy and uncertainty about paternity.

5.72 **LIUDMILA KOVALEVA, Moscow**
Show Concern!
The design illustrates the unhappiness of children in state orphanages and points to the harm that results from institutionalisation, when the children can cease to exist and value themselves as individuals. The sign reads 'Dormitory no. 17'.

5.73 **ANATOLII GUSAROV, Leningrad, 1941**
Provision For Old Age
'In our land 23 million people receive a pension of less than 80 roubles (a month). Ten million are single people and invalids who are completely alone in the world.' The old lady here is semi-transparent, unnoticed.

5.74 **NATALIA VERDI, Leningrad, 1958**
Tax on Childlessness
The tax demand is pinned to a parent's official notification of a son's death in Afghanistan. In the later period of the war parents who became childless in this way were exempted from the tax.

5.75 **A. LEKOMTSEV, E. MOROZOVSKII, O. STAIKOV, Odessa**
Pension Subsidy
The design criticises the smallness of the state pension, which creates a situation in which some poor pensioners go around looking for discarded deposit bottles, in order to collect a few kopecks to supplement their official benefit.

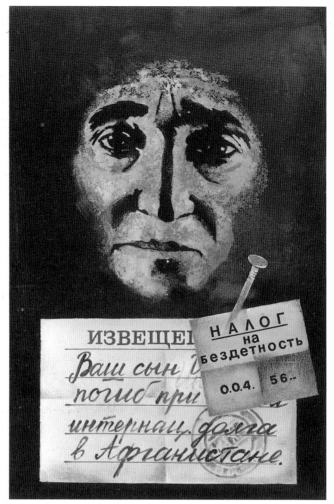

5.74

6.1

St Petersburg

The elegant, aristocratic city of St Petersburg was the location of the events that triggered off the most radical social transformation of modern times. But the Revolution of 1917 was the second great upheaval in Russian life in as many centuries. The rapid building of the city in the early 18th century marked a planned transition from the traditional Muscovite way of life that was a change of similar magnitude. St Petersburg presents two paradoxes: first, the city that stands for the Enlightenment's vision of a rational human environment was built by methods of inhuman despotism. Second, this architectural embodiment of classical harmony ultimately gave birth to tumultuous social upheaval. The city's image of grace and beauty conceals both the trauma of its birth and the hectic expansion of the final St Petersburg decades, when the fairytale capital became one of the largest industrial cities in the world.

Visions of an Imperial Capital

by Lindsey Hughes, School of Slavonic and East European Studies, University of London

I love thee, Peter's proud creation
Thy princely stateliness of line,
The regal Neva coursing, patient
'Twixt sober walls of massive stone
Aleksandr Pushkin, The Bronze Horseman, 1836

The square and the chalk-line accord so well with the point of view of absolute sovereigns that right angles become one of the attributes of despotic architecture.
Marquis de Custine, St Petersburg, 1839

On 16 May 1703 Peter I of Russia laid the foundations of a fortress on Zaiachii (Hare) Island in the Neva delta, recently captured from the Swedes. Just three years later he was referring to this still largely unpopulated wasteland as 'paradise'. In 1713 'Sanktpeterburgh' replaced Moscow as the capital of Russia and in 1721 was further upgraded when Russia became an empire.

The rise of a major European capital and sea port in a virtually landlocked country which until recently Europeans had dismissed as uncivilised to the point of barbarism was remarkable. Foreigners who in the previous century had sneered at Moscow's lack of 'architectural order' (while admiring the occasional 'exotic' edifice such as the wooden palace built by Peter's father in the 1660s, **ill**), hailed the new city as a 'brilliant spectacle'. 'In regard to regularity ... and embellishment but few capital cities in Europe can compare', wrote a German visitor in the 1790s.

Tsar's wooden palace at Kolomenskoe, built 1667-81, demolished 1767. 18th-century engraving

Yet many have argued that this 'artificial' city should never have been built at all. Its location made it an inconvenient, even hazardous place to live. Foundations subsided in the marshy ground. There were freezing, dark winters, floods in spring and autumn, mosquitoes in summer, and the sun shone for only 30 days a year. Food, building materials and other supplies had to be transported great distances. Small wonder that the Moscow magnates had to be herded there by imperial decree. Yet these very disadvantages also shaped it aesthetically: the northern climate provided the charm of snow and icy riverscapes in winter and the magical lighting effects of 'white' nights in summer; vivid colour washes were applied to facades in an attempt to counteract winter gloom; spacious riverscapes created a spectacular setting for the 'Venice of the North'.

For Peter, the visual potential of the setting was of minor significance. Passionate about boats since boyhood, for him the city was a promise of future naval might as well as a symbol of military prowess. Only after the Russian victory at Poltava in 1709 did he begin to think of it as a political capital. But Peter's personal orientation towards the West also determined that his new city would be more than Moscow-by-the-sea. Childhood alienation from the Muscovite court, contacts with foreigners and visits to Moscow's foreign quarter of orderly houses, finally — in 1697-8 — journeys to Western Europe itself, convinced him that in matters architectural as in almost everything else 'Europe' was technically superior. What impressed him initially had little to do with art, much to do with efficiency and practicality. His insistence that his nobles become 'decent beardless Europeans' clad in Western dress required a milieu of secular buildings, custom-built on Western lines to meet Russia's new requirements. There were to be churches of course, but ecclesiastical architecture was no longer to play the role it had in the heyday of Holy Russia.

There was an additional and vital factor; Peter had a passion for regularity and uniformity which expressed itself not only in architectural proportions but also in edicts. An example is the famous Table of Ranks, by which officers and officials proceeded up the promotional ladder in orderly sequence. New arrivals in the capital were thus issued with model plans for residences in

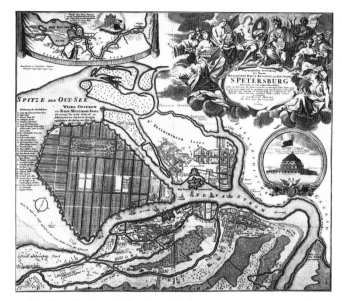

6.20 Plan of St Petersburg in 1716

keeping with their status. Facades were to follow the line of the street. If we also take into account Peter's lack of confidence in his subjects' commitment to reform ('Even if something is useful and necessary', he complained, 'our countrymen won't undertake it unless forced to do so') and his realisation that foreign skills must be assimilated as quickly as possible, then we have the essential formula for the first decades of St Petersburg. It was to be plain North European in style, with mainly secular buildings designed by foreigners and regularly laid out according to prescriptions in government edicts. Surviving examples include Domenico Trezzini's grid plan for Vasilevskii Island (**6.20**), the straight line of Nevskii Prospekt, the identical linked facades of the Twelve Colleges, the old Summer Palace with its formal gardens. Such priorities were reflected in the first Russian architectural textbook, a translation of Vignola's *Rules of the Five Orders of Architecture*, which opens with sections on foundations and masonry, but also included engravings of St Peter's in Rome, suggestive of more grandiose visions. There is one final factor of course. Peter was an autocrat and Russia still had serfdom: the city was constructed by people performing compulsory labour. At Peter's death in 1725 the city still had a temporary feel to it, with many wooden and wattle buildings, some painted to imitate brick. His immediate successors lacked the founder's personal commitment to the city and for a brief period the court even returned to Moscow. Nonetheless, the outline plan was there,

and projects started by Peter were completed and extended. In 1737 the Commission on St Petersburg Construction was founded, ensuring that development was centrally planned.

The next major phase of growth is associated with the reign of Peter's daughter Elizabeth (1741-61) and with her leading architect Bartolomeo Rastrelli. The textbook cliché about Elizabeth is that she was indolent and extravagant, the 15,000 sets of clothes allegedly discovered after her death suggestive of conspicuous consumption far exceeding the scale of a Marcos or Ceausescu.

The court followed this lead, succumbing, in the words of a later commentator, to a 'voluptuousness' which led to 'the ruination of noble houses and the corruption of morals'. Rastrelli's buildings are themselves 'voluptuous': the white and gold ballrooms and dining rooms (habitable only a few months each year) of the Catherine Palace at Tsarskoe Selo (now Pushkin) with its 300-metre long blue and gilded facade; the blues and golds of Baroque-domed Smolny Cathedral, commissioned in a phase of religious repentence; the Winter Palace, built 'solely for the glory of Russia' with its 1,945 windows and 1,050 rooms.

Although Elizabeth's reign produced some remarkable individual monuments, the ruler who influenced the shape of the contemporary city more than any other was Catherine II (1762-96). It is no coincidence that Falconet's statue, *The Bronze Horseman* (1782), Pushkinian emblem of the city, bears the inscription 'From Catherine II to Peter I' (**6.26**). Catherine, German by birth, shared Peter's practical bent and devotion to work, and considered it self-evident that Russia was an integral part of Europe. Peter would have approved of her decrees for the remodelling of four hundred of Russia's provincial towns following a disastrous fire that destroyed the city of Tver in 1763. She was determined to get away from the 'heap of edifices huddled together' which characterised Moscow. In the provinces new plans created orderly squares with solid civic buildings, while in St Petersburg, a plethora of grand edifices and large-scale ensembles in prominent locations were erected in the Classical style favoured by the Empress herself. It was arguably Catherine who created the imperial city which Peter had envisaged but not completed. Columned porticoes redolent of civic virtues, the arts and the sciences of Greece and Rome, suggest a city altogether less frivolous than Elizabeth's. It was Catherine who ordered the granite-faced embankments for the Neva and canals, 30 kilometres of them, a task which took 25 years to complete. (It is said that she found a city of wood and left one of stone.) Public buildings sprang up,

6.26 *Unveiling of the Monument to Peter the Great*, 1782

designed in the Classical style by the best architects — Quarenghi, Vallin de la Mothe, Velten, Cameron — monuments to Enlightened Absolutism.

Of course, the city was not entirely the work of autocratic ukase. It is the town houses of the late 18th-century nobility which, away from the public squares, still give the city its character. Embellished with Classical porticoes and pilasters, colour washed in yellows and ochres, pinks, olives and browns, they line the streets and canals. Each is different, but uniformity of scale (rusticated plinth supporting two upper storeys) and compliance with rules on following the line of the street ensured a harmonious impression (see, for example, 6.50). Yet these monuments to the wealth of the imperial court raise certain questions. Just as Trofimov in Chekhov's *Cherry Orchard* sees long-dead serfs peeping out from the gorgeous blossoms, so spectres may be glimpsed hovering behind the elegant porticoes of the mansion of some Prince Iusupov or Count Stroganov, which may well have been not only constructed by serf labourers and serviced by serf lackeys but also designed by serf architects. St Petersburg's streets and squares also call to mind the 'little men' of 19th-century Russian literature, insignificant beings not so much inspired by sweeping vistas as dwarfed by aristocratic grandeur, driven insane by imposed patterns and statues come to life. The capital was a show place for the court, a backdrop for the bureaucracy, and, from the turn of the 18th century, a parade ground for the troops.

The last ruler substantially to shape it was Catherine's grandson Alexander (1801-25). The Empire Style of Alexander's Petersburg presents a Russian variant of European Neo-classicism of the Napoleonic era. Like his predecessors Alexander was for-

tunate in his architects and firm in his commitment to a grand city, his vision inspired by the retreat of Napoleon from Moscow in 1812 and the entry of the Russian armies into Paris in 1814. Military honours were reflected in such projects as Palace Square, with the magnificent sweep of Carlo Rossi's Main Staff Headquarters punctuated by its Triumphal Arch. The patriotic military theme resounds again in the area behind Palace Square — the Field of Mars, flanked by Guards' barracks — or Voronikhin's Cathedral of Our Lady of Kazan, once a depository for war relics.

'The aim is not abundance of decoration but majesty of form and nobililty of proportion', wrote Rossi in the 1820s, indicating that Classicism was still a powerful force. By the 1830s, however, it was giving way to an eclectic style, and from the 1860s industrial and commercial developments intruded. But the comparative newness of a city shaped in the era of Classicism discouraged retrospectives to a medieval past. The pattern of streets and squares was too strong to allow substantial redevelopment, despite a sprinkling of pseudo-Russian, neo-Byzantine, mock-medieval and Art Nouveau buildings, and a burgeoning of industrial suburbs far more squalid than anything in the West. One must be grateful, too, that there was no attempt to replace the imperial city with a utopian socialist one (the architectural visionaries of the early years of Soviet power lacked the means to put their ideas into practice) or a fascist one (Hitler failed to take it), and that Stalin's architects were directed to a Classical style which itself harked back to the imperial era. The spirit of Peter's creation remained intact, despite the change of name.

Ultimately the vision that created St Petersburg was a cumulative one, stimulated by a climate and setting simultaneously difficult and inspiring, facilitated by the presence of talented architects and bound labour, and shaped by the conviction shared by all the major rulers of 18th-century Russia and most of the nobility that their country was a great *European* power and that St Petersburg was its symbol. The fact that the work of so many different hands has a harmonious integrated appearance can be attributed partly to the respect of subsequent generations for Peter's principle of regularity and to the fact that most of the city was completed in the era of Classicism, but mostly to the dominant role of the state, which wielded both the wealth and the power to organise vast projects and discourage individual aberrations. The result is an ambiguous city. The Frenchman de Custine wrote: 'It is the result of an immense force of will and if one does not admire it, one fears it — which is almost to respect it.' Others, like Pushkin, have loved it.

6.17 *Palace Embankment, c. 1810*

Petersburg in Image and Myth

by Aleksandr Margolis, history department, Museum of the History of Leningrad

Artists' images of a city mark the phases in the development of its life and culture like the yearly rings on the cut trunk of a tree. Paintings and engravings made of St Petersburg throughout its history, early photographs and postcards of the city, present the changing architectural landscape of this great capital: the ceremonial, festive and everday life of its people seen through contemporary eyes. The city on the Neva has also been a theme of Russia's great writers, Pushkin and Gogol, Dostoevsky and Bely. The theatrical and picturesque character of its townscape has been created in words, but in the many poems, stories and novels in which it plays a prominent role St Petersburg's history and the effort of will and imagination it represents have also taken on active life, giving birth to its own legends.

Unlike most cities, whose growth is slow and gradual, keeping pace with the development of the surrounding area, St Petersburg appeared in a short time, as the result of exceptionally intense and deliberate construction. But precisely because of its 'eccentric' location on the very edge of such a huge country, this maritime capital very quickly became the major port and an important industrial centre of Russia.

The broad Neva, the main 'avenue' of St Petersburg, played an essential role in the plan of the city from the first. At the time of its founding Peter had captured the strategically important island of Kotlin, which screens the Neva's mouth from the Gulf of Finland to the west, on which he immediately constructed the fort and docks later known as Kronshtadt (see **6.20**). Peter's emphasis on naval power and his desire to establish links with Western Europe gave the Neva central importance, and the dominant elements in the city's design were focused on the river.

United later by the severe slabs of granite embankments and the graceful arcs of bridges, the grand palaces form a unique panorama, strIking in its extensiveness and architectural cohesion. On the whole it is the waterways, more tellingly than the streets, that bear witness to the specific character of the planned layout, the architectural landscape and spriritual climate of the city. This is reflected in the work of artists, where appreciation of the historic buildings is heightened by their interaction with the watery expanses (see **6.17, 6.31**).

The interrelation of squares and avenues that give the city its particular character were only incidentally part of the original conception. When St Petersburg became the Russian capital in 1712, Peter envisaged the central part of the city on Vasilevskii Island, which was laid out in accordance with his instructions. The plan (**6.20**) shows how the island was broken up by straight streets running north to south, along which canals were to excavated: at right angles to the vertical elements, three broad thoroughfares would

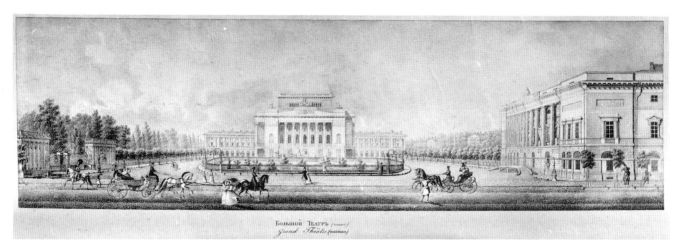

6.58-9 *Panorama of the Nevskii Prospekt* (detail), 1835. Alexandra Theatre, Imperial Public Library, Gostinnyi Dvor

run east to west. The south-east tip of the island, the Strelka, was set aside for an administrative centre that would include a cathedral and the main government offices. But not all these plans came to fruition. Particularly, only a few of the canals were laid, gradually becoming increasingly shallow until by the end of the century they were all filled in. The basic scheme, with its neat grid of parallel streets ('lines' in Russian) intersected by avenues, remains as planned, providing a unique record of Petrine town planning — but it is not the essential image that the mature Baroque and Classical cityscape provides.

Peter's idea of establishing the centre of his capital on the island was not fulfilled. By the 1730s a new centre of St Petersburg had already begun to develop on the left, mainland bank of the Neva, beside Peter's Admiralty. The scale of the construction achieved after 50 years is clearly shown in the drawings of the mid 18th-century artist Mikhail Makhaev, made as the basis for engravings and paintings to mark the half-century of the northern capital (see 6.2-3,6.23-4). The move of the city's hub to the left bank was fully confirmed in the early 1760s, when the final version of the Winter Palace was completed there.

The work of the city's great architect, Rastrelli, the Winter Palace is the supreme example of St Petersburg Baroque, a style combining in an original way both West European influences and traditional Russian architecture, which represents the extravagant luxury that is a major ingredient in the city's character. But the palace was also the last Baroque building in the city, as from the 1760s ornate ostentation was superceded by Classicism. Now the 'noble simplicity and quiet greatness' (Pushkin) of ancient monuments became the aesthetic ideal. The complex of buildings along the Neva known as the Hermitage, erected alongside the Winter Palace in the 60s, 70s and 80s to house the imperial art collections, embodies the gradual evolution of architectural forms from the extremely picturesque and plastic richness of the Baroque to the severity, prescision and balance of Classicism. It was now that the river embankments were faced with granite, the massive stone quays of the left bank extending almost four kilometres. Rhythmically marked by the curves of bridges and the softly sloping descents to landing stages, they gave the panorama of the Neva classical clarity and unity.

The outline layout of the centre of the city established in the mid 18th century has not had any serious changes made to it. Its basis are the three main thoroughfares (the 'Nevskii trident') radiating from the central spire of the Admiralty on the Neva's left bank. Although planned, the 'trident' only took shape gradually, beginning with what is now the Nevskii Prospekt. The strict regularity of the plan is emphasised by solid facades alongside streets, with independent houses abutting closely to one another. Building height was limited to 23.4 metres, the height of the Winter Palace. This rule was observed until the beginning of the 20th century, and helped to ensure the characteristic silhouette of the city; a 'background' of buildings similar in height, among which the vigorous verticals of major elements — the towers, cupolas and spires of the cathedrals, churches, monasteries and public buildings — stand out strongly (see **6.61**, for the drama of the Admiralty spire framed by the tight facades and even height of the buildings of the Nevskii Prospekt).

ИМПЕРАТОРСКАЯ ПУБЛИЧНАЯ БИБЛІОТЕКА.
Bibliothèque publique.

Вид Загороднаго дома
Его Сиятельства Графа Строгонова.

Vue de la maison de Compagne
de S. E. Monsieur le Comte de Strogonoff.

6.31 *Stroganov Villa on Chernaia River*, 1801

6.55 *Petersburg Cries: Flowerseller, c.* 1830   6.57 *Meat-seller, c.* 1830

The late 18th century and early 19th saw the flowering of Russian Classicism. Such masters as Giacomo Quarenghi, Antonio Rinaldi, Andrei Voronikhin, Andreian Zakharov, Thomas de Thomon, Vasilii Stasov and Carlo Rossi were working in St Petersburg. Especially the first third of the 19th century was the high point in the design of architectural urban ensembles; at this time St Petersburg became renowned as the 'Palmyra of the North', one of the most beautiful cities of the world. It is worth describing the way its spacious harmony is achieved.

In 1806-23 the Admiralty, the pivotal centre of the city's plan, was completely rebuilt to Zakharov's design, its facade facing the city being changed by the introduction of powerful colonnades. At the same time, the complex of squares being laid out around the Admiralty were conceived as part of a larger scheme.

On Palace Square, the massive building of the Main Staff of the Russian Army was erected to Rossi's design, with its great Triumphal Arch dedicated to Russia's victory in the war with Napoleon. Rossi also designed the Senate and Synod buildings to front Senate Square; this square, which is today named for the Decembrists, completed the western side of the central ensemble, while itself remaining open on its north side to the Neva. The south side of Admiralty Square took on a strict uniform facade, as its western corner was closed by Quarenghi's building for the Horse Guards Riding School (the 'Manezh'). These three central squares make up a single St Petersburg 'forum': a well-designed expanse, striking in the scale and grace of its buildings.

Yet other crucial elements in the central cityscape were built at this time. Since the 1780s Senate Square had had as its focus the *Bronze Horseman* (**6.26**), the equestrian statue to Peter the Great. It was almost one hundred years before the panorama of the square was completed by the huge presence of St Isaac's Cathedral: commissioned from Auguste de Monferrand in 1818, this was not fully finished until 1858. Across the river on Vasilevskii Island, the Exchange building with its flanking Rostral columns (**6.41**), designed by the Classical architect Thomas de Thomon, form a complementary architectural grouping. This handsome profile is in itself a link in the circle of townscape surrounding the central expanse of the Neva. Finally, in this period of major construction, the Nevskii Prospekt, integrated and harmonious, strict and ceremonial, was laid out as the principal thoroughfare of the northern capital (**6.58**). Here too, Classicism is the main influence.

While artists were inevitably stimulated by the grace of the city and the speed of its construction, hastening to record its architectural face, they were also attracted to portray its human life. As well as the grandees and soldiers who inhabited this governmental and military capital, print-makers and painters chose as subjects the artisans, traders and pedlars of its street scene (**6.54-7**, for example). From the earliest period they also paid attention to the city's 'street art' (*ploshchadnoe iskusstvo*), which played an important part in the urban culture. Twice a year, for a week, in one of the central squares or on the ice of the Neva, a 'pleasure village' would be erected, with swings, slides and fairground booths. There would be performances by actors, tightrope walkers, and magicians, by puppet and shadow theatres. Almost the whole city would gather for these carnivals (see **6.70** etc). The popular festivals of the 18th and 19th centuries were the starting point for many entertainment forms — circus, street advertising, cinema, variety, side shows, competitive sport — which later took on independent life.

The middle of the 19th century was a turning point in the history of St Petersburg, as a new period began that was to provide the context for the revolutions of 1905 and 1917. The city was rapidly becoming one of Russia's major industrial centres and huge factories — the Putilov, Obukhov, Baltic Shipbuilding and other works — were being built on its outskirts. Beside the plants and foundries, worker settlements sprang up in totally unplanned fashion: clusters of huge barrack-like hostels, lodging houses and rough shacks. The capital of Russia was characterised by the sharp contrast between the wretched fringes and the advanced centre: industrial zones enclosed the historic nucleus in a huge ring. The face of the Nevskii Prospekt was also changing, as it became the business centre of Russia, the St Petersburg 'City', with banks and commercial offices, fashionable shops and hotels.

The intense development of industry brought about a rapid rise in the population, with an influx of people from other parts of Russia. If in 1860 there were barely more than 500,000 inhabitants, by the start of the 20th century the number had grown to 1.5 million. Residential construction rose fast, and the new buildings typically being erected were apartment blocks of five to six floors built round a system of courtyards. Constructed for investment, the architecture of this rented accommodation defined the face of extensive areas of St Petersburg. The apartment blocks were drawn up solidly along the street, seeming to fence themselves off from the unsightly 'underside' of seedy dwellings.

The varied architecture of the second half of the 19th century is in sharp contrast to Classicism, to the harmony and clarity of its compositional devices. However, there was much that was positive in the contemporary town planning. New streets were built, old ones widened and straightened; gardens, squares and boulevards were laid out. Many buildings were constructed for commerce and banking, for educational, entertainment and medical purposes. Permanent bridges were built across the Neva and its subsidiary channels. The first decade of the new century then saw a return to the general tenets of Classicism and the town planning legacy of old St Petersburg, in an attempt to recreate a harmonious building style appropriate to the city's historic face. The energetic activities of photographers in these years recorded for posterity the appearance of the city on the Neva — and its population (see **6.79**)— on the eve of the revolution of 1917, which marked the end of St Petersburg.

Over the two hundred years of its history the city captured the imagination of Russia's greatest writers, who made St Petersburg one of the central themes of Russian literature. Thus interpreted in words, but also in paintings and sculpture, the reality of St Petersburg took on the features of a myth, one that was constantly recreating itself. And this legend of Petersburg, was born almost at the moment of the city's founding.

None of the other great European cities were built so quickly. The famous European capitals grew gradually, a natural and largely spontaneous growth. The city on the Neva appeared as if overnight and strictly to plan. Many foreigners visiting St Petersburg saw something miraculous in such a sudden rise: 'You could never imagine', wrote Madame de Staël, 'that such a beautiful city could be created in so short a time.' The city was seen as the fulfilment of the grand design of the 'miracle-worker' and reformer of Russia, Peter the Great. To build on a marsh in the face of a constant threat of catastrophic flooding from the sea meant the subduing of nature itself. This achievement was seen as a triumph of human will and reason over the elements.

But there were two aspects to this picture of St Petersburg. Exultation and glorification were countered by doubts about the wisdom of building the city and even prophecies of its downfall. This contradiction was contained in the history of its very creation; this up-to-date European city embodying to the full the experience of western civilisation was built by barbarous methods in the tradition of the most cruel eastern despotism.

From the very outset St Petersburg was a historical actor, and for two centuries the destiny of all Russia was a reflection of its complex character. The Russian political thinker and memoirist Aleksandr Herzen used the term 'the Petersburg period of Russian history' to refer not only to the strengthening of despotism and state bureaucracy: it was precisely the Petersburg period that

6.79 Petrograd metal-workers. Photograph, 1917

also gave rise to classical Russian culture, Russian democracy, and the Russian revolution. The 'city of tragic imperialism' referred to by N. Antsiferov, became a spiritual motherland for many.

Although to inattentive eyes and those not illumined by love St Petersburg may seem no more than the sum of a collection of eclectic architectural quotations, it has its own unity and is — by virtue of its destiny — a very Russian city.

6.61 *Nevskii Prospekt Looking Towards the Admiralty, c. 1840*

The Fortress Museum

by Olga Chekhanova, deputy director (research), Museum of the History of Leningrad

The Museum of the History of Leningrad is one of the most-visited and widely-known museums in the Soviet Union. Its displays trace the formation and development of the city that began as St Petersburg, became Petrograd in 1914, and then Leningrad, covering its whole history from 1703 to the present day. There are 12 permanent independent exhibitions of general-historical interest, which also relate to domestic and private life: several displays serve as memorials to the tragic peroid of the Blockade of Leningrad, 1941-4. The Museum is visited by over two million Russian and foreign tourists annually. Over recent years it has developed links with colleagues in similar institutions in other European countries and the United States.

The idea of creating a museum to chronicle the events in the city's rich history was first mooted in connection with the bicentenary of the founding of St Petersburg. The first attempt at showing views of the city in chronological sequence was thus made in 1903, in a jubilee exhibition in Peter the Great's original palace in the Summer Gardens. Over the following decade several more exhibitions were put on, each emphasising different aspects of the city's history, but the most important event was the setting up in this period by the Society of Architects and Artists of an actual museum, called 'Old Petersburg'.

The museum's founders were passionate enthusiasts, among whom were such figures as the artist and theatre-designer Alexandre Benois; his brother Leontii, the architect; their nephews Evgenii and Nikolai Lanseray, artist and architect; the artists Mstislav Dobuzhinskii and Anna Ostoumova-Lebedeva; the architects Ilin, Shchusev, Kurbatov and Stolpianskii. The basis of the museum's collections were such valuable materials as original designs and plans by the major St Petersburg architects, but also received were engravings, paintings and documents relating to the whole period of the city's planning and development, all donated by members of the Society and other collectors and amateur historians. For its first ten years the museum was housed in the home of Count Siuzor, president of the Society of Architects and Artists.

A year after the October Revolution of 1917, legislation established that a City Museum should be created in Petrograd. Its brief was to acquaint visitors with the architecture of foreign cities, also to familiarise them with St Petersburg's past, with tasks of preservation and restoration of its architectural monuments, and with the way of life of its inhabitants. In later years, the museum's function was updated and changed, when in 1953 it became the State Museum of the History of Leningrad. This determined the nature of the current collections, which total more than seven hundred thousand items, including documents and prints, paintings by pre- and post-revolutionary artists — mainly relating specifically to the city — and furniture and decorative materials from the 18th-20th centuries.

The original plans by the city's architects make up one unique part of these collections, but so too do the applied art objects from palaces and private villas which came to the museum after the buildings were nationalised. Of particular interest are paintings and drawings from the 1920s and 30s, including works by Mikhail Matiushin, a leader of the Russian *avant-garde*, and his circle. Paintings by Leningrad artists relating to the Second World War and children's drawings made during the Nazi blockade of the city are also of special significance. The museum's collections from the pre-revolutionary era include objects of everyday use: samovars, painted city signboards, beadwork and silver, costumes, embroidery and lace.

The museum administers a total of 86 buildings of historical and architectural interest. Among these are the Rumiantsev mansion on the Neva embankment, St Pantaleimon's Church on the Fontanka, and the poet Aleksandr Bloks's house museum, all in Leningrad itself; it is also responsible for the former Shlisselburg Fortress, now called Petrokrepost, upstream on the Neva and close to the river's source in Lake Ladoga. But the essential nucleus of the museum is the Peter-Paul Fortress. This is where the exhibitions relating to the early period are housed, and of course the main architectural structures are open to visitors. The fortress itself presents a unique and unusual architectural ensemble, including both fortified and civil buildings. Taken as a whole it is a monument to military engineering as well as architecture:

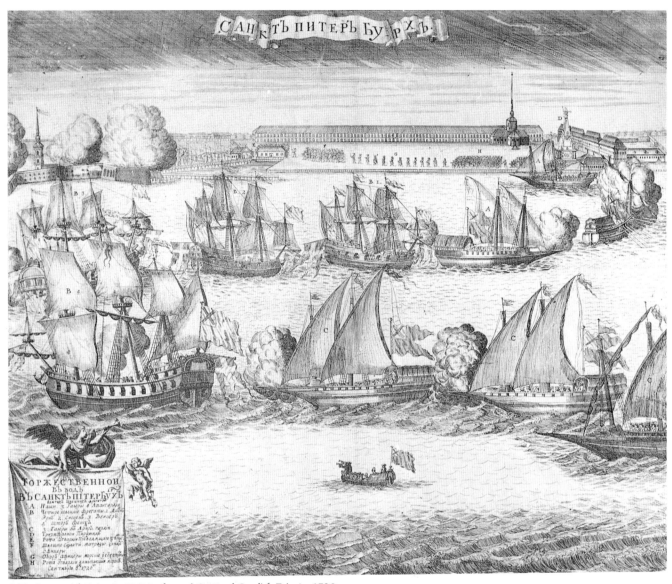

6.22 *Ceremonial Entry to St Petersburg of Captured Swedish Frigates,* 1720

similar bastion fortifications exist in Western Europe, but only those at Lucca, Perpignan and Valletta are as well preserved.

The most important of the buildings is the Peter-Paul Cathedral, whose design marked a new direction in the development of Russian architecture. Of its internal furnishings, the gilded oak carvings of the iconostasis (1722-6) are particularly interesting as an outstanding work of the Baroque. The cathedral was the burial place and still houses the tombs of the Russian tsars from Peter the Great to Alexander III, with the exceptions of Peter II and Alexander II, who were buried in Moscow.

Our fortress has links with crucial turning points in Russian history: the Great Northern War with Sweden, which liberated the Neva delta; the Decembrists' Uprising of 1825, whose leaders met their death within its walls, and the October Revolution of 1917. Its conversion into a historical musuem thus serves two purposes, providing an authentic, stimulating background to the teaching of history and ensuring the preservation of the buildings themselves. Restoration is a constant concern for all the buildings, but especially the cathedral: much work was done in 1956-9 and is again in progress now.

CATALOGUE

Catalogue notes are by Galina Vasileva, senior curator and keeper at the State Museum of the History of Leningrad, from which all the materials come.

Paintings

6.1 Artist unknown, mid 18th century
Portrait of Peter the Great*
Oil on canvas; 86 x 70.5; inv. 1-A-486-Zh.
From the original by Jean-Marc Nattier, painted in Holland in 1718. Nattier also painted Peter's wife, later the empress Catherine I.

6.2 Artist unknown, second half 18th century
Palace Embankment near the Winter Canal
Oil on canvas; 70 x 118; inv. 1-A-184-Zh.
Based on a drawing by Mikhail Makhaev. On the embankment is the second Winter Palace, built for Peter the Great, architect G.J. Mattarnovi; *right*, Kushelev house. Between them is the canal and bascule bridge. The wooden embankment predates the granite slabs installed in the 1760s-80s.

6.3 Artist unknown; second half 18th century
Nevskii Prospekt near the Anichkov Palace
Oil on canvas; 58 x 111; inv 1-A-256-Zh..
Based on a drawing by Mikhail Makhaev. The palace is *left* beyond the bridge, built to plans by M. Zemtsov completed by Bartolomeo Rastrelli. The gallery facing the Fontanka River has not survived; nor has the small canal, joining an internal pool with the Fontanka. See also 6.15, 6.64.

6.4 Artist unknown, 1760s
Peter-Paul Fortress from Palace Embankment
Oil on canvas; 77 x 142; inv. 1-A-200-Zh.
Copy from painting by J.B. Leprince. Across the Neva are Vasilevskii Island, *left*, and the former Petersburg Island (now called Petrograd Side). For the fortress, see 6.10.

6.5 FĚDOR ALEKSEEV (?), early 19th century
Potëmkin Street
Oil on canvas; 66 x 111; inv. 1-A-204-Zh.
The Tauride Gardens, one of the oldest parks in Leningrad, is *left*, facing the barracks of the Chevalier Guards, built in 1806 to plans of Luigi Rusca. Prince Potëmkin was given land for his skill in annexing the Crimea (Tavriia) in 1783. The gardens were laid out by William Gould, whose house is *left foreground*.

6.6 Artist unknown, 1830s
Sleigh in Vladimir Square
Oil on canvas; 36x48.5; iv. 1-A-180-Zh.
Vladimir Cathedral, *left*, was built in the late 18th century.

6.7 L. RODIOVOV, 1835
Alexander Column and the Arch of the Main Staff
Oil on canvas; 84 x 62; inv. 1-A-205-Zh.
The column was erected in 1834, to commemorate Alexander I's victory over Napoleon in 1812 (see also 6.60); on top is an angel with a cross, trampling a serpent. *Foreground*, is the Victory Arch of the Russian Army Main Staff, built by Carlo Rossi in 1819-20 over Herzen Street. See also 4.7-12.

6.8 ALEKSEI MAKSIMOV, 1837
Alexander Nevskii Lavra
Oil on canvas; 56 x 75; 1-A-187-Zh.
The monastery was founded by Peter in 1710, to a scheme of Domenico Trezzini. The Church of the Annunciation, *left*, 1722, is by Trezzini. A lavra is a senior monastery; there were only four then in Russia. Peter believed the location was the site of the battle where Prince Alexander of Novgorod defeated the Swedes in 1240; historians consider this to be wrong. The hero's remains were brought here from Vladimir in 1724.

6.9 I.K., an unknown artist, mid 19th century
Fair Booths (Balagany) on Admiralty Square
Oil on canvas; 35.5 x 42.5; inv. 1-A-177-Zh.
In the foreground is an ice-cream seller; *left*, a crowd gathers round a peepshow. See also 6.37, 6.42-3, **6.70**, 6.72 and **2.88-9**.

6.10 ALEKSEI BOGOLIUBOV, mid 19th century
Peter-Paul Fortress
Oil on canvas; 55 x 44; inv. 1-A-429-Zh.
The founding of the fortress in 1703 marked the beginning of St Petersburg. Earthworks were soon replaced by Trezzini's stone bastions. Trezzini was also architect of the Peter-Paul Cathedral inside the walls, whose 122-m spire is the city's highest landmark.

6.11 FĚDOR SADOVNIKOV, 1855
Neva River looking towards the Nicholas Bridge
Oil on canvas; 66 x 93; inv. 1-A-207-Zh.
From *left*, on the embankment are the Winter Palace and the Admiralty, with the dome of St Isaac's Cathedral behind; *right*, is Vasilevskii Island with the University and Kunstkamera. The latter, built 1718-34, housed curiosities collected by Peter the Great. The central tower had Russia's first observatory at the top, but was destroyed in 1747 and only restored 200 years later. The building is now the Museum of Anthropology and Ethnography. The bridge was re-named for Leitenant Shmidt, a hero of the 1905 revolution. See also 6.68.

6.12 Artist unknown, 1867
Winter Roadway on the Neva
Oil on metal; 56.3 x 73; inv. 1-A-230-Zh.
In winter, when the ice on the Neva was two metres thick, roads were laid out, bounded by fir trees. The pontoon bridge leads to Senate (now Decembrists) Square and the Senate and Synod, the most important state offices of tsarist Russia; centre is St Isaac's Cathedral, 1818-58 by Auguste de Monferrand. See also 6.71.

6.13 ALEKSANDR BEGGROV, 1881
New Admiralty from the Neva
Oil on canvas; 54 x 84; inv. 1-A-233-Zh..
View is from the Bolshaia Neva, near the Gulf of Finland, showing the second Admiralty, the ship-building yard constructed early in the 19th century on the site of Peter's galleon dock.

6.14 V. MAZARAKII, 1879-80
Pokrovskaia Square
Oil on canvas; 62.5 x 84.5; inv. 1-A-211-Zh.
The square (now named after Turgenev) is in an area of the city known as Kolomna, west of Kriukov Canal. At the time of the painting it was inhabited by poor civil servants and retired soldiers. Kolomna is famous in Russian literature as the home of Evgenii, the unhappy clerk in Pushkins great Petersburg poem *The Bronze Horseman* of 1833 (see also 6.16).

6.15 ALEKSANDR BEGGROV, 1886
Nevskii Prospekt and Anichkov Bridge
Oil on canvas; 60.5 x 89.5; inv. 1-A-220-Zh..

The bridge (see also 6.3 etc), is a landmark on the Prospekt because of the statues of rearing horses at each corner. The horse-drawn railway was installed along the Prospekt in 1863.

6.16 B. KAMYKOV, early 1900s
Monument to Peter the Great on Senate Square
Oil on canvas; 54 x 74; inv. 1-A-231-Zh..

Known as the Bronze Horseman, the statue was designed by Etienne Falconet on orders of Catherine the Great, with an inscription reading 'To Peter the First from Catherine the Second'. It gets its name from Pushkin's poem (see 6.14), where it symbolises the oppressive power of tsarism. Senate Square was renamed after the revolution in honour of the Decembrists, aristocratic young officers who in 1825 attempted to overthrow Nicholas I. See 6.26.

Drawings and Watercolours

6.17 W. BART, 1810s
Palace Embankment**
Gouache; 29.6 x 45; inv. 1-A-1020-A.

The artist came to St Petersburg from the Royal Porcelain Factory in Berlin. On the embankment, from right: Winter Palace, built by Bartolomeo Rastrelli, 1754-5; the Small Hermitage, 1767, by Vallin de la Mothe; the Old Hermitage, 1771-87, by J. Velten. With the New Hermitage (6.62), all these buildings now make up the great art museum; before the revolution the 'hermitage' buildings housed the imperial art collections, while the Winter Palace was the main residence of the imperial family.

6.18 Artist unknown, first quarter 19th century
Red Bridge over the Moika River
Watercolour with white heightening; 50 x 68; inv. 1-A-768-A.

The bridge carries Gorokhovaia (now Dzerzhinskii) Street over the river. Four similar bridges were constructed early in the 19th century, of which only this one retains its original form.

6.19 ALEKSANDR BEGGROV, 1892
Malaia (Lesser) Neva
Watercolour; 70 x 57; inv. 1-A-787-A.

Cargo is unloaded from a boat at the Tuchkov Embankment on Vasilevskii Island. On the far bank are hemp warehouses (1764-70) known as Tuchkov Buian (wharf), designed by A. Rinaldi, also architect of the Prince Vladimir Cathedral, whose dome and belltower is seen beyond. The river is spanned by Tuchkov Bridge, named for a hero of the war with Napoleon.

Prints: Engravings

(Unless otherwise stated, the names given are those of the print-maker).

6.20 Published by I. KHOMAR
Plan of St Petersburg in 1716*
Hand-coloured; 50.5 x 59.5; inv. 1-A-10406-G.

Shows clearly the regular grid of Trezzini's street layout of Vasilevskii Island, also the key position of Peter-Paul Fortress at the southern tip of Petersburg Island, and the central location of the (then fortified) Admiralty, on the left bank of the Neva, with two projected arterial roadways already radiating from it. Detail, top left, maps the currents in the Neva, from its source in Lake Ladoga to the Gulf of Finland; top right, allegorical figures representing the arts and sciences admire a portrait of Peter the Great; centre right, the fortress of 'Kronshlot' (Kronstadt) on Kotlin Island.

6.21 ALEKSEI ZUBOV, 1720
Peter-Paul Fortress (detail of panorama)
50 x 61; inv. 1-A-1006-G.

Fortress from the Neva side, showing the cathedral belltower under construction. The Peter Gate, also shown, is the only triumphal entrance of the Petrine period surviving today. See also 6.10.

6.22 ALEKSEI ZUBOV, 1720
Ceremonial Entry to St Petersburg of Captured Swedish Frigates*
50.3 x 59.7; inv. 1-A-1004-G.

Celebration of the victory of the Russian navy off the Aland Islands, which helped end the Great Northern War with Sweden (1700-21). The key shows the Swedish vessels 'B', and the Russians 'A' and 'C', making clear the contrast between the large Swedish deep-water men-of-war and the mobile, shallow-draught Russian 'galleys' that Peter introduced in the Baltic, which could outwit the Swedes by keeping close to rocky islands and fjords. In the background, centre, on Trinity (now Revolution) Square, Swedish prisoners ('F') are paraded in front of a 'triumphal pyramid' ('D'); left, Peter-Paul Fortress, cannon blazing.

6.23 G. KACHALOV, from a drawing by M. Makhaev, 1753
Old Admiralty from Nevskii Prospekt
49.7 x 69.4; inv. 1-A-1102-G.

A fortified shipyard was built on this site in 1704, replaced seven years later by the first Admiralty. The building here (1738), by I. Korobov, has ramparts and the first, Baltic-style spire. Right, is the old Winter Palace, Rastrelli's first version, rebuilt in 1754. Nevskii Prospekt, foreground, is tree-lined, with meadows either side.

6.24 E. VNUKOV, from a drawing by M. Makhaev, 1753
The Twelve Colleges
50.3 x 69.2; 1-A-1132-G.

The colleges (1722-44), by Trezzini, each housed one of Peter's government ministries. From 1819, they became part of Petersburg-Leningrad University. Right, is old Gostinnyi Dvor ('bazaar'), commercial warehouses close to the docks, later replaced. The canal, linking the Bolshaia and Malaia Nevas, was soon filled in, and riverside granite embankments were installed.

6.25 ALEKSEI GREKOV, from a drawing by M. Makhaev, 1753
The Summer Palace of the Empress Elizabeth
49.2 x 70; inv. 1-A-1118-G.

The luxurious wooden palace was built by Rastrelli, 1741-4, with the current Summer Gardens beyond its northern facade. The Palace was demolished in the late 1790s to make way for the Michael Castle (see 6.38).

6.26 A. MELNIKOV, from a drawing by A. Davydov, 1782
Unveiling of the Monument to Peter I on Senate Square*
51.8 x 78.6; inv. 1-A-2175-G.

For the statue and square, see 6.16. The unveiling, on the centenary of Peter's accession to the throne in August 1782, was attended by Catherine II on the balcony of the Senate, left. The construction surrounding the monument fell away accompanied by a salvo of rifles from the circle of Guards. Beyond the monument is the spire of the Old Admiralty, see 6.23.

6.27 -30 Works from a series published in the 1790s by the German engravers Christian-Gottfried-Heinrich Geisler and Christian Gotthelf Schonberg, who had lived in Russia. These show St Petersburg street trades, and were so popular in Russia that they were published there in 1799. All: watercolour with white heightening; 18.6 x 12.2. See also 6.47-8, 6.54-7, 6.78-9.

6.27 Match-seller
Inv. I-A-2321-G.

6.28 Comb-seller
Inv. I-A-2316-G.

6.29 Seller of Easter Eggs
Inv. I-A-2317-G.

6.30 Milk-seller
Inv. I-A-2307-G.

6.31 I. CHESKII, from a drawing by Andrei Voronikhin, 1801
Stroganov Villa on Chernaia River**
35.5 x 45.5; inv. I-A-551-G.
Country villa of the art patron and president of the Academy of
Arts, Count A.S. Stroganov (1733-1811), constructed to plans of F.I.
Demertsov at the end of the 18th century. The small Chernaia (Black)
River flows into the Bolshaia Neva from the mainland immediately
north of Petersburg Island. The Stroganovs were among the earliest
Russian entrepreneurs, basing their wealth on salt and iron conces-
sions in the remote north-east, and being responsible for opening
up Siberia in the late 16th century. The villa was pulled down early
this century.

6.32 Drawn and engraved by IVAN IVANOV, 1815
Trinity Holiday on Vladimir Square
41 x 60; inv. I-A-1248-G.
The church was built to house the icon *Virgin of Vladimir* in 1769,
with belltower by Quarenghi added in 1783. Trinity was celebrated
in Russia with birch twigs to symbolise palms.

6.33 Drawn and engraved by E. KARPEEV, 1820s
Skating on the Neva
24.5 x 31.8; inv. I-A-2276-G.
A favourite pastime of upper-class youth.

6.34 Artist unknown, 1820s
The Great Petersburg Flood of 7 November 1824
19.4 x 34.6; inv. I-A-2266-G.
This was the worst of many floods in the city's life. The river rose
by over four metres, covering most of the streets: thousands died
and low-lying areas were destroyed. The disaster plays a major role
in Pushkin's *Bronze Horseman*, see 6.16.

6.35 MARTENS, 1837-8
Tsarskoe Selo Railway
15.7 x 23.1; inv. I-A-2218-G.
This was the first public railway in Russia, 25 kilometres from the
capital to Pavlovsk, a royal park where public entertainments were
promoted in order to encourage passengers. This is the origin of
the Russian word for railway station, *vokzal*, after the Vauxhall
pleasure gardens in London. Tsarskoe Selo (tsar's village), with the
Summer Palace, was in easy reach. The railway opened in 1837.

**6.36 A. APPERT from a drawing by Joseph Charlemagne, late
1850s**
Birdseye Panorama of St Petersburg
52.3 x 83.3; inv. I-A-1193-G.
The view of the Neva delta shows clearly how 10 per cent of the
city is waterways. *Foreground*, is the central Petersburg island, which
was not developed until the end of the century. *Right*, is Vasilevskii
Island, showing the earliest street plan and the Gulf of Finland
beyond; *left*, the Vyborg Side, soon to see massive industrial building.
Beyond the Neva is the Admiralty Side, the main centre of the city.

Prints: Aquatints

6.37 Drawn and engraved by JOHN ATKINSON, 1804
Public Holiday on Palace Square
26.3 x 37.7; inv. I-A-2274-G.
Atkinson, an Englishman, lived more than 16 years in St Petersburg,
and published many engravings on his return to London in 1801.
Catherine II built the 'Lantern' balcony on the Palace Square facade
of the Winter Palace, from which courtiers could watch popular fetes
below. The holiday here is during the reign of Alexander I, with
tents pitched in the square. See also 6.9 etc. For the square and
Winter Palace facade, see 1.22, and 4.7-9.

**6.38 M. DUBOURG and JOHN CLARK, with hand colouring,
from a drawing by Mörner, 1815**
Field of Mars
23.8 x 34.2; inv. I-A-1360-G.
This was St Petersburg's military parade ground, also used for training and manoeuvres. For its use after the revolution, see 4.2. *Distance
left*, is the Michael Castle, built for the emperor Paul in 1800, now
known as Engineers Castle. *Foreground*, is the obelisk by Brenna
erected in 1799 to mark Rumiantsev's victories in the Turkish wars.

**6.39 M. DUBOURG and JOHN CLARK, with hand colouring,
from a drawing by Mörner, 1815**
Parade on Palace Square
23.8 x 34; inv. I-A-1358-G.
St Petersburg was a military city, because of the guards regiments
stationed there: in the 1820s one in ten inhabitants was a soldier.

6.40 Unknown artist, with hand colouring, 1820s
Bolshoi Theatre
29.9 x 44.7; inv. I-A-1317-G.
The building was erected on what is now Theatre Square in 1783,
when it was the largest theatre in Europe. In 1889, it was declared
unsafe and soon replaced by the Rimskii-Korsakov Conservatory.

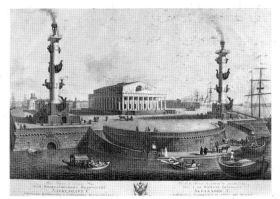

6.41

**6.41 I. CHESKII, with hand colouring, from a drawing by M.
Shatoshnikov, 1820s**
Strelka on Vasilevskii Island
48 x 76; inv. I-A-1344-G.
The Strelka, a main landmark of St Petersburg-Leningrad, is at the
tip of Vasilevskii Island where the Greater and Lesser channels of
the Neva divide. From the 1730s, the city's port was here. The complex of the central Exchange building with flanking Rostral Columns
(from *rostra*, ships' prows), designed by Thomas de Thomon in 1810,
served the port, the columns acting as lighthouses. The port moved in the 1880s, but the Exchange functioned until 1917.

Prints: Lithographs

6.42 GUSTAVE-ARMAND HOUBIGANT, hand coloured, 1817
Ice Mountains

23.3 x 36; *inv.* I-A-2515-L.

Ice toboggan slides were erected in winter: made of wood and decorated with fir-trees. The French artist never came to Russia, but made free use of the engravings of John Atkinson (see 6.3).

6.43 GUSTAVE-ARMAND HOUBIGANT, hand coloured, 1817
Swings

24 x 35.7; *inv.* I-A-2515-L.

Swings of different kinds would be brought out for holidays. Here, *left*, are also fair booths for all kinds of show. See 6.9 etc.

6.44 Artist unknown, with hand colouring, 1820s
Palace Embankment near the Summer Garden

29.6 x 45.4; *inv.* I-A-4365-L.

The Summer Garden railings (1770-84), by J. Velten, are outstanding in the wealth of fine St Petersburg ironwork. In the 18th century Russia became the world's largest iron exporter, and the material was used to handsome effect in St Petersburg (see 6.49-50).

6.45 ZEIDEL, 1820s
View from the Winter Canal to the Peter-Paul Fortress

37 x 54.5; *inv.* I-A-2125-L.

The small canal runs beside the Hermitage (see also 6.2). The large arch links the Old Hermitage with the Hermitage Theatre.

6.46 KARL-JOACHIM BEGGROV from a drawing by K. Sabata and S. Shifflard, 1820s
Sadovaia Ulitsa (Street)

29.7 x 42.7; *inv.* I-A-1953-L.

Sadovaia (Garden) Street is one of the oldest streets in the city. Making an inner (half) ring road, along the line of the Fontanka. *Left*, is the former State Bank (1780s), by Quarenghi, with Gostinnyi Dvor (1785; formerly a bazaar, now a department store) beyond.

6.47 Hand coloured, from a drawing by A. Orlovskii, 1820s
Baker's Boy

25.3 x 17; *inv.* I-A-2378-L.

One of the many urban pedlars, often peasants from the countryside. The boy is in front of the cabin where Peter the Great lived, 1703-9. See 6.27 etc.

6.48 With hand colouring, from a drawing by K. Kalman, 1820s
Fish-seller

16.8 x 22.1; *inv.* I-A-2131-L. *See* 6.47

6.49 KARL-JOACHIM BEGGROV from a drawing by W. von Traitteur, 1824
Pantaleimon Bridge

35.8 x 56.7; *inv.* I-A-2131-L.

Traitteur was the designer of some of the most beautiful small bridges in St Petersburg. This example, unusual for ironwork and over the Fontanka near the Summer Garden, was the city's first suspension bridge. It was replaced in 1907. See also 6.50, 6.44.

6.50 KARL-JOACHIM BEGGROV, 1828
Lion Bridge over the Catherine Canal

36.5 x 57.8; *inv.* I-A-2114-L.

Suspension footbridge (1826), also by Traitteur, over the Catherine (now Griboedov) Canal. The cast-iron lions were sculpted by Pavel Sokolov. Bankovskii Bridge, another Traitteur design, is very similar, but supported by gold-winged griffons. See also 6.49 and 6.44.

6.49

6.51 1823-5
The Admiralty from Palace Square

30 x 45.5; *inv.* I-A-1468-L.

The building on which the plan of St Petersburg pivots was completed in its final form by Andreian Zakharov in 1823. *Right*, is the south-west corner of the Winter Palace. See also 6.13.

6.52 Published by ALEKSANDR PLUCHART, 1826
Vista of the English Embankment

22.5 x 35; *inv.* I-A-1823-L.

One of the earliest steamships on the Neva: a regular service to Kronshtadt in the Gulf of Finland began in 1816. See also 6.65.

6.53 KARL-JOACHIM BEGGROV, 1828
Trinity Bridge across the Neva

36.2 x 57.5; *inv.* I-A-1918-L.

The pontoon bridge (1826), crossing to the Petersburg Side, survived 70 years. On its site today is the Kirov Bridge.

6.54 PĒTR IVANOV, with hand colouring, from drawings by
-7 Vasilii Sadovnikov, 1830s
Petersburg Cries. See also 6.27 etc.

6.54 Pieman

14 x 10.8; *inv.* I-A-2398-L.

6.55 Flowerseller**

14 x 10.5; *inv.* I-A-2400-L.

6.56 Glazier

14 x 10.7; *inv.* I-A-2401-L.

6.57 Meat-seller**

14 x 10.7; *inv.* I-A-2402-L.

6.58 PĒTR IVANOV, with hand colouring, from a drawing by
-9 Vasilii Sadovnikov, 1835
Panorama of the Nevskii Prospekt*

Right side, 15 x 714.7; *inv.* I-A-3418-L.

Left side, 15 x 829.5; *inv.* I-A-3419-L.

The distance covered is about 1.5km, from the Admiralty to the Fontanka River, about one third of the Prospekt's full length. In 1835, this stretch included the Kazan Cathedral, five other churches, and such landmarks as Gostinnyi Dvor (see 6.46), the Alexandra (now Pushkin) theatre, the Public Library, the city Duma building, the Stroganov (see 6.61) and Anichkov (6.3) palaces.

6.60

6.60 BICHEBOIS and BAILLOT from a drawing by Auguste de Monferrand, 1836
Erection of the Alexander Column on Palace Square
36 x 47.8; inv. 1-A-2364-L.
It took one hour 45 minutes to raise the 704-ton granite monolith, which is supported only by its own weight. The drawing is by the column's designer, also architect of St Isaac's Cathedral. See also 6.7.

6.61 J. ARNOUT, 1840s
Nevskii Prospekt Looking Towards the Admiralty**
25.5 x 36.3; inv. 1-A-1733-L.
Left, Stroganov Palace (1752-4), by Rastrelli; *right*, the Dutch Church, by P. Jacot, incorporating the pastor's house and other accommodation. Police (now Narodnyi, 'People's') Bridge is over the Moika River, and beyond is the Kotomin house, on whose ground floor was Volf and Beranger's café, frequented by Pushkin and other writers.

6.62 L.-J. JACOTTET and AUBRUN from a drawing by Joseph Charlemagne, 1855-60
New Hermitage from the Winter Canal
33.7 x 45.2; inv. 1-A-1652-L.
Russia's first purpose-built art gallery, by Leo von Klenze, architect of the Munich Glypothek and Pinakothek, the building was completed in 1852, beside the Winter Palace. See also 6.45.

6.63 L.-J. JACOTTET and REGAMEY from a drawing by Joseph Charlemagne, 1850s
Nevskii Prospekt by Moonlight
32.8 x 45.5; inv. 1-A-1762-L.
Snow usually covers the streets from December to April. Gas lighting was introduced in the city in the 1830s.

6.64 From a drawing by Joseph Charlemagne, 1850s
Anichkov Bridge
33.4 x 44.8; inv. 1-A-1775-L.
Opposite view to 6.3 and 6.15. Beyond the bridge is the Beloselskii-Belozerskii palace (1846-8).

6.65 L.-J. JACOTTET from a drawing by J. Charlemagne, 1850s
English Embankment
33.5 x 45.7; inv. 1-A-1837-L.
The Neva bank west of Senate Square got this name from the presence of the British community, the embassy and the English Church, a Quarenghi building of 1814. The British settled here originally because of the proximity of the shipyards, where many skilled workmen were foreigners. See also 6.52.

6.66 G. BERNARDAZZI from a drawing by Bachelier, mid 19th century
St Petersburg Panorama
34 x 229.5; inv. 1-A-2136-L.
Viewpoint is the belltower of the Peter-Paul Fortress (see 6.10), whose bastions are in the foreground, looking towards Palace Embankment. The panorama was presented to Nicholas I.

6.67 From a drawing by J. Arnout, mid 19th century
Sennaia Square (Haymarket)
27 x 36; inv. 1-A-1987-L.
The market, then on the Moscow road at the edge of the city, functioned from 1737, selling food, livestock, and household goods as well as horse fodder. In the 19th century it was the best and cheapest market in the city and the centre of low life, figuring in Dostoevsky's *Crime and Punishment*. The haymarket was removed in the 1930s; after the war it was renamed Peace Square.

6.68 F. ZILBER, 1850s-60s
Chapel on the Nicholas Bridge
26.2 x 36.6; inv. 1-A-1929-L
The bridge (1850; initially called Annunciation, now named for Leitenant Shmidt) was the first permanent raisable bridge over the Neva to Vasilevskii Island: before this pontoons were used. The chapel was built in 1854, dedicated to St Nicholas the miracle-worker.

6.69 From a drawing by Joseph Charlemagne, 1850s
University Embankment by Moonlight
33.3 x 46.6; inv. 1-A-1895-L.
Foreground, *left*, is the Academy of Arts (1753-88), by Aleksandr Kokorinov and J.-B. Vallin de la Mothe. The landing place (1832-4) was made to accommodate sphinxes transported from Thebes.

6.70 Wilhelm Georg Timm, 1858
Shrovetide (Maslenitsa) on Isaac Square
35 54; inv. 1-A-3205-L.
Shrovetide had been celebrated with popular festivals since the mid 18th century. Isaac Square was one of several large spaces where tents, booths, swings and slides were erected. In the centre is the ticket-seller for a mumming play. See also 6.9 etc.

6.71 A. AVNATAMOV and B. BREZE from a drawing by Joseph Charlemagne, 1859
Sleigh Races on the Neva
39 x 58; inv. 1-A-2530-L.
A course would be set up on the ice in front of the Winter Palace. Roadways for the arrival of the horsedrawn sledges, lit and marked out with fir-trees, are laid out here from the Strelka, *right*, and Palace Embankment. See also 6.12.

6.72 L.-J. JACOTTET from a drawing by Joseph Charlemagne, mid 19th century
Popular Pleasure-ground on Admiralty Square
22.8 x 44.3; inv. 1-A-2532-L.
Festivals were customary here from the mid 18th century, with 'ice-mountain' slides and fair booths. See also 6.9 etc.

6.70

Magazine Illustrations

6.73 N. NEGADAEV in *Vsemirnaia illiustratsiia* (World illustration), 1872
Smolensk Cemetery
22.6 x 32.4; inv. 1-A-3830-P.
Satirical drawing of the new, more urban population's celebration of All Saints Day. Compare the traditional holidays in 6.9 etc.

6.74 1870s
Large Dock of the Baltic Shipbuilding Works
14 x 20; inv. 1-A-1882-P.
Largest shipbuilder in the city was this state-owned yard in the industrial area in the south-west of Vasilevskii Island, built in 1856.

6.75 G. BROLING in *Vsemirnaia illiustratsiia* (World Illustration), 1870s
Main Customs House
22.5 x 32.5; inv. 1-A-2100-P.
St Petersburg was Russia's largest sea port, as well as its foremost industrial centre. After the port moved away from the city's heart in the 1880s the customs house, on the north side of the Strelka, became the Institute of Russian Literature (Pushkinskii Dom).

6.76 V. NAVOZOV in *Niva* (Neva), 1884
The Imperial Academy of Art
25.5 x 37.8; inv. 1-A-1560-P.
The Academy was founded in 1757; no longer imperial, it moved to Moscow in 1947 and its old building (see also 6.69) now houses the Repin Art Institute. The interiors here are, *top*, grand staircase, life class, Academy church; *centre*, Russian sculpture hall, composition class; *below*, Academy gallery, council chamber, Kushelev-Bezborodko Gallery.

6.77 Photograph by K. Bull in *Niva* (Neva), 1903.
Bestuzhev Advanced Classes for Women
16.8 x 25.4; inv. 1-A-9103-P.
The first opportunities for female higher education came in 1869. Konstantin Bestuzhev-Riumin, a distinguished professor of Russian history, was the formal founder in 1878 of the first women's courses with university status.

Большой док Балтийского завода

6.74

Early 20th-Century Photographs

6.78 **Tradesmen.** See also 6.27 etc.

   a) **Fireman** *c.* 1900

   b) **Hot-drink seller** c. 1910. The drink is made with honey and spices; cloth wrappings help to keep it hot. The vendor carries glasses in a special tray tied round his waist (see also **2.89**).

   c) **Postman** *c.* 1910. He is delivering a copy of the journal *Ogonëk* (Small Light).

   d) **Knife-grinder** 1913. He is carrying a treadle-driven lathe.

   e) **Kvass-seller** 1913. Kvass is rye-beer, still sold in Russian streets. but in far larger metal drums.

6.79 The 'working class'. See also 6.27 etc.

   a) **Beggar-woman** end 19c. A bag-woman of the St Petersburg 1890s, with a well-peeled stick, carefully stitched patches and bast shoes (see 3.1).

   b) **Day-labourer** 1913. This man had no job security; his heavy linen overall and ruddy face suggest he still has close links with peasant life in the countryside.

   c) **Workman** 1913. This man is called '*masterovoi*', a permanent worker. His clothes are urban, and he had probably lost his ties with the land, even been born in the capital.

   d) **Metal-workers*** 1917. These men belonged to the labour élite, as part of the 13,000-strong workforce of the state-owned Obukhov steel plant, occupied solely with defence orders. Their smart clothes and confident air suggests they were skilled workers who had benefited from the wartime boom in Petrograd industry.

6.78b

Select Bibliography

1 Russian Faces, Soviet Lives

John Bowlt, *Russian Art of the Avant-Garde: Theory and Criticism*, Thames & Hudson, revised edition, 1988.

David Elliott, *New Worlds: Russian Art and Society 1900-1937*, Thames & Hudson, 1986.

Mark Etkind (intro), *Boris Kustodiev*, Collets, Wellingborough, for Aurora, Leningrad, 1983.

Mikhail Guerman (intro), *Soviet Art 1920s-1930s: Russian Museum, Leningrad*, Penguin, Harmondsworth, 1988.

C. Vaughan James, *Soviet Socialist Realism: Origins and Theory*, Macmillan 1973.

Iurii Rusakov, *Kuzma Petrov-Vodkin*, Collets Wellingborough, for Aurora, Leningrad, 1986.

Vladimir Syssoiev (intro), *Alexandre Deineka*, Aurora, Leningrad, 1982.

2 The Russian Lubok: Two Hundred Years of Popular Prints

Catherine Claudon-Adhémar, *Imagerie populaire russe*, Paris, 1961.

Pierre-Louis Ducharté, *L'Imagerie populaire russe et les livrets gravés 1629-1885*, Paris, 1961.

Iurii Ovsiannikov, *Lubok: Russkie narodnye kartinki* (with English translation), Aurora, Leningrad, 1968.

Alla Sytova, Natalia Rudakova, et al, *The Lubok: Russian Folk Pictures, 17th to 19th Century*, Aurora, Leningrad, 1984.

3 Bolshevik Posters 1917-25

Nina Baburina, *The Soviet Political Poster 1917-1980, from the USSR Lenin Library Collection*, Penguin, Harmondsworth, 1988.

Mikhail Guerman (ed), *Art of the October Revolution*, Collets, Wellingborough, for Aurora, Leningrad, 1979.

David King and Cathy Porter, *Blood and Laughter: Caricatures from the 1905 Revolution*, Cape, 1983.

Stephen White, *The Bolshevik Poster*, Yale UP, Newhaven, 1988.

E. H. Carr, *The Bolshevik Revolution 1917-1923*, 3 vols, Macmillan, 1950-53.

E. H. Carr, *The Russian Revolution from Lenin to Stalin 1917-1929*, Macmillan 1979.

Evan Mawdsley, *The Russian Civil War*, Allen & Unwin, 1987.

Robert Service, *The Russian Revolution 1900-1927*, Macmillan, 1986.

4 Street Art of the Revolution: Petrograd 1918

Vladimir Tolstoy, Irina Bibikova and Catherine Cooke (eds), *Street Art of the Revolution: Festivals and Celebrations in Russia 1918-33*, Thames & Hudson, 1990.

Also: David Elliott, *op cit* (section 1), and Mikhail Guerman, *op cit* (section 3).

5 Posters of Perestroika

Alexander Yevorov and Victor Litvinov (intro), *The Posters of Glasnost and Perestroika*, Penguin, Harmondsworth, 1989.

6 St Petersburg

Robert Auty and Dimitri Obolensky (eds), *An Introduction to Russian Art and Architecture*, Cambridge University Press, 1980.

James Bater, *St Petersburg: Industrialisation and Change*, Arnold, 1976.

W. Brumfield, *Gold and Azure: 1000 Years of Russian Architecture*, Boston, 1983.

James Cracraft, *The Petrine Revolution in Russian Architecture*, Chicago, 1988.

G. H. Hamilton, *The Art and Architecture of Russia*, Penguin, Harmondsworth, 1983.

Lindsey Hughes, 'Russia's first architectural textbooks: a chapter in Peter the Great's cultural revolution', *Architectural Design*, vol 53, 5-6, 1983, pp4-13.

Laurence Kelly (ed), *St Petersburg: A Traveller's Companion*, Constable, 1981.

C. A. Marsden, *The Palmyra of the North*, Faber, 1932.

Evan and Margaret Mawdsley (eds), *The Blue Guide to Leningrad and Moscow*, Benn, 1980. This was particularly helpful for preparing the notes in section 6, and is essential reading for the history, architecture and topography of Leningrad. A new edition is planned from Adam and Charles Black in 1991.

Brief Chronology of Russian and Soviet History

Kievan Russia ('Rus') A group of princedoms centred on the River Dnieper, the trading route between northern Europe and Constantinople, and the city of Kiev. The princes, who may have been of Scandinavian origin, gave the peoples, Slav tribes occupied in agriculture, the name Rus. Riurik and Oleg are early Kievan princes in the mid 9th century; the flourishing of Kievan Russia is associated with the adoption of Christianity under St Vladimir in 988, with the reign of this prince (980-1015) and of Iaroslav the Wise (1019-54). Kiev adopted eastern, Orthodox Christianity, and the Slav language was written down in adapted Greek characters. The Kievan state was weakened by division into smaller princedoms. The Prince of Suzdal sacked the city in 1169, moving the capital to Vladimir in the northeast. In 1240 Mongol invaders razed Kiev and conquered Kievan Rus.

Novgrod A city whose influence extended as far as the Urals, over huge areas of northern Russia, Novgorod was subordinate to Kiev, but largely independent of it. It is known for its democratic traditions, its healthy commerce and for its prince, Alexander Nevskii (1219-63), who defeated the Swedes and the Teutonic Knights (1240-2). Novgorod came to an accommodation with the Mongols, averting occupation.

Mongol Rule Mongol and Tatar khans dominated Russia between 1240 and 1480, succeeding because of singleness of purpose, mobile horsemen, and efficient tax collection. At the Battle of Kulikovo on the Don in 1380, Prince Dmitri ('Donskoi') of Moscow dented their power; in 1480 Mongol sway was finally rejected by Ivan III of Moscow. Pushkin later wrote that Russia's martyrdom now 'saved' Christian civilisation, by holding down the invasion from the east that might otherwise have enveloped Western Europe.

The Rise of Moscow Moscow rose to prominence because of its strategic position on the river network and the administrative talents of its princes as agents of the khans. Especially under Ivan I (1325-40), 'Moneybags', Muscovite territory expanded; the head of the Orthodox Church moved to Moscow from Kiev. Dmitrii Donskoi (1359-89) fended off forces of Lithuania, the city of Tver, and the Volga Bulgars, as well as the Golden Horde. In the 1430s-60s the eastern overlords' territories split into separate khanates: the Crimea, Kazan and Astrakhan. Constantinople and the Crimea fell to the Turks, increasing Russian isolation from the rest of the world.

Muscovite Russia In the reign of Ivan III (1462-1505) Moscow formalised its independence of Mongol domination; Muscovy was consolidated by absorbing such rival centres as Novgorod and Tver. In 1493 Ivan took the title of Sovereign of All Russia (*gosudar*) and on his marriage to a Byzantine princess he began to use the title *tsar* (derived from *caesar*): the idea arose of Moscow as 'the third Rome', the refuge of christendom after the fall of the churches of old Rome and Constantinople. Much of the Moscow Kremlin and its churches were built now; democratic traditions ended as the cities of Novgorod, Pskov and Viatka, with their *veche*, or town meeting, became part of the authoritarian Muscovite system.

Ivan the Terrible Ivan IV (1533-84), the first ruler to be crowned 'tsar', began his personal rule in 1547 auspiciously. Defeats of the Kazan and Astrakhan khanates led to huge territorial gain; there were legal, church and administrative reforms; the influx of West Europeans, skilled in the arts, sciences and trade, begun under Ivan III, gathered pace. But on the death of his wife (1560), the tsar's conduct changed, and he waged a fierce campaign of terror (the 'Oprichnina', 1565-72) against the power of the boyar nobles. Muscovy attempted expansion to the Baltic, unsussessfully. After the conquest of Kazan mineral deposits in the north-east were increasingly developed by Muscovite entrepeneurs; in 1579 one of these families, the Stroganovs, organised an army which, under Ermak, penetrated far beyond the Urals, defeated the Siberian khan and established Russian control of western Siberia.

The Time of Troubles 1598-1613. Destabilised, recently expanded Muscovy was held together after Ivan's death by the regent Boris Godunov; the country's position was enhanced by the establishment of a Russian patriarchate; Orthodox Georgia, beyond the Caucasus, asked for Muscovite protection from threatening Moslems. But Boris's position as the inheritor of an exhausted dynasty was made untenable by a series of disasters, including famine (1601-3), epidemics, and accusations that he had murdered the true heir. Legal migration of peasants was abolished, to try to ensure the position of the land-owning gentry, effectively enserfing the whole working population. Those who could escape joined free societies of cossacks establishing themselves in the new borderlands. When a pretender, 'False Dmitrii', claimed the throne, Boris turned against the boyars. His sudden death in 1605 brought momentary success to the pretender, soon followed by disagreement with the boyars, a succession of rulers, invasion, cossack rebellion, and anarchy.

The Romanovs Polish attempts to conquer Moscow failed, thanks to armies led by plebian Kuzma Minin and Prince Dmitrii Pozharskii. The victors convened a Land Assembly (*zemskii sorbor*), which elected Michael Romanov, aged 16 and from an influential boyar family, as tsar. The reigns of Michael and of his son Alexis were more stable, although there were popular rebellions over taxation, principally that led by Stepan (Stenka, Stëpka) Razin. Important were the code of laws (*ulozhenie*), of 1649, the church reforms of Partiarch Nikon (1650s), which were to lead to serious schism, and the annexation of the Ukraine.

Imperial Russia Peter the Great ruled 1682-1725, at first with his half-brother. His experience of violence during the revolt of musketeer regiments (*streltsy*) against his mother's family at the time of his accession, when he was 10, may account for some of his own rough treatment of the traditional side of Russia the streltsy represented; his declared aim was West European efficiency. Peter's major reforms affected all areas of life: the calendar , the alphabet, public service, the army and its weapons, government education, the position of the church, architecture: even personal dress and style of beard and hair-cut. Peter's final victory in the long series of campaigns and wars in the Russian north and south was partly the result of his founding of a navy. The victory permitted further orientation towards the West because of the conquest of a north-west sea-shore; the building of a city-port there — St Petersburg — permitted the permanent creation of physical evidence of change. St Petersburg became the capital in 1712; at the end of the Northern War, in 1721, Russia was declared an Empire.

Catherine the Great Catherine II (1762-96), of German origin and widow of murdered Tsar Peter III, affirmed Western cultural values and promoted enlightened ideas of government, before the widespread Pugachëv revolt of 1773-4 and the events of the French Revolution made her more cautious. Legislation now strengthened serfdom. Russian territorial expansion continued through the partitions of Poland and annexation of the Crimea and the Black Sea coast. But a periodical press was established and cultural life flourished. The principle of female education was established and better schooling spread to the provinces, although this did not extend to the bulk of the people. The first modern Russian poet, Derzhavin, and dramatist, Fonvizin, published; the major work of social criticism, *Journey from Petersburg to Moscow*, was written by Aleksandr Radishchev.

Napoleon Optimism among the generation born in post-Petrine Russia who saw the West European world during the Napoleonic campaigns and experienced the victory, was dashed by the failure of the victor of Europe, Alexander I (1801-25) to continue his country's move into the modern world by social and political reform. A succession of brilliant literary works appeared, beginning with Karamzin's *History of the Russian State*, through playwrights, poets and thinkers like Griboedov, Tiutchev, Chaadaev, Zhukovskii and the fable-writer Krylov, and reaching full maturity in Lermontov, Pushkin and Gogol. But after the Decembrists Revolt of 1825, when young officers in favour of constitutional rights to basic freedoms organised a mutiny on Senate Square, oppressive conservatism prevailed under Alexander's brother and successor, Nicholas I (1825-55).

The 'Great Reforms' Russia's poor performance in the Crimean War (1853-6) drew attention to the country's inefficiency, especially its poor communications. Conservative elements had feared any opportunity for the population to become more mobile. Reforms began under Alexander II, 'the Liberator', with the abolition of serfdom in 1861-2, the setting up of rural self-government by local councils (*zemstva*), and a more modern legal system. The rail network was quickly established and expanded; foreign businesses were influential in industrial expansion, while the government attempted to make Russia's own businessmen competitive.

Slavophiles and Westerners Debate about the future of Russia among the growing Russian intelligentsia, became more political. Two generations of thinkers are seen here: the 'fathers': Herzen, Bakunin, Belinskii, followed by more radical, less socially refined 'sons'. Chernyshevskii, Dobroliubov, Tkachev. One oppositional movement crystallised in Populism, which believed in a specifically Russian native wisdom and was fearful of change in the industrial West European manner. Failure of any popular response to overtures made to peasant villagers by idealistic young people in 1873-4 led some groups to adopt more violent tactics, to promote chaos and force the pace of change.

The Revolutionary Movement In 1881 Alexander II was assassinated by 'People's Will', a terrorist group. The regimes that followed, under Alexander III and Nicholas II were mainly repressive. Industrial development proceeded especially fast in the 1890s and 1900s. In these circumstances, and following the publication of Marx in Russia in the 1880s, the political debate now centred on Marxists, who saw Russian industrialisation as producing the conditions for political and social change, and Populists, many of whom believed in terrorism to provoke change. The labour movement that grew in circumstances of factory expansion was the hope of the former group (Social Democrats), while the second (Social Revolutionaries) believed the evident and continuing unfairness with which the peasant land issue was being settled under the Reforms would finally result in peasant upheaval. Strikes and peasant violence increased.

Revolution of 1905 Russian defeat in the war against Japan fueled discontent. Demands for change were frequent. On 'Bloody Sunday', 22 January 1905, police fired on a huge demonstration of workers coming to the Winter Palace with a petition, killing at least 130. Disturbances increased, culminating in a general strike 20-30 October, during which St Petersburg workers organised their first *soviet*, or council, with Leon Trotsky as its leader. The Tsar conceded the 'October Manifesto', guaranteeing civil liberties and a Duma, or parliament with legislative functions. In June 1907 much of this was revoked: high property qualifications cut worker and peasant representation in the electoral system severely; union activity was curtailed; the Tsar resumed various autocratic powers.

First World War The war came as industry was expanding and strike activity was again buoyant. Land reform introduced by Pëtr Stolypin to create a class of independent farmers, the 'wager on the strong', had not progressed far. Many Russian socialists opposed the war from the beginning: although the Social Democrats had split into Bolsheviks and Mensheviks (groups of the 'majority' and 'minority') in 1903 on the issue of a narrow-or broad-based membership, the leftist wings of both groups denounced the war as potential fratricide for the European working class. The army was badly supplied, lacking even rifles, as well as boots and clothing. Public criticism led to the involvement of local government, industrialists and even workers groups in administering the war effort.

February 1917 Revolution In February food riots and demonstrations were reinforced by soldiers' support and followed by the setting up of two anti-tsarist organs of authority: the Provisional Government, of liberals, emanating from the Duma; and the Petrograd Soviet of workers' and soldiers' deputies, based on the councils of 1905. On 3 March the Tsar was persuaded to abdicate. Workers were involved in the organisation of industrial production, where managers or owners had fled; factory and military hierarchies were democratised.

Lenin In April Lenin spoke out for an end to the war, for workers' control of factories and against socialists' cooperation with the Provisional Government. In the countryside peasants began cultivating landlords' land. The liberals became compromised in popular minds by their commitment to tsarist undertakings given to the Allies and their allegiance to authoritarian factory management and private land ownership. The Provisional Government was finally discredited by an unpopular military offensive in June, wavering policies on the food question and its apparent support for the attempted coup of General Kornilov in August. Bolshevik policies first put forward by Lenin were justified; electoral support rallied to Bolshevism.

October 1917 Revolution On 25 October, after occupation of key points in the capital by armed militias, the cruiser *Avrora* fired a blank shell and rebels entered the Winter Palace to arrest Provisional Government ministers. The All-Russian Congress of Soviets, meeting in Petrograd with representatives from all over the country assumed power. In the Council of People's Commissars, now running the country, Left Social Revolutionaries joined the Bolsheviks; elections to the Constituent Assembly predated this split in the SR party. The economic crisis which had grown over the war years was a severe test for the new government, as was public dismay at the terms of the humiliating Treaty of Brest-Litvosk taking Russian out of the war. In March the capital moved to Moscow as a German advance threatened; the Bolshevik party adopted the designation 'Communist'.

Civil War, 1918-20 White, anti-government armies sprang up in the southeast, the south and the north-west; non-Russian forces attempted intervention in the north, south and far east. The Red forces' strength was their physical position as a unified whole; although the huge mass of peasants disliked the grain requisitioning necessary to feed the army and cities, they also feared the return of the landlords. Lack of food and industrial supplies caused a massive exodus from the cities.

New Economic Policy In the spring 1921 strikes and a revolt in Kronshtadt against the waning of democratic rights led the government to make economic concessions to the peasants and legitimise small private businesses. However, with industrial plant in need of renewal after long years of war it was hard to generate industrial-agricultural exchange. Lenin, very much the driving thinker of the new regime, envisaged large-scale investment in industry to rejuvenate the country. After his death in 1924, decisions were taken to move fast in this direction, although there remained anxiety about feeding the cities.

Stalinism Heavy taxes on better-off peasants brought more falls in grain marketing. Stalin emerged as the dominant figure in Soviet politics in the late 1920s as difficult decisions were taken. He began the use of force, of 'administrative-command methods' to secure food supplies and silence critics of crash industrialisation. This degenerated into terror through the forced collectivisation of agriculture; arrests, intimidation and show trials eliminated whole sections of the Communist party and the main part of the army officers corps.

The Second World War After failure to negotiate a joint front with Britain and France in 1939, Russia concluded a non-agression pact with Germany, allowing the Red Army to move into eastern Poland and the Baltic republics; the pact was broken in June 1941 by headlong German advance along USSR's western front. The defence of Moscow, Leningrad's refusal to surrender in spite of the 900-day blockade when hundreds of thousands died, and the battle of Stalingrad turned the tide against the German army.

Stalinism Resumed Political repression, relaxed during the war, resumed at its end and was gathering force when Stalin died in 1953. The 'cold war' was identified by Churchill when the Red Army remained in the postwar period in the East European countries it had liberated.

The 'Thaw' International relations eased; millions returned from forced labour camps; Soviet society was liberalised and cultural life resumed. Khrushchev, who in 1956 denounced Stalin's crimes in a secret speech to the Communist Party, was the leader until 1964, when his earthy diplomatic style and often over-hasty policies at home led to his removal.

Years of Stagnation Under Leonid Brezhnev (1970-82), at first part of a collective leadership, economic performance fell off, there was corruption and neglect of reform. An attempt was begun to reverse this under Iurii Andropov (1982-3), but reform only became the official aim in 1985, when Mikhail Gorbachev initiated policies of open-ness about past and present failings (Glasnost) and restructuring (Perestroika), for economic efficiency.

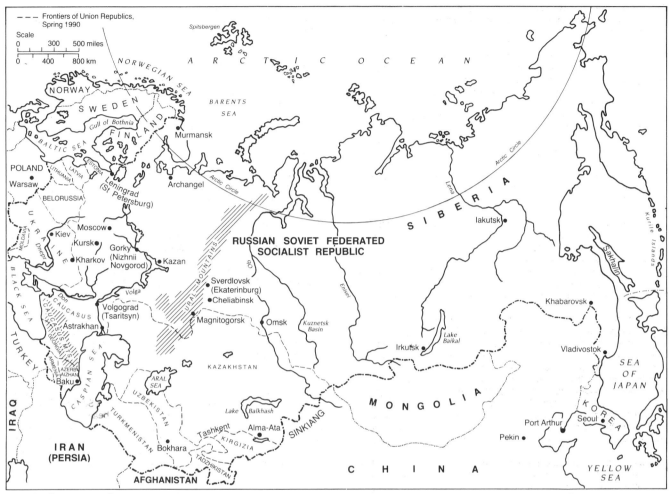

Map 1. The Union of Soviet Socialist Republics

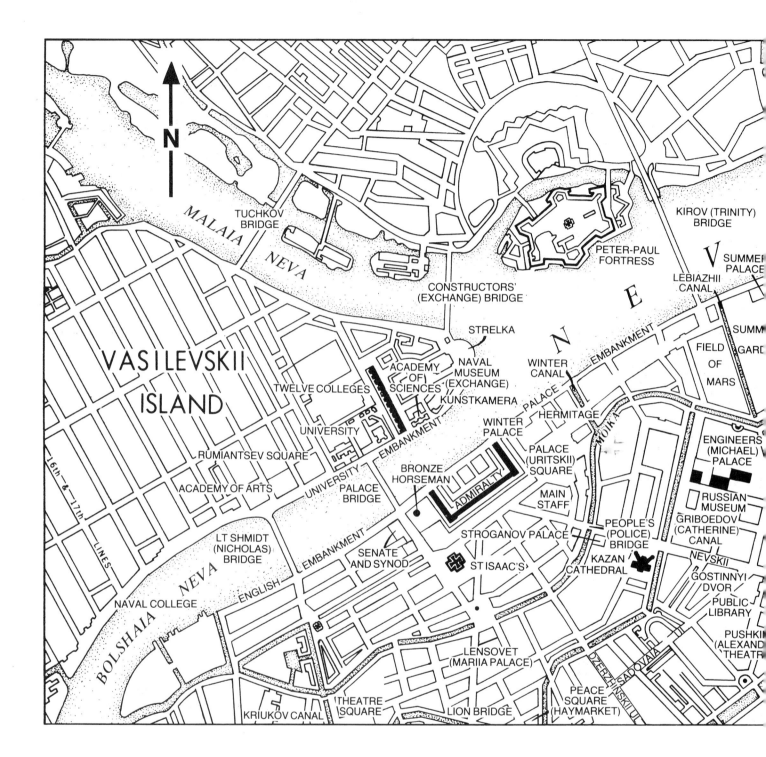

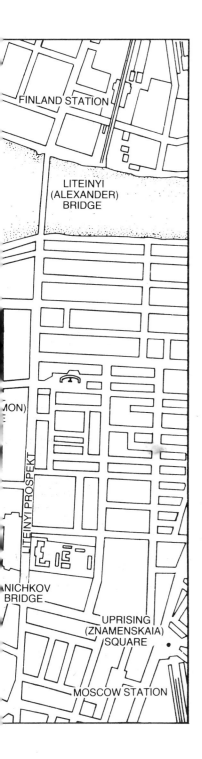

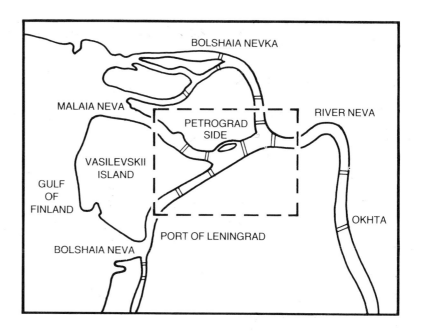

Map 2. The central area of Leningrad-Petrograd-St Petersburg, with pre-revolutionary names in brackets. The small map shows the position of this area in relation to a wider view of the city.